PHYSICS

Published simultaneously in Canada by McClelland and Stewart, Ltd.

Published in the United Kingdom by Constable and Company Limited, 10 Orange Street, London W.C.2.

This new Dover edition, first published in 1963, is a revised and enlarged version of the second (1955) edition of the work first published for *Metal Industry* by The Louis Cassier Co. Ltd. in 1948.

Library of Congress Catalog Card Number: 63-17905

Manufactured in the United States of America

Dover Publications, Inc.
180 Varick Street
New York 14, N.Y.

ELECTRONS, ATOMS, METALS AND ALLOYS

By

WILLIAM HUME-ROTHERY
O.B.E., F.R.S.

Isaac Wolfson Professor of Metallurgy, University of Oxford

Third Revised Edition

DOVER PUBLICATIONS, INC.

NEW YORK   NEW YORK

Contents

Page

PART I—THE NATURE OF AN ATOM

Chapter

PART II—THE NATURE OF A METAL

PART III—THE NATURE OF AN ALLOY

PART IV—THE STRUCTURE OF THE NUCLEUS

Preface to Dover Edition (1962)

THE reprinted edition is being prepared sixteen years after the original manuscript first appeared in *Metal Industry*, and six years after the revised printing of the original book. In the intervening period there have been remarkable advances in the theory and knowledge of dislocations, in the science of semi-conductors, and in nuclear physics and metallurgy. At the same time, the development of the electron theory of metals and alloys has shown that some of the earlier and more simple theory is really not so satisfactory as was first imagined. These later developments can only be appreciated after the earlier views are understood, and for this reason most of the original book has been left unchanged. In order to preserve the dialogue form, the later advances have been dealt with in a series of "Epilogues" in which the Older Metallurgist (OM) and Young Scientist (YS) of the original book are imagined to meet after an interval of sixteen years, when the now Retired Metallurgist (RM) and Middle-aged Scientist (MAS) consider the bearing of the later work on their original discussion.

It must again be emphasised that the book is still one describing what the new theories are about, rather than what they are, and for a real understanding the references and suggestions for further reading must be consulted. In view of the appearance of numerous books on semi-conductors and on nuclear science, no attempt has been made to expand Chapters 27 and 40 through 44. Except for minor corrections, these have been left in their original form.

W. HUME-ROTHERY

Oxford, England
May, 1962

Preface (1948)

THE work of the last thirty years has led to great advances in the theory of the structure and properties of metals and alloys, and much interest has been aroused in this subject. In recent years the present author has been engaged in the preparation of a general introduction to the theoretical work, which has been published by the Institute of Metals under the title of " Atomic Theory for Students of Metallurgy," and is intended for University honours students. In the course of its preparation, part of the manuscript was submitted for criticism to some industrial metallurgists. These replied that they found much of it unintelligible. One critic went so far as to say that the only kind of book he had time to deal with was one which could be read with " enjoyment, and without hard work." It says a great deal for the broad-mindedness of the Institute's Publication Committee that they proceeded with the publication of the book for the benefit of the University student, but it was clear that a quite different approach was needed for some industrial readers.

This led the present author to consider why the average physical textbook often proves unattractive to readers outside Universities. One reason appeared to be that the usual textbook not only requires a considerable power of continuous concentration, but also expects the reader of any one chapter to retain clearly the lessons learnt in earlier chapters. For University students these requirements are entirely reasonable, but it can readily be understood that they cannot be satisfied by those who are busily occupied in metallurgical industry.

In the hope of overcoming these difficulties, the author was led to experiment with a presentation of the subject matter in the form of a dialogue. The method has obvious dangers, but it has the advantage that the readers' attention may be stimulated by the deliberate raising of questions, or discussion of difficulties, and that direct attention may be drawn to cases in which a knowledge of previous chapters is being assumed. The author has attempted to make " Electrons, Atoms, Metals and Alloys " as much as possible a discussion of the points at issue, but he must confess that in some places it has proved difficult to prevent it from becoming merely " question and answer." The manuscript was first published in *Metal Industry* and the author must express his thanks to Mr. L. G. Beresford, the Editor, for his help and advice.

The criticism may be made that the questions of the Older Metallurgist are sometimes unduly naïve, and if so the author may perhaps suggest that fundamental principles are sometimes revealed by questions of the simplest nature. If any readers feel that the Older Metallurgist has been made too much of an Aunt Sally, the author offers his apologies, and assures them that if they chose to instruct him in the technique of foundry practice they would find that his own ignorance of such matters exceeded anything they had imagined.

It will be appreciated, therefore, that the book is intended for those who prefer to study the subject in small instalments, and that the treatment will become increasingly less attractive as the reader has more time or inclination to give the work steady and continuous thought. It is essentially a book describing what the new theories are about, rather than what they are, and the University student should realise that if he is tempted to read its pages his duty as a student is to proceed to the study of the books referred to at the ends of the chapters. He must not think that a reading of the present book has given him any real understanding of the new theories.

The author must express his gratitude to many friends who have read and criticised part or all of the present book. In particular Dr. H. J. Axon, must be thanked for having read the whole manuscript in its early stages, whilst Mr. G. MacDonald, O.B.E., and Dr. D. K. C. MacDonald have also given valuable assistance. Thanks are due to Mr. J. W. Christian, Mr. S. J. Carlile, and to the author's father for help with the proof corrections. It need scarcely be said that the fact that the friends mentioned above have read the manuscript in no way commits them to the views expressed in the book.

W. HUME-ROTHERY

The Inorganic Chemistry Laboratory,
University Museum,
Oxford.

NOTE ON THE REVISED PRINTING, 1955

THE continued demand for this book since its original publication in 1948 has made a reprint necessary. The period 1948–54 has seen great advances in the theory of dislocations (Chapter 32) and in the science of nuclear structure (Part IV). As both of these subjects lie outside the main scope of the book, no attempt has been made to bring the sections concerned completely up to date. The text has been corrected so that nothing, it is hoped, is incorrect in view of recent work, but the reader should be warned that the description is at an elementary level, and that the " Suggestions for Further Reading " should be consulted. If this policy is criticised, it may be pleaded that the dialogue form is not well suited for the description of the theory of dislocations, which requires familiarity with crystallographic notation, whilst the interest in nuclear energy has resulted in the publication of many elementary books on nuclear structure. The remainder of the book is substantially unchanged, although a few sections have been rewritten where new work has rendered the old description incorrect. It should also be noted that although they remain correct as illustrating general principles, the equilibrium diagrams should not now be used for accurate measurement without checking whether they have been modified by later work.

Electrons, Atoms, Metals and Alloys

The reader is asked to imagine the following conversation as taking place between a young scientist and an older metallurgist. The young scientist has taken an Honours Degree in Physics or Physical Chemistry sometime between 1930 and 1945, that is, since the establishment of the Quantum Theory. The older metallurgist took a high Honours Degree in Metallurgy or Chemistry in the period 1910–20, since when he has been occupied (with conspicuous success) with industrial problems. The two are to be regarded as having met by chance after the meeting of a Metallurgical Society in which they are both interested, the date of the meeting being 1945.

PART 1—THE NATURE OF AN ATOM

1—The Problem

OLDER METALLURGIST: You know, it's very sad, but I'm getting more and more depressed about the state of metallurgical science nowadays.

YOUNG SCIENTIST : Oh, I say ! What has been getting you down ?

OM: Well, I thought I'd like a bit of a change from all my production worries. So I went for four days to the conference on the Theory of Alloy Structures arranged by the new Institute of Physical Metallurgy.

YS: Ah ! Now that was a good show, that was ! The mathematical physicists began to come clean, and one could really see what was going on. It was a great contrast to the usual kind of stunt, where men repeat all the catch phrases, and then discreetly shirk the real difficulties. You must have learnt a lot there, so why all this depression?

OM: To be quite honest, I couldn't understand a word of what was going on. There was a lot of talk about wave functions, and some strange symbol ψ, and weird things called Brillouin Zones, and a lot of men wrote equations on the blackboard involving $e^{2\pi i}$, and something about structure factors. This went on for about two days, and then the chairman said one must remember that all the theory referred to the simple model of the ideal crystal, and that the strength of actual metals depended on the much more difficult problem of the secondary structure of the real crystal.

YS: I see. What then ?

OM : Well, I felt that, having spent two days not being able to understand the simple stuff, it wasn't much good staying longer.

YS: So you gave it up?

OM: Yes! It seems to me there is a real danger nowadays that

9

metallurgical science may become split up into two watertight sections
—the practical kind of work with which I deal, and this new theoretical
work done by young mathematical physicists who speak a language
which nobody else can understand.

YS : Well, it takes all sorts to make a world, so you mustn't be too
impatient. After all, I don't know much about casting alloys, but there
are plenty of things in mathematical physics which I understand and
you don't.

OM : That's not the point. You don't know much about casting
ingots, but I can explain to you how it is done. Your mathematical
friends, on the other hand, either won't or can't explain what they are
doing, at any rate in such a way that I can understand them. They
don't seem to realise that to the average man their symbols are meaningless, and they have no idea of the gap between their own ideas and
the limited mathematics of the ordinary metallurgist. They seem
quite unable to give a simple and straightforward account of their
new ideas. After all, I'm not very unreasonable. I'm a practical
man, dealing with metals all day long, and here are these young
men saying that the whole idea of what constitutes a metal has been
revolutionised in the last thirty years, and then, when I ask for a
simple common-sense explanation of what they are doing, they just
can't give it.

YS : Tell me how far back you want to begin.

OM : Well, as a matter of fact, I took papers on elementary physics
and chemistry when I took my degree in metallurgy.

YS : I see—elementary physics and chemistry—mathematics ?

OM : That was not one of my strong points—still, I do know what
$\frac{dy}{dx}$ and $\int y dx$ stand for ; but as for $e^{2\pi i}$—no.

YS : All right. Now what exactly is it you want ?

OM : I want a simplified common-sense account of these new
theories of metals. It isn't much to ask for, is it ?

YS : If you won't think me too pedantic, what exactly do you mean
by common sense ?

OM : What do you mean ?

YS : I mean exactly what I say. What do you mean by " common
sense " ?

OM : Surely that's obvious, isn't it ?

YS : No, I don't think so. If you used the expression literally, it
would, I suppose, mean some experience with which you were acquainted by means of your five senses—sight, hearing, smelling, taste
and touch.

OM : Oh ! Look here, have we really got to be as philosophical as
all this ?

YS : I generally tick off my students unless they can explain the words they use. Still, we may as well meet you half-way, so shall we say that by a common-sense description, you mean a description in terms of events with which you are familiar in daily life ?

OM : That's all right.

YS : Well, doesn't it strike you that you are making a colossal and quite arbitrary assumption ?

OM : What do you mean ?

YS : You said that you had passed examinations in elementary chemistry and physics, so I suppose you've realised that the atoms out of which metals are made are very small things ?

OM : You know that was one of the things which struck me all along. The imagination seems simply to boggle at the smallness of the atom. If I remember rightly there are about 10^{22} atoms in a gram of aluminium.

YS : Yes, that's right. The number of molecules in the gram molecular weight of a substance is called Avogadro's Number and equals about 6.0247×10^{23}. The same number gives the number of atoms in a gram atom of an element ; the atomic weight of aluminium is 26.96, so that 26.96 grams of aluminium contain 6.0247×10^{23} atoms, and one gram of aluminium contains 2.23×10^{22} atoms.

OM : Numbers like that are almost inconceivable. I find I can imagine numbers up to about 10^{10}, but beyond that I just can't grasp them. That's what makes it all so fascinating ! It's amazing to think one can work out the positions of atoms in crystals when the whole scale of things is so small. That's why I'm so interested in it all, and why I so much want a simple common-sense description of the atomic theory of metals.

YS : Yes. But can't you see what a big assumption you're making ?

OM : But I'm not making any assumption at all.

YS : Oh yes, you are. What you are assuming is that in spite of the immensely small scale of the atom its behaviour can be described in terms of principles resembling those which hold for the events on the enormously larger scale with which you are familiar. Your continual demand for a common-sense description is really an assumption that atoms of the order 10^{-23} gram, or their constituent particles if there are such, will behave in the same way as particles of the order, say, 10^{-3} grams and upward, with which your senses are familiar.

OM : But why shouldn't they ?

YS : Well, why should they ? It is surely a matter for experiment.

OM : Are there any experiments about it ?

YS : Oh, yes ! Quite a lot of information has been gathered about atomic processes and, although some of it is a matter of inference rather than of direct observation, it is quite definitely established that many processes on the atomic scale cannot be understood in terms of what you would call " common-sense " principles.

OM: Do you mean that there are two sets of laws, one applicable to events on the atomic scale and the other to large-scale phenomena ?

YS: No, that's not quite the right way to put it. The same laws hold throughout, but when one deals with events on the ordinary scale some of the laws or equations can be expressed in a relatively simple form. Perhaps the following very crude illustration may help you. Let us suppose that we have two quantities x and y, which are connected by the equation

$$y = a \left(x + \frac{1}{x^4} \right).$$

Then if x is very large, $\frac{1}{x^4}$ is so much smaller than x that there is very little error in writing

$$y = ax.$$

Conversely, if x is very small, $\frac{1}{x^4}$ is very large compared with x, and we are justified in writing

$$y = \frac{a}{x^4}.$$

The same equation holds throughout, but if one always dealt with cases where x was large one would imagine one had a simple proportionality, and one might have great difficulty in recognising that the inverse 4th power law was the same equation applied to small values of x. This example mustn't be pushed too far, because it is one in which both the terms ax and $\frac{a}{x^4}$ can be readily understood in terms of everyday mathematics, whereas the theory of atomic structure leads one into more difficult branches of mathematics. But the general principle is the same, and you just have to accept it as a fact that some of the new atomic theories cannot be understood in terms of " common sense."

OM: Then, do you mean that it is impossible for the theory to be understood by the ordinary man ?

YS: If you speak of understanding the theory, I think we may recognise three main lines of approach. There is first of all the man who wants to do the thing thoroughly, and who aims at original work on the subject. That is quite beyond your powers and, to be honest, I shouldn't advise you to encourage your son to try his hand at it either. It is a job for a first-class mathematician only, and there are already too many men wasting their time on it when it is all too clear that their mathematics isn't good enough.

Secondly, there is the man who is prepared to leave the mathematics to others, but who wants to get a real understanding of the underlying principles, so that he can keep an eye on the subject and see how new investigations may bear on his own work. This is possible for some men, but it requires considerable mental effort, and frankly I don't advise it for you, although I think you should do all you can to encourage your son to make the effort. This will mean that if you are going to take him into your works you must be prepared to take him from his university without a knowledge of technology. In a four years' course there is not time for a man to read both technology and theory of metals, and one or other must be sacrificed. I can quite understand how attractive it is to you to have a man coming into your works knowing exactly how the different machines are used, but you will find that in the long run your son will be a better investment if he comes to you with a real knowledge of what constitutes a metal, and then learns his technology after he joins you. There are very few universities where the right kind of instruction is given now, and on the whole I should advise you to let him read physical chemistry, and then turn over to metallurgy. This will give him a good general background, and you will find that if he is any good he will pick up the works practice pretty quickly.

Finally, there is the third type of man represented by you, my friend. You are too busy, and, if you won't mind my saying so, too much in the old groove ever to go really thoroughly into the new work, but there is no reason why you should not understand the general ideas, and grasp what the new men are after.

OM : Will it mean a lot of work?

YS: It is not so much a question of difficulty or of time, as of being prepared to think. The subject is not one to read in spare time in railway carriages, or while lunching in a restaurant. But if you are willing to sit down quietly from time to time, and think things out, there is no reason why you should not grasp what is going on—at any rate you could get a general idea so that some of the stuff at this new Institute would be more interesting to you.

OM : Well, look here, will you give me a list of books or papers, and I'll make an effort?

YS: The truth is, I'm afraid, that there is very little that is suitable. The " popular " accounts are mostly too early—some of them contain puzzling mistakes—or are too much concerned with showing how the mathematics works for simple problems. There are several deep books on metals—Mott and Jones is the best[1]—but they assume much too great a knowledge on the reader's part.

OM: Then what can I do?

YS: The only thing I can suggest is for me to give you some tutorial discussion.

[1] *The Theory of the Properties of Metals and Alloys*, by N. F. Mott and H. Jones. Since the completion of the MS. the following two books have appeared: *Atomic Theory for Students of Metallurgy*, by W. Hume-Rothery, and *An Introduction to the Electron Theory of Metals*, by G. V. Raynor. Both are published by the Institute of Metals.

OM : Oh, I see. Well, look here, is it really worth my while ?

YS : That depends on what you mean. If you mean, will it enable you to go back to your works and make better castings, the answer is " No." On the other hand there may be some very definite advantages.

In the first place, as you yourself have pointed out, the present position is unsatisfactory. It's almost absurd that a so-called " metallurgist " should be one of the last people to be able to understand what a metal is.

Secondly, there is always the possibility of practical applications and new discoveries. There is a good deal of work going on to test these theories in one way and another, and one never knows what may turn up—remember Faraday and the dynamo ! But, apart from this, there is no saying when these new theories will be of practical use. In some connections, such as magnetism or thermionic emission, this stage has already been reached. In problems such as those regarding the strength of metals, the electronic theory is probably farther from direct application. It may be five years or it may be fifty, but the important thing is that when the time comes metallurgical industry shall be in the hands of men who understand what is going on. If it is left in the control of those who cannot understand the new ideas, there is a distinct possibility that they may suddenly find themselves confronted by new and better alloys produced elsewhere by what may at first seem to them to be good luck, but which is in reality the result of a shrewd application of the theory of alloys to practical problems. In this case success will go to the country whose metallurgists can understand the new ideas, and this implies a method of thinking which cannot be acquired in a hurry. You must not imagine that the situation could be saved by suddenly calling on physicists and mathematicians to help you. Such men would be too much out of touch with the practical side of metallurgy. The best solution to the problem is to bring up a generation of metallurgists to whom the underlying ideas of the electron theory of atoms are as familiar as they already are to a well-trained chemist. Meanwhile people like yourself should obtain a general idea of the new outlook.

OM : Can this be done so that we deal only with metals and alloys ?

YS : No. The electron theory of metals and alloys is very complicated, and its ideas can be understood only if a number of much more simple problems are dealt with first. As you will soon realise, it is by no means easy to describe the nature of a single atom, and all these difficulties have to be overcome before there is any chance of your understanding the assembly of atoms which builds up a metallic crystal. We shall, therefore, have to discuss many things which have no direct reference to metals, and if you are not prepared to do this, you had better give up the whole idea.

2—Elementary

OLDER METALLURGIST : Before we begin, there is one point I should like cleared up. You gave the values of Avogadro's Number as 6.0247×10^{23}, but the value I have found in my textbooks is 6.06×10^{23}. How has the difference arisen ?

YOUNG SCIENTIST: In the last fifteen years it has become generally recognised that the previously accepted values of many of the physical constants were slightly in error. The reasons for this were discussed fully by R. T. Birge[1] in 1941, and if you want to understand the details you should read his two papers. There was an unfortunate period in which some books continued to print the old values of the physical constants, although original papers used more accurate values. In recent years J. W. M. Du Mond and E. R. Cohen[2] have given a list of what they consider the most probable values, and some of these differ slightly from those of Birge.

OM : I see. I suppose you'll now want to find out how much I know ?

YS : Yes, that would be the most sensible thing. You said before that you understood the significance of Avogadro's Number as giving the number of molecules in a gramme molecular weight of a substance. You realise, do you, that a knowledge of Avogadro's Number, when combined with the known densities of metals, enables us to get a rough idea of the sizes of atoms, in so far as these are indicated by the distances between atoms in solids ?

OM : Well, I can see that since the specific gravities of most metals are of the order 1 to 20, the distances between atoms in metals will be of the order 10^{-7} to 10^{-8} cm.

YS : That's right. The usual scale of length employed in describing atomic phenomena is the Angstrom Unit, which is equal to 10^{-8} cm, and is denoted by the symbol Å or A. The closest distances between neighbouring atoms in metallic crystals are of the order 2 to 4A, so that the sizes of metallic atoms lie within quite a narrow range.

OM : Hasn't there been some muddle about the Angstrom unit ?

YS : Yes, I'm afraid there has. The determination of inter-atomic distances in crystals is carried out by X-ray diffraction methods, and these require a knowledge of the wave lengths of X-rays. The wave lengths usually employed are those tabulated by Siegbahn, and although at the time these tables were drawn up the values were as accurate as possible, later work has revealed a slight systematic error, and what the crystallographers used to call Angstrom units

[1] *Reviews of Modern Physics*, 1941, Vol. 13, page 223. Also *Reports on Progress in Physics*, 1941. Physical Society of London, page 91.

[2] J. W. M. Du Mond and E. R. Cohen. *Reviews of Modern Physics*, 1953, Vol. 25, page 691.

really required multiplying by 1.00202 in order to convert them into true Angstrom units of 10^{-8} cm. I'm afraid the theory of metals isn't yet sufficiently advanced for this difference to be worth bothering about nowadays as regards the theory. But you should note that there is an increasing tendency nowadays to express crystallographic results in true Angstrom units of 10^{-8} cm. At the moment of writing (1953), there is I am afraid considerable confusion, because recommendations have been made to express all results in true Angstrom units, but these have not been universally accepted, and the symbol A is still sometimes used both for kX units and for true Angstroms. For accurate lattice spacing work, you must always verify what the author means when he refers to A units, although the difference between A and kX does not affect results to two places of decimals. You should also note that some writers have used the expression " crystal Angstroms " to describe kX units, although this practice is now dying out.

OM: Sometimes I've come across diagrams referring to " atomic units " of length. What are these?

YS: The atomic unit of length is equal to 0.5292 A. I'll explain its significance later when we come to deal with the structure of the hydrogen atom.

OM: Am I right in thinking that it is now definitely established that atoms possess a structure, and that they are no longer regarded as analogous to minute billiard balls as they were in the early days of chemistry?

YS: Oh, yes. That's now quite certain. From the experimental point of view, one may say that the story begins with the discovery of the electron at the end of the nineteenth century. In this work it was shown that certain conditions, such as electrical discharges in gases, or the heating of metals to high temperatures (thermionic emission), resulted in the emission of what were first called cathode rays. It was found that these rays were deflected by electric and magnetic fields as though they consisted of streams of negatively-charged particles, and by suitable methods it was possible to determine the charge and mass of these particles, which were then called *electrons*. The important discovery was made that electrons always possessed the same charge and mass, regardless of the substance from which they were produced. The values of the electronic mass (m) and charge (e) now accepted are

$m = 9.1085 \times 10^{-28}$ gram.

$e = 4.8029 \times 10^{-10}$ electrostatic units.

The mass of the electron is thus about $\dfrac{1}{1,840}$ that of hydrogen atom, and the facts suggested clearly that all atoms contained electrons as part of their structures.

The second important point was that the charge on the electron was the same as that on a univalent negative ion, that is, an ion such as the Cl' ion.

OM: How do you make that out?

YS: Well, as you will know, the charge on the gram molecular weight of a univalent ion is called a faraday, and is equal to 96,520 coulombs. Since Avogadro's Number is equal to 6.0247×10^{23}, the charge on a single univalent ion is $\dfrac{96,520}{6.0247 \times 10^{23}} = 1.60207 \times 10^{-19}$ coulombs.

Now 1 coulomb $= 2.99793 \times 10^9$ electrostatic units, and so the charge on a univalent negative ion is equal to $1.60207 \times 2.99793 \times 10^{-10}$ $= 4.8029 \times 10^{-10}$ electrostatic units, which is the value given above for the electronic charge.

OM: I see. So a univalent negative ion contains one extra electron above the number required to make the atom or group of atoms electrically neutral?

YS: That's right. And a univalent positive ion contains one electron fewer than the number required for a neutral atom or group of atoms.

OM: But I don't see why that follows. Can't there be positive electrons as well?

YS: No. That point was settled by the mass spectroscopic work of J. J. Thomson and F. W. Aston. In their work streams of ions or charged atoms or electrons were deflected by electric and magnetic fields arranged so that the ratio of the charge to the mass could be determined. These experiments showed that negative charges were associated both with electrons and with particles (negatively-charged ions) whose masses were the same as those of atoms or molecules. Positive charges, on the other hand, were found associated only with particles whose masses were those of atoms or molecules (positive ions). These experiments showed clearly that, so far as atomic structure was concerned, there was an essential difference between positive and negative electricity—the relatively light negatively-charged electrons could be lost by the atom, but the positive electricity seemed to be more deeply bound.

OM: But haven't I read something about positive electrons lately?

YS: Yes. Some of the more recent developments of nuclear physics have led to the production of positive electrons which are much lighter than the hydrogen atom. But these phenomena do not concern metallurgy, and I think we had really better leave them alone for the present, although we shall refer to them in Chapter 42.

OM: But just what is nuclear physics?

YS: Well, we've seen that the evidence suggested that the positive electricity associated with an atom was somehow held more firmly than the negative electricity. The next great step was due to Rutherford, who studied the scattering of α-particles by matter—α-particles are particles which are ejected in some radioactive transformations and they are He^{++} ions, that is helium atoms which have lost two electrons. A study of the scattering process (see Chapter 43) showed that atoms consisted of a minute positively-charged nucleus, whose dimensions were of the order 10^{-12} cm, surrounded by extra-nuclear electrons which occupied a region whose dimensions were of the order 10^{-7} to 10^{-8} cm. The nucleus is thus very small compared with the " size " of an atom, but almost the whole mass of the atom is contained in the nucleus, and the nucleus contains a positive charge of $+Ze$, where Z, the so-called *atomic number*, gives the position of the element in the Periodic Table of Mendeleev (Fig. 1). I imagine you will have met it in your young days.

OM : Yes, that's right. I understand the general periodic repetition of properties of the elements, but I seem to remember that there were one or two places where the table went wrong. The table as I knew it was in the order of increasing atomic weights, but cobalt has a higher atomic weight than nickel, although it comes before it in the periodic table. Similarly tellurium has a higher atomic weight than iodine, although the properties suggest the order antimony→tellurium→ iodine, and this is the order you have put in your table. It seems to me that the table is a bit of a fudge in one or two places.

YS : That difficulty has now been cleared up. The real characteristic of the periodic table (Fig. 1) is that it is in order not of increasing atomic weight, but of increasing atomic number. Thus copper is the twenty-ninth element in the table, and the atom of copper has a nuclear charge of $+29e$, and is surrounded by 29 electrons. Cobalt and nickel have atoms with nuclear charges of $+27e$ and $+28e$ respectively, and their order in the table is the order of increasing nuclear charge. The order of the elements in the periodic table was first established by Moseley in 1912.

OM : So the nucleus is even more minute than the atom ?

YS : Yes, but the nucleus contains almost the whole mass of the atom.

OM : If that is so, isn't it rather strange that the atomic weights of the different elements are such a curious jumble of odd fractions ? One would have expected some kind of regular scheme.

YS : That difficulty has been cleared up by the discovery of what are called *isotopes*. The original discovery here was in connection with the radioactive elements. These elements and their compounds were found to give off different kinds of radiation, and in some of these changes it was found that the radioactive element was changed into a new element belonging to a different group of the periodic table. This, of course, was in complete contrast to ordinary chemical changes, in which, although the state of combination of an element may alter, the element itself and its atoms are indestructible. The work on radioactive transformations also showed that some elements, notably lead, could exist in forms which were chemically indistinguishable,

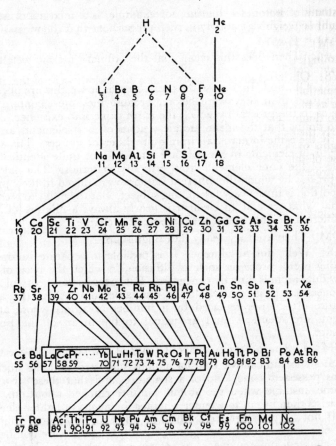

[*Courtesy Clarendon Press*

Fig. 1—Periodic table of the elements in graphic form

but possessed different atomic weights. These were called isotopes of the elements concerned, because the different isotopes were chemically indistinguishable and so occupied the same place (*iso* = **equal**, *topos* = **place**) in the periodic table. The development of this subject was due mainly to Soddy, and it was clear that the radioactive transformations involved something quite distinct from ordinary chemical change, and it was soon recognised that radioactive changes involved changes in the nuclei of the atoms, and that the isotopes of a given element were all characterised by the same charge on the nucleus—all the isotopes of lead for example have atoms with a nuclear charge of $+82e$, surrounded by 82 extra-nuclear electrons.

The methods of mass spectroscopy developed by J. J. Thomson and F. W. Aston then showed that nearly all the elements were really mixtures of isotopes—chlorine, for example, is a mixture of isotopes of atomic weights 35 and 37 in such proportions that the mean atomic weight is 35.457.

OM: Then does this mean that the ordinary atomic weights are meaningless?

YS: Oh, no ! In a sense the ordinary atomic weights are of greater fascination than they were before, because they must contain some clue as to the process by which the earth came into existence. There is no doubt that the mean atomic weights of most elements are very nearly the same in materials from quite different sources. The atomic weights of elements in meteors are almost if not quite identical with those of the same elements from ordinary materials. The nature of the process by which the different isotopes were mixed in their present proportion is thus a very fascinating subject. But the point to recognise is that what we call an element is nearly always a mixture of atoms of different weights but of the same nuclear charge.

OM: Then are they really indistinguishable?

YS: Well, not absolutely. It is possible to separate isotopes by making use of processes such as diffusion, in which the mass of each individual atom is directly concerned. But so far as the theory of alloys is concerned it is nearly always justifiable to consider the actual mixture of isotopes replaced by a number of atoms whose atomic weights are identical, and are equal to the mean of the isotopic mixture.

OM: I seem to have read about artificial isotopes. What are they?

YS: The radioactive transformations suggested that the nuclei of atoms possessed some kind of a structure, and that these structures became unstable when the atomic number reached about 90. The physicists then began to wonder whether the nuclei of lighter elements might not be disintegrated or broken up, and they found that this kind of change could be brought about if substances were bombarded with charged ions moving at extremely high velocities. In this way the science of nuclear physics has been developed and has led to the various atomic energy projects. In the course of this work many new isotopes of common elements have been prepared and identified.

OM: Then does this concern metallurgy?

YS: Up to a few years ago, the answer to that question would have been " No." In the ordinary processes of chemistry and metallurgy the characteristics of an element depend essentially on the nuclear charge, and the different isotopes of an element can be regarded as identical, so that nuclear physics need not be considered. You will know, however, that in the period 1940 to 1945, work was carried out which led to the development of atomic bombs, and to the prospect of the direct utilisation of atomic energy. In these processes we are concerned directly with changes in the nuclei of atoms, and the immense possibilities which have been opened up have led to many problems in which the metallurgist is directly or indirectly interested.

These problems are so distinct from those of ordinary metallurgy that it will probably be better to discuss nuclear structure separately. (*See* Chapter 40.)

You should, however, note that, apart from the work on atomic energy, the nuclear physics is of interest to metallurgy in connection with the study of processes such as diffusion. The atoms of some of the new artificial isotopes are unstable, and undergo further transformations with the emission of rays similar to those of the radioactive changes whose study led to all these developments. In this way it is possible to produce radioactive isotopes of some common metals, and these isotopes can be used to study processes such as self-diffusion. One can, for example, plate a radioactive isotope on to the ordinary non-radioactive form of the element, and then heat the specimen, and see how far the radioactive atoms migrate in a given time. This kind of work offers many possibilities because it enables one to distinguish between atoms which so far as their ordinary chemical properties are concerned, are almost identical.

OM: Then it amounts to saying that the general idea of an atom is a minute positive charge of $+Ze$ surrounded by Z electrons?

YS: That's right. And the general problem of atomic structure is the way in which an assembly of Z electrons will move round a nucleus of charge $+Ze$.

OM: It must be pretty complicated.

YS: Oh, I assure you it is! For this reason we had better begin with the simplest case of all. This is, of course, the hydrogen atom, because it possesses only one electron.

3—The Hydrogen Atom: Early Theory

YOUNG SCIENTIST : Well, we agreed to start with the structure of the hydrogen atom. From what we have already said, you will have got the general idea that the hydrogen atom consists of one electron of charge $- e$, in motion round a nucleus of charge $+ e$, the dimensions of the nucleus being of the order 10^{-12} cm, whilst the region covered by the motion of the electron is of the order 10^{-8} cm.

OLDER METALLURGIST : Yes, that's all right. But is it necessary to do all this to understand the nature of a metal ?

YS : Yes ! The nucleus and the electron of the hydrogen atom are held together as a stable structure because of the electrostatic attraction between the positive and negative charges. When one gets down to the bottom of things, it is this kind of attraction which is responsible for the cohesion in metals. As we shall see later, this attraction may take forms or produce effects which cannot be described in terms of " common sense," but the hydrogen atom is the simplest example of all, and unless you understand it fairly thoroughly you will have little chance of understanding the structure of a metal. We have seen that the experimental evidence led to the idea of a nuclear atom with planetary electrons revolving in orbits round the positively charged nucleus. The simplest case will clearly be that of a circular orbit, and we will consider this first.

OM : But what is your justification for assuming a circular orbit ? Surely there are many other possibilities ?

YS : The circular orbit is assumed as being the most easy to deal with mathematically. After all, it is only common sense to try a simple assumption first. If it works, then well and good ; if it doesn't you can make your more elaborate assumptions later.

OM : Does the circular orbit work ?

YS : Now ! Now ! You mustn't cheat ! The theory of the atom isn't like a detective story where the dishonest reader can look at the last chapter first, and then say there is no need to read the rest of the book. There's no taking short cuts like that !

Let us assume that we have an electron moving in a circular orbit of radius r, as shown in Fig. 2. Then since the electron has a charge of $-e$, and the nucleus a charge of $+e$, the electron will be attracted towards the nucleus with a force equal to $\frac{e^2}{r^2}$. If the electron is moving in a stable orbit, this inward force of attraction must be balanced by the outward centrifugal force which is equal to $\frac{mu^2}{r}$, where u is the velocity of the electron and m is its mass.

We have, therefore,

$$\frac{mu^2}{r} = \frac{e^2}{r^2}$$

and hence the kinetic energy of the electron, which is equal to $\frac{1}{2}\,mu^2$, will be given by

$$\frac{1}{2}mu^2 = \frac{1}{2}\frac{e^2}{r}.$$

The *total energy* of the electron will be the sum of the kinetic energy and the potential energy, and when we measure the potential energy we have always to assume some arbitrary zero. For this purpose it is customary to take the zero as being that of an electron at rest at an infinite distance from the nucleus. In this case, as the electron approaches the nucleus, its potential energy will become increasingly negative, and a simple integration of the inverse square law of force will show you that the potential energy of the electron at a distance r from the nucleus is equal to

$$-\frac{e^2}{r}.$$

OM : That's what always puzzles me. It doesn't seem sense to talk about negative energy. Surely energy must be positive ?

YS : No. It's just a matter of the definition of where you start from. Let's take a simple example. Suppose you have a hill and

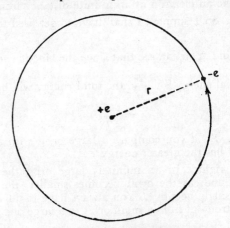

Fig. 2—To illustrate the circular orbit assumed in the older theory of the hydrogen atom

The electron of mass m and charge −e is assumed to move in a circular orbit round the nucleus of charge + e. If the radius of the circle is r, and the velocity of the electron is u, the outward centrifugal force is equal to $\frac{mu^2}{r}$, and this is balanced by the inward attraction which is equal to $\frac{e^2}{r^2}$ (inverse square law of attraction).

a valley, and you call the potential energy of a man in the valley zero. Then when he climbs the hill his potential energy will be positive. That all clear?

OM: Yes. That's right.

YS: But, after all, that is purely arbitrary. If the man had a house on the top of the hill, he might quite reasonably call his potential energy at home zero, and in this case when he went down into the valley his potential energy would become increasingly negative. Isn't that clear?

OM: I see. You mean that he could adopt whichever system he chose, and that all the energy values in the one system would differ by a constant amount from those in the other system?

YS: Yes. Whenever we include potential energy, there has to be an arbitrary zero.

OM: Well, then, why not choose a more sensible zero, and so avoid these negative quantities?

YS: Well, what would you suggest?

OM: Anything that makes it positive.

YS: The difficulty there is that one can't get a uniform zero for different atoms. If you take the zero of potential energy as being that of an electron at rest at an infinite distance from the nucleus, then all atoms can be compared on the same scale, because in each case you can imagine an electron at an infinite distance from the nucleus.

OM: I see. So I suppose I shall have to get used to the negative values?

YS: You will! You can see that since the kinetic energy is $+ \dfrac{1}{2} \dfrac{e^2}{r}$, and the potential energy is $- \dfrac{e^2}{r}$, the total energy will be

$$- \dfrac{1}{2} \dfrac{e^2}{r}.$$

OM: I see. So if you compare a large orbit with a small orbit, the larger orbit has the greater energy?

YS: That's right. In an infinitely large orbit the total energy would be zero and, as the orbit becomes smaller, the total energy becomes increasingly negative. You always have to do work in order to push an electron out from a small orbit to a large one.

Further, you can see that since the kinetic energy equals $+ \dfrac{1}{2} \dfrac{e^2}{r}$, the kinetic energy becomes smaller as the orbit becomes larger. So if we compare an electron in a large orbit with one in a small orbit, we may say that the electron in the large orbit has the smaller kinetic energy, but the larger potential energy and the larger total energy.

OM: Does this apply to the more complete and recent theories?

YS: In a general way, yes. As you will learn later, we have to deal with electronic motions which cannot be expressed in terms of simple orbits. But the general idea holds, and we have to do work in order to push an electron out from a state of motion near the nucleus to one farther from the nucleus. In a general way we may also say that the farther an electron is from the nucleus, the greater is its potential energy and its total energy, and the smaller is its kinetic energy. The early theory which we have just considered has undergone drastic modification, but it did express a great deal of the truth.

OM: Then, if I understand you rightly, the early theory said that the electron of the hydrogen atom could move in an infinite number of possible orbits, and that if the orbit had a radius r, the electron had a total energy equal to $-\dfrac{1}{2}\dfrac{e^2}{r}$, and a kinetic energy equal to $+\dfrac{1}{2}\dfrac{e^2}{r}$.

YS: That's right.

4—The Hydrogen Atom : The Bohr Theory

OLDER METALLURGIST: I've been thinking over what you have just told me, and I've come to the conclusion that the theory doesn't work.

YOUNG SCIENTIST: Oh! What do you think is wrong?

OM: In the first place, I don't see why you should get a stable atom. The theory seems to allow the electron to move in an infinite number of possible orbits, and I should have expected the electron to move gradually closer and closer to the nucleus. Further, if changes in the energy of the electronic motion resulted in the emission of energy in the form of radiation, there would seem to be an infinite number of possibilities, and I should expect the emission spectrum of hydrogen to be continuous over a wide range of wave lengths. But if I understand it rightly, the hydrogen spectrum consists of a number of sharp lines. It seems to me, therefore, that the theory you have described accounts neither for the stability of the atom nor for the occurrence of sharp spectral lines.

YS: You're perfectly right, but you must not think that I have been wasting your time. The theory which I have described contains a considerable element of truth. The general relation between the size of an orbit, and the accompanying potential and kinetic energies, applies to the more complete theories, and must be thoroughly grasped. But you are quite right in saying that the early theory could account neither for the stability of the atom nor for the existence of sharp spectral lines.

OM: Well, tell me, how one does account for the stability of an atom?

YS: I'm afraid it is rather a long story. I suppose you have grasped that light, and in fact all radiation, is a form of energy?

OM: Oh, yes! That's all right. Even people like myself did problems about the loss of heat by radiation.

YS: Well, the first theories of radiation were based on the assumption that energy could change continuously. But it was found that this led to difficulties, and that some of the facts could not be explained satisfactorily. For our purpose we need not go into details, but in brief there was a complete hold-up until Planck in 1901 introduced the revolutionary idea that energy could be absorbed or emitted only in definite units or *quanta*, and that radiation of frequency v was associated with quanta of magnitude hv, where h is the mysterious Planck's Constant, and is equal to 6.625×10^{-27} erg sec. In the case of sodium, for example, the well-known yellow line in the spectrum (the D line) has a wave length of 5,893A. The velocity of light is equal to 2.99793×10^{10} cm per second, and consequently the frequency of the D line equals

$$\frac{2.99793 \times 10^{10}}{5893 \times 10^{-8}} = 5.087 = 10^{14}.$$

The corresponding quantum of energy is thus

$$h\nu = 6.625 \times 10^{-27} \times 5.087 \times 10^{14} = 3.370 \times 10^{-12}$$

ergs, and the D line of sodium is regarded as the result of a transition in which the energy of the atom falls by 3.370×10^{-12} ergs.

OM: What sort of a change is that in terms of grams of sodium instead of a single atom?

YS: The number of atoms in a gram atom is given by Avogadro's Number, so the energy change per gram atom will be $3.370 \times 10^{-12} \times 6.0247 \times 10^{23} = 20.30 \times 10^{11}$ ergs per gram atomic weight of sodium. Now 1 joule is equal to 10^7 ergs, and 1 calorie is equal to 4.1855 joules. The energy change per gram atomic weight is thus $\frac{20.30 \times 10^{11}}{4.1855 \times 10^7} = 4.85 \times 10^4$ calories = 48.5 kilo-calories per gram atomic weight. The atomic weight of sodium is 22.997, and so the energy change per gram will be equal to $\frac{48.5}{22.997} = 2.109$ kilo-calories.

The D line of sodium is thus the result of an atomic process, the energy change of which is equivalent to 2.109 kilo-calories per gram. It is in this way that Planck's Constant can be used to indicate the magnitude of the energy change associated with the emission of radiation of known frequency.

OM: Does the same constant apply to the lines of an absorption spectrum?

YS: Yes. A line of frequency ν in an absorption spectrum is the result of a large number of atomic processes each involving the absorption of a quantum energy equal to $h\nu$. This idea of quanta of energy was then extended by Einstein to the problem of specific heats of solids. It was generally accepted that the thermal energy of a crystal was the result of atomic vibrations, whose amplitude increased with rise of temperature. But the older views could not account for all the facts, and it was left to Einstein to introduce the concept that a vibration of frequency ν was associated with quanta of energy of magnitude $h\nu$. The original theory of Einstein was but a first approximation, and there have been many developments, some of which we shall deal with later. For our present purpose it is sufficient to note that in many atomic processes radiant energy or vibrational energy appears to exist in the form of definite quanta, whose magnitude is given by the fundamental relation $E = h\nu$. Now you have already pointed out that the hydrogen spectrum consists of sharp lines of definite frequencies. Can't you begin to see how this bears on our previous theories of the orbital motion of an electron round the hydrogen nucleus?

OM: Wait a minute while I think. You mean that since the frequency of each spectral line is fixed, the quanta of energy are fixed by the relations $E = h\nu$, and hence each spectral line will correspond with a definite change in the energy of the atom. It looks as though the atom could somehow exist in a series of states each with a definite energy.

YS: That's right. That's the point, the significance of which was first appreciated by Bohr in 1913. Bohr in his first great theory of the atom, from which everything else has followed, made the fundamental assumption that of all the conceivable orbits which the classical theory allowed, only certain orbits were actually possible, and that, when the electron moved in one of these orbits, it was in a *stationary state* in which it neither gained nor emitted energy. If an electron jumped from a stationary state of energy E_1 to a stationary state of energy E_2 (less than E_1) the transition was imagined to correspond with the emission of a quantum of energy whose frequency was given by the relation

$$h\nu = E_1 - E_2.$$

In the same way the lines of the absorption spectra corresponded with transitions from a state of lower to one of higher energy.

OM: Does all this apply to other atoms, or only to hydrogen?

YS: It's perfectly general. Other atoms contain more electrons, so that the electronic motion is more complicated, but each atom is again imagined to possess a number of stationary states, and the sharp spectral lines are the result of the electronic motion changing from one stationary state to another.

OM: It seems to me that the assumption of stationary states is a rather obvious *ad hoc* assumption.

YS: Now! Now! You're being wise after the event! It was certainly an *ad hoc* assumption, made with the deliberate object of obtaining a stable atom, and of accounting for sharp spectral lines. But, however simple it may seem now, the assumption of stationary states was anything but obvious when it was first made. You didn't suggest it yourself although I'd given it you almost ready labelled. The introduction of simple ideas which everyone has missed is the hall mark of genius, and Bohr is a genius of the first order.

OM: How was it possible to choose the stationary states?

YS: Well, to understand that you will have to go a little more deeply into things. You have already pointed out that the spectrum of hydrogen consists of a number of sharp lines. Examination showed that these lines could be grouped together in series, and that the frequencies of the different lines could be expressed by equations of the type

$$C\left(\frac{1}{n_1^2} - \frac{1}{n_2^2}\right)$$

where n_1 and n_2 were whole numbers and C was a constant. There was, for example, one series of lines whose frequencies were given by the relation

$$C \left(\frac{1}{1^2} - \frac{1}{n_2{}^2} \right)$$

where $n_2 = 2, 3, 4 \ldots$ etc. Another series of lines had frequencies given by the equation

$$C \left(\frac{1}{2^2} - \frac{1}{n_2{}^2} \right)$$

where $n_2 = 3, 4, 5 \ldots$ etc.

OM: Was all this found out by Bohr?

YS: Oh, no! The classification of the lines was made much earlier. The first series was discovered by Balmer in 1885. Bohr realised that these series relations contained the clue to the stationary states of the hydrogen atom, and he found that the correct results could be predicted if it were assumed that the only possible circular orbits of the electrons in the hydrogen atom were those for which the angular momentum was a whole number multiple of $\frac{h}{2\pi}$, where h is Planck's constant.

OM: What's the angular momentum of an electron in a circular orbit?

YS: The angular momentum, or moment of momentum of an electron in a circular orbit, is equal to mur. You can see that mu is the momentum of the electron, so that mur is the moment of the momentum about the centre of the orbit.

OM: What is the significance of it?

YS: Well, if you look upon momentum as a measure of the quantity of movement, then angular momentum is a measure of the quantity of movement and its turning effect. The importance of angular momentum is that in processes such as collisions, it is conserved.

OM: Then you mean that Bohr's assumption is equivalent to saying that

$$mur = \frac{nh}{2\pi}$$

where n is a whole number?

YS: That's right. Further, you will find that if you combine this relation with the earlier equations, the energies of the electrons in the different stationary states are given by

$$E = - \frac{2\pi^2 \, me^4}{h^2} \times \frac{1}{n^2}$$

In this way transitions of the electron from stationary states for which $n = 2, 3, 4 \ldots$ to the stationary state for which $n = 1$, will give energy changes proportional to terms of the form

$$\frac{1}{1^2} - \frac{1}{n^2}$$

so that the general type of spectral series is accounted for. This in itself is not so very remarkable, because the assumptions were chosen with this end in view. That is to say, Bohr saw that the series laws required the angular momentum to assume whole number multiples of some common unit. What was remarkable was that the numerical values came out almost correct. It is common practice to deal, not with the frequency ν, but with the wave number, that is, the number of waves per unit length. If λ is the wave length of a spectral line and c the velocity of light, the wave number $\frac{1}{\lambda}$ is equal to $\frac{\nu}{c}$. The Bohr theory of circular orbits thus required the wave number associated with a transition from an orbit of quantum number n_1 to one of quantum number n_2 to be

$$\frac{1}{\lambda} = \frac{2\pi^2 m e^4}{ch^3}\left(\frac{1}{n_1^2} - \frac{1}{n_2^2}\right) = R\left(\frac{1}{n_1^2} - \frac{1}{n_2^2}\right)$$

where R, the so-called Rydberg constant, was equal to

$$\frac{2\pi^2 m e^4}{ch^3}.$$

It was then found that the above value for R was almost exactly that required by experiment. This was quite unforeseen, and showed that a discovery of the first importance had been made. Planck's Constant, which had been discovered in quite different connections, suddenly appeared as playing a vital part in problems of atomic structure.

OM: You said that the constant term was very nearly correct. Should it not have been exactly so?

YS: No. So far we have been making one simplifying assumption: namely, that when the electron revolves round the nucleus, the latter may be considered as fixed. Strictly speaking, this is justified only if the nucleus is infinitely heavy compared with the electron. In the actual problem the electron revolves round the common centre of gravity of the nucleus and electron. When this small correction was applied, the constant R was found to have the correct value.

OM: Is that the whole story of the Bohr theory?

YS: Oh, no! You yourself pointed out that circular orbits were only one out of many possible types. The more general case is that of an elliptical orbit, and the Bohr theory was extended to the case of elliptical orbits, for which the stationary states required the introduction of two quantum numbers.

OM: Wait a minute. What's a quantum number?

YS: Well, in the case of the circular orbit, the possible states were defined by the relation

$$mur = \frac{nh}{2\pi}$$

as we have already explained (page 29). The term n can assume the whole number values 1, 2, 3 . . . and these are called quantum numbers. The total energy varies as $-\frac{1}{n^2}$, so that the energy becomes greater with increasing quantum number.

OM: What then is the significance of the two quantum numbers in an elliptical orbit?

YS: The first and second quantum numbers are denoted by the symbols n and k, and in the case of the hydrogen atom the major axis of the ellipse is proportional to n^2 whilst the minor axis is proportional to kn, so that $\frac{k}{n}$ gives the ratio of the minor axis to the major axis, and so determines the eccentricity—when $n = k$ the orbit is circular. The secondary quantum number k may have any value up to, but not greater than n. In a hydrogen atom the energy of the electron is proportional to $-\frac{1}{n^2}$, so that all orbits of a given n have the same energy. The secondary quantum number k is a measure of the angular momentum of the electronic orbit, the angular momentum being equal to $\frac{kh}{2\pi}$. You will see that for a circular orbit where $n = k$, this is equivalent to our previous statement that the angular momentum was equal to $\frac{nh}{2\pi}$.

OM: In the theory of the elliptical orbits, can one have a series of orbits of the same n but different k?

YS: Oh, yes! If $n = 3$, for example, one can have the three orbits defined by $n = 3, k = 1; n = 3, k = 2; n = 3, k = 3$. Of these the last will be circular, and the first will be the most eccentric. You will probably have read popular accounts of the theory of relativity?

OM: Yes, that's all right. The ordinary laws of motion go wrong for very high velocities, don't they?

YS: Yes, and in the more advanced developments of the Bohr theory that had to be taken into account. In an eccentric elliptic orbit, the distance of the electron from the nucleus varies as it goes round the orbit, and this causes an alteration in the velocity—the velocity of the electron is greatest when it is nearest to the nucleus. All this had to be considered theoretically, and the result was a very satisfactory theory of the hydrogen atom.

OM: Did the theory apply to other atoms as well?

YS: In a general way, yes. The problem becomes enormously more complicated when more than one electron is present, because the motion of each electron is affected by the fields produced by the other electrons, and these are all moving. But Bohr was the first to produce

31

a general scheme showing how the electrons were divided into different groups. The details have been slightly modified or extended by later workers, but it is to Bohr that the whole idea is due.

OM: What do you mean by saying that the electrons are divided into groups?

YS: Well, we've already seen that the periodicity summarised in Mendeleev's table (page 18) suggested that some kind of repetition occurred in the process by which atoms were built up with increasing numbers of extra-nuclear electrons. We have also seen that in the hydrogen atom, the one electron can enter a series of possible electronic states defined by the quantum numbers $n = 1, 2, 3 \ldots$ Bohr's general idea was that in going down the periodic table, electrons entered a group defined by one or more quantum numbers, and that when this group contained a certain number of electrons, a stable arrangement was produced, so that on passing to the next element the extra electron had to enter a new group, and in this way the periodicity of properties was explained.

For example, a large number of facts indicated that the alkali metals contained one relatively loosely-bound electron, and Bohr concluded that the valency electrons of lithium, sodium, potassium, rubidium, and caesium were in orbits with the principal quantum number $n = 2, 3, 4, 5$ and 6, respectively, and the secondary quantum number $k = 1$. The remaining electrons of these elements were then regarded as filling groups of lower quantum numbers.

OM: Then do you mean that the energies of the valency electrons of the different alkali metals are all related by terms of the type

$$-\frac{1}{n^2}?$$

YS: Oh, no! The simple $-\frac{1}{n^2}$ terms of the hydrogen atom are the result of the electron being under the influence of the one nucleus of charge $+ e$. In the alkali metals, the nuclear charge is greater but, as far as the valency electron is concerned, most of the nuclear charge is neutralised or screened off by the other electrons, and the problem is complicated.

OM: So it amounts to saying that the quantum numbers of the valency electrons of the alkali metals are no longer so simply related to their energies?

YS: That's right. But the general character of the elliptical orbits was assumed to be retained. The orbit of the valency electron in caesium ($n = 6, k = 1$) was regarded as more eccentric than that of the valency electron in lithium ($n = 2, k = 1$). But it is not worth our while worrying about the details of the elliptical orbits because, although the Bohr theory was the first great step forward, the whole viewpoint has now been changed. Much of the detail of the Bohr theory has been discarded, and we have even had to reject the idea of motion which can be visualised as that of an electron in an orbit. But the great landmarks of the Bohr theory still stand. The electrons in atoms do occupy stationary states, and these are characterised or defined by quantum numbers. The spectral lines are the result of transitions from one stationary state to another, and the equation $E_1 - E_2 = h\nu$ does relate the frequency of the quantum of radiation to the energies of the two stationary states. Further, the division of electrons of the atoms of the elements into the main groups and sub-groups which was first made by Bohr still stands. The theory contains an immense element of truth, and you must understand its main ideas if you are to appreciate what follows.

Suggestions for further reading.

For a detailed account of the Bohr theory, the following books may be recommended:
The Structure of the Atom, E. N. da C. Andrade, 1927 (G. Bell & Son, London);
The Electronic Theory of Valency, N. V. Sidgwick, 1927 (Clarendon Press, Oxford).

5—Electron Waves and Light Waves

OLDER METALLURGIST: I've been thinking over what you said and, if it isn't impertinent for a mere metallurgist to say so, it seems to me that the Bohr theory isn't so satisfactory as you made out.

YOUNG SCIENTIST: Well, let's hear your objections.

OM: It's rather difficult to explain what I mean, but it seems to me that you are really trying to unite two quite different points of view. On the one hand, you've been speaking of electrons in orbits, and for these you have been using the equations of ordinary schoolboy dynamics. Then you have suddenly introduced these whole numbers, and you've planted them down on the top of ordinary dynamics without any justification or reason. I can quite well see the fascination of the whole-number relations for the spectral series, but it seems to me that your procedure is logically unsatisfactory.

YS: You're quite right. The Bohr theory, in spite of its great success, was logically unsatisfactory. As you have pointed out, the electron in its orbit was assumed to behave like an ordinary " classical particle," and then the apparently quite arbitrary whole number or quantum relations were superimposed. This was quite illogical, and the whole theory was a rather confused jumble of the older mechanics, and what seemed to be quite arbitrary whole number restrictions. Further, some facts were found which did not agree with the Bohr theory, and it became apparent that although the theory was an immense step forward a fundamentally different outlook was required.

OM: Is it possible for me to understand the next stage?

YS: As you pride yourself on being a practical man, it will probably be best to keep in touch with experiment as far as possible, and we may say that considered experimentally—this is not the historical order of things—the secret to the mystery lies in the fact that electrons are found to exhibit interference effects, and to behave in some ways as though they were waves. Have you heard anything about this?

OM: Well, I know that it is possible to determine crystal structures by means of electron diffraction methods, but I don't know much about the details.

YS: You know how electrons are given off by a metal if it is heated to a high enough temperature?

OM: You mean as in thermionic valves?

YS: Yes, that's right. Well, if you take a stream of electrons, and let them fall through a known potential difference, you obtain a beam of electrons moving with a velocity which can be calculated. It was first shown by Davisson and Germer (1927), and by G. P. Thomson (1927), that a beam of electrons of velocity u underwent diffraction

34

effects, as though it consisted of waves of wave length λ given by the relation

$$\lambda = \frac{h}{mu}$$

If, for example, a beam of electrons of velocity u is allowed to strike a specimen of metal filings, it is not scattered uniformly in all directions but produces diffraction rings quite analogous to the rings formed by X-rays in the Debye-Scherrer method of X-ray crystal analysis. Fig. 3 shows examples of electron diffraction patterns.

OM: You mean that if you change the velocity of the electrons, you alter the wave length?

YS: That's right. The faster the electrons are travelling, the shorter is the wave length, as you can readily see from the above equation. The reciprocal of the wave length, $\frac{1}{\lambda}$, is often called the wave number,

and is given by

$$\frac{1}{\lambda} = \frac{mu}{h}$$

so that the wave number, or number of waves per centimetre, is proportional to the momentum of the electrons in the beam.

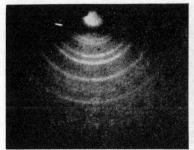

Spluttered platinum; normal pattern

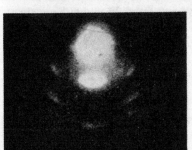

Spluttered platinum [111] orientation

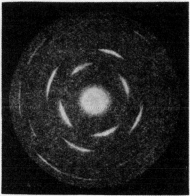

Beaten gold foil (Trillat and Oketani)

Fig. 3—Examples of electron diffraction patterns

[Illustrations reproduced from " Theory and Practice of Electron Diffraction " (Thomson & Cochrane), by courtesy of Macmillan & Co., Ltd.

OM: That's all very interesting, but what has it got to do with the structure of atoms or of metals?

YS: Doesn't it strike you that it is going to be very difficult to reconcile these wave-like properties with the existence of the electrically-charged particles which we have imagined to move in orbits? It is surely the essence of a particle that it is all together in one place, whereas these interference effects seem to require continually expanding wave fronts which may reinforce or may neutralise one another according as they are in phase or not.

OM: Well, if you are going to argue like that, surely exactly the same applies to what you have said about the quantum theory of light? Everybody knows that light is a wave motion of the ether, and this requires continuously expanding wave fronts, whereas you have said in almost so many words that light travels about in little bundles, or particles, or quanta, or whatever-you-like-to-call-them of energy. You can't have it both ways—either light is a wave-motion, or it is a stream of particles—it can't be both.

YS: The comparison you have made is quite a fair one, and the difficulty of reconciling the wave-like and particle-like aspects of light is quite analogous to the difficulties in connection with the particle and wave aspects of the electron.

OM: It seems to me that this is a case where the physicists have been frankly dishonest. They have used a wave theory where it suited them, and a particle theory where it suited them, and they seem to have ignored the fact that the two ideas are in plain contradiction.

YS: Well, as a matter of fact, the modern theory is concerned largely with the problem of reconciling the two points of view.

OM: You can't have it both ways. It must be one or the other—waves or particles—not both.

YS: Suppose you ask yourself exactly what you mean by the wave theory of light. Have you ever watched light waves, or read of any experiments of that kind?

OM: No. That's not my line of work. I should like to hear about the experiments, though.

YS: Well, to be candid, there aren't any. Nobody has ever seen light waves in the act of waving.

OM: But surely the interference experiments must mean that there are light waves?

YS: Now! Now! You say that you are a sound practical man, so suppose you think for a minute, and ask yourself what are the actual observable quantities in an interference experiment.

OM: Well, I suppose you measure light patches and dark patches on a screen or on a photographic plate.

YS: Exactly! The observables are the relative intensities of light at different places. These intensities are what you observe or measure, and nobody has ever observed an actual light wave. Further, nobody has ever detected the hypothetical ether to which you referred. For a long time people imagined that light was a vibration in an actual physical ether, and all sorts of hypotheses were advanced about the nature of the vibrating medium. But there was a complete failure to detect the medium, or even to be able to detect motion through it. The celebrated Michelson-Morley (1887) experiment was an attempt to detect the motion of the earth relative to the ether, but it failed completely, and all other attempts to reveal the presence of the ether have failed.

So, as a sound practical man, you must accept it that the observable quantities in an interference experiment are the intensities of light.

OM: But, surely people still use the wave theory? Why, the equations of the wave theory are used in X-ray crystal analysis!

YS: Now! Now! You must think more carefully! What you do in X-ray diffraction work, or in any optical interference experiment, is to calculate the relative intensities of the radiation at different places by means of certain mathematical equations. These equations are the same as those for a wave motion, and the function which expresses the intensity of the radiation is proportional to the square of what would be the amplitude if the equations referred to an actual wave motion. It is of course perfectly true that, historically, the equations were deduced on the assumption of a wave theory of light but, as a practical man, what you use is the mathematical equation, and you are not concerned with the historical background.

OM: But surely the fact that the equation is that of a wave motion must mean that light is a wave motion?

YS: Oh, no! That doesn't follow at all. The following example was, I think, originally due to F. A. Lindemann (later Lord Cherwell), and may perhaps help you. You know what is meant by a steel rod in torsion?

OM: You mean a rod held at one end and twisted at the other?

YS: That's more or less right. Well, there is a certain mathematical equation which gives the stress in a rod under torsion. D'you know anything about soap bubbles?

OM: About what?

YS: About soap bubbles.

OM: But what have soap bubbles to do with steel rods in torsion?

YS: Well, when you blow a soap bubble, there is a certain mathematical equation which expresses the curvature of the bubble. It was noticed by G. I. Taylor in 1917 that the equation for the curvature of the soap bubble was of the same mathematical form as that for the stress in a rod under torsion. The mathematical correspondence was so complete that in cases where the torsional problem was too difficult to be solved, it was possible to blow the appropriate soap bubble—sometimes they blew out a thin rubber membrane instead— and then by measuring its curvature it was possible to solve the problem in torsional stress.

OM: That was clever work.

YS: Yes, it was very ingenious, and you can understand how a group of men who were continually solving stress problems by these methods might become so familiar with them that they began to visualise the torsional problem in terms of the appropriate soap bubble. In this way they might begin to build up a kind of " soap-bubble statics " in which all the problems investigated were those of torsional stress, whilst all the equations used could be visualised in terms of soap-bubble curvature. But, however far this correspondence was carried, they would clearly never be justified in saying that a rod of steel in torsion was the curvature of a soap bubble.

OM: I begin to see what you are after. You mean that the fact that the mathematical equations used in interference problems are the same as those of wave motion does not mean that light itself is a wave motion.

YS: That's right.

OM: Then how am I to think of light?

YS: You should think of a light ray as consisting of a stream of light particles, or *photons*, each of energy $h\nu$, where ν is the frequency and h is Planck's Constant. The intensity of the light at any place is proportional to the density of the photons, or to the number of photons per unit volume at the place concerned. When you want to calculate this intensity, you use the equations of the wave theory, with the interpretation that the square of the amplitude at each place is proportional to the density of photons, or in other words to the probability of finding a photon at the place concerned. In this way you drop all attempts to think of a mechanical vibrating medium, or ether, and your wave theory remains merely as a form of mathematics which enables you to calculate the density of photons at different places. In an interference experiment for example, the places of bright illumination are those where there is a high probability of finding a photon, and are the places where the amplitude is high. The dark regions are the places where the amplitude is zero, or at any rate very small, and are the regions where the probability of finding a photon is small. In this way you think of light as consisting of particles, and you interpret the intensities on a probability basis, the probabilities being calculated by means of the equations of the wave theory.

OM: Then does this mean that all the properties of light can be interpreted in terms of the same theory?

YS: Yes. The early form of optical theory, *geometrical optics*, dealt with light rays, and was concerned with the relatively large-scale phenomena such as reflection and refraction. This branch of optics failed entirely to explain interference phenomena, and these were explained by the wave theory. It could, however, easily be shown that the wave theory led to the laws of the older geometrical optics when the scale of events was much larger than a wave length. So the wave theory included the older geometrical optics, but seemed at first to be in contradiction to the quantum phenomena. The line of approach which I have described reconciles these two aspects of light. It does not, of course, provide an explanation of why light behaves in this way, but it reduces the facts to order. We can accept the fact that we meet light in the form of photons, and at the same time we can accept the wave theory as giving a means of calculating the photon densities of light at different places.

OM: Then does this line of approach mean that it is no longer correct to speak of light waves?

YS: Oh, it's perfectly all right to speak of light waves, and to think in terms of light waves, provided that you remember that it is nothing more than a means of visualising your mathematical equations—there is no harm in the engineer visualising his problems of torsional stress in terms of soap-bubble curvature, provided that he doesn't mistake soap for steel!

OM: Then you mean that I have got to get used to the idea of thinking of the wave theory of light as nothing more than a method of calculating the probabilities of finding photons at different places?

YS: That's right. In a sense the waves may be called probability waves—where the amplitude of the waves is large the probability of finding a photon is great.

Suggestion for further reading. For work on electron diffraction reference may be made to *Theory and Practice of Electron Diffraction* G. P. Thomson and W. Cochrane (Macmillan and Co., Ltd.).

6—Electron Waves

OLDER METALLURGIST: From the hints you have dropped, I suppose you are going to tell me that the electron waves are to be treated in the same way as light waves?

YOUNG SCIENTIST: That's more or less right.

OM: But the more I've thought about that, the more it seems to me that it isn't sense. What I mean is this: light has always been rather a funny thing—it travels about, but it has no weight, and its wave properties are very pronounced. I think I did begin to understand what you meant about the probability theory of photon density, but it all seems rather mysterious, and quite different from electrons which are, after all, quite definitely particles.

YS: Well, to be honest, I think you are wrong there, and that you are being influenced by the historical order of things. In the case of light you were thoroughly used to a wave theory before the " photon " or " particle " properties of light were discovered. In the case of electrons, on the other hand, you were acquainted with the " particle " properties before the wave-like properties were discovered. But you must remember that in the case of an electron diffraction experiment, the wave-like characteristics are just as pronounced as those in optical diffraction. Conversely, in a photo-electric experiment the photon behaves very definitely like a particle. In each case there is a dual particle and wave behaviour.

OM: Then do you mean that the waves of an electron have no physical existence, and are simply to be interpreted as probability waves?

YS: Exactly. Just as you are to think of light as consisting of photons whose density is given by the amplitude of a wave equation, so you are to think of electrons as particles, and then when you want to calculate the density of electrons at a given place, or in other words the probability of finding an electron in a given small volume, you are to use a wave equation whose amplitude is to be a measure of the electron density. In an electron diffraction experiment, for example, a beam of electrons is reflected from a crystal, and a diffraction pattern is produced on a film. In this case the spots on the film are the places where the electron density is high, and these are the places where the amplitude of the wave equation is large. In this way the interference effects produced by electrons can be interpreted in terms of probability waves, just as was the case for light.

OM: Ah! Now that brings me to my second objection. All this talk about interference is very interesting, and if I were going in for electron diffraction work I should like to know about it. But I can't see that it has much to do with the structure of atoms, or of metals.

Surely what we need is the way in which electrons move around or between atoms, and we needn't bother about interference.

YS: Oh! But it's all part of the same general problem. Suppose we imagine an electron diffraction experiment which I have sketched in Fig. 4. Here a beam of electrons is reflected from a crystal X, and produces a diffraction pattern ab on the photographic film F. Then surely the principles which explain why the electrons travel in the directions Xa and Xb, and not in other directions, will just be one particular example of the very laws for which you are asking, namely, the principles which govern the motion of electrons round and in between atoms?

OM: Then do you mean that the wave-like properties of the electron are connected with what one might call the dynamics of the electron?

YS: If by dynamics you mean the way in which electrons move, then certainly yes. You must remember that we always meet a whole electron, and so the " particle probability " interpretation of a diffraction experiment clearly means that electrons travel in some directions and not in others, and this means that we are getting down to the dynamics of the electron.

OM: But, surely the trajectory of a particle is quite a different matter from the propagation of a wave?

YS: Now! Now! You are getting back into the old groove again! The electron waves are not material waves. They are merely mathematical functions from which you calculate the probability of finding the electron at different places. These probabilities must clearly be connected with the way in which the electron moves, and since the equations can be visualised in terms of wave motion, it follows that trajectories of electrons are somehow connected with the wave-like properties.

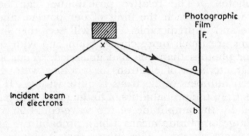

Fig. 4—To illustrate an electron diffraction experiment

A parallel beam of electrons strikes a metal crystal X. If the crystal is suitably orientated, diffracted rays are produced in the directions Xa and Xb. If the electrons have a velocity u, they are diffracted by the crystal as though they possessed a wave length of $\lambda = \dfrac{h}{mu}$. The process is analogous to the production of X-ray diffraction patterns, and it must be emphasised that the effect illustrated will occur only if the crystal is suitably orientated relative to the electron beam.

OM: Now that doesn't seem to me to follow at all, and it brings up an objection I was going to have raised about your probability theory of photons. In all this discussion you've been talking about rays of light and beams of electrons—that is to say, immense numbers of photons or electrons. Now I don't profess to understand your probability waves, but I can dimly imagine that a number of electrons might affect one another so that they travelled in some directions and not in others, and I suppose the same thing might apply to the photons in a beam of light. But now suppose you were to pass one single electron through a diffraction apparatus. Then the electron must go somewhere—if it's a particle it can't interfere with itself—so it seems that your methods work with streams of electrons but not with a single electron, and the same objection would apply to a single photon in the case of light.

YS: Ah! Now you are getting down to something very fundamental. Let us suppose that we do pass a single electron through the diffraction apparatus of Fig. 4. Then we find that the position is as follows: We cannot calculate or predict where the electron will travel. There will be a certain probability that the electron travels in the direction Xa, and another probability that it travels in the direction Xb, and so on. The amplitudes of the wave function are a measure of these probabilities, and the relative probabilities can be calculated exactly, but we cannot calculate or predict which path the electron· will take.

OM: But that seems to me absurd. You seem to suggest that if the experiment were repeated, the electron might go one way on one occasion and another on a second occasion, even though the conditions of the experiment were identical.

YS: Exactly! The new viewpoint implies that there is a degree of uncertainty as regards the behaviour of the individual electron or individual photon. The relative probabilities can be calculated exactly, but we then reach the limit of our powers, and the rest is indeterminate and unpredictable. You will see, therefore, that the wave-equations are much more closely bound up with the dynamics of electrons or photons than you had imagined. Your idea that the wave-like characteristics of electrons or photons were due to inter-action between numbers of electrons is quite wrong. If we consider one single electron, the probabilities of finding it at different places are still measured by the amplitude of the wave-equation at the places concerned—large amplitude means a high probability—and the same applies to a single photon. This means that if you try to visualise your equations as waves you have to admit that one electron can interfere with itself but, as I've already emphasised, the waves are means of visualising the equations, and the waves have no actual physical existence.

7—Heisenberg's Principle

OLDER METALLURGIST: What you have told me about the single electron is really most extraordinary, but even though a single electron has to be thought of as interfering with itself in the sort of experiment you have indicated in Fig. 4, I don't see that it has much to do with the problem we are considering in the case of the hydrogen atom. We are concerned with the trajectories or paths of motion of an electron round the nucleus, and surely this is a straightforward problem in dynamics, and need not involve any interference effects or wave-like properties at all?

YOUNG SCIENTIST: Well now, you are a practical man, so suppose you tell me just what you mean by a straightforward problem in dynamics.

OM: Oh! That's easy enough! I mean a problem dealing with quantities like velocity, momentum, kinetic energy, and so on.

YS: Have you ever asked yourself exactly what you mean by these quantities, and how you would measure them in the case of an electron?

OM: What does that matter? We all know what they are—it's self evident.

YS: There, I think, you are fundamentally wrong. It seems to me that when you say an electron is at a certain position in space, or that it possesses a certain momentum, you must be able to describe some experiment which serves as a measure of the values you give. Otherwise it seems to me that your statement has no real meaning.

OM: Oh, look here! Must we be as philosophical as this?

YS: In this particular case, yes! If you are going to understand the behaviour of electrons, you must understand exactly what your expressions imply. After all, it is a matter of some importance. If you said that an electron was at a position x, and I contradicted you and said that it was at y, would you say it was merely a matter of opinion?

OM: Of course not. I'd most certainly show you that it was at x. I must confess that I am not enough of a physicist to know exactly how I would do it, but I'd make it reveal its presence somehow or other.

YS: Now you are getting down to it! You mean that you would carry out an experiment in which the electron interacted with its surroundings, and revealed itself by something like the movement of a galvanometer, or the emission of a quantum of light.

OM: That's the sort of thing I meant—and exactly similarly for momentum, energy, etc. You'll know much more than I do about the actual experiments, and if it will help you I'll agree that the appropriate

43

experiment should be made, although frankly I think you are bothering me with a lot of philosophical twaddle.

YS: The truth of the matter is that one comes across a most awkward fact, namely that any experiment by which the electron is revealed results in a disturbance of the electron. This difficulty is really present whenever we measure anything, and you will find that when you speak of quantities like position, momentum, etc., in ordinary schoolboy dynamics, you are really assuming that you can ignore the disturbance caused by the act of measurement.

OM: Give me an example of what you mean.

YS: Well, suppose you are going to measure the length of something. You will want to compare it with a standard scale and, if you press the scale against it in order to make " contact," the pressure will cause a slight deformation, and you will be uncertain about the extent of this.

OM: I shouldn't dream of doing it like that. I should put the two side by side and look at them through a travelling microscope. What is more, I'd get the optical conditions right and in order to obtain good resolution, I'd use light of very short wave length, and an objective of high numerical aperture. I'll grant you that there is a limit to the resolving power, but in principle I could use light of infinitely short wave length, and get the measurement exact. And what is more, I could detect the position of an electron in the same way, because I have read about electrons scattering light.

YS: Well, as a matter of fact, if you did try that method you would find that a beam of light exerts a small pressure on anything which it strikes, and this pressure increases as the wave length diminishes.

OM: But surely that sort of effect is so small that we can ignore it?

YS: If we are measuring objects of the order 1 gram, these effects are negligible, but when we deal with single electrons, things are very different. As you yourself have said, electrons can scatter light, and the scattering process may be regarded as the result of a collision between a photon and an electron. As a result of this collision, the electron undergoes a recoil, the direction and magnitude of which can be calculated if one knows the angle through which the light has been scattered, that is the angle through which the photon has been deflected. This process is known as the Compton effect, and it is one of the phenomena in which the particle properties of light are very marked. Furthermore the recoil of the electron increases as the wave length of the light diminishes, so if you did use light of very short wave length to measure the position of an electron, you would disturb the electron tremendously.

OM: That is very interesting, but I don't see why it should worry us. Even though we did disturb the electron by our measurement, we could in principle measure its exact position before it was disturbed.

YS: What you say is quite right although it is only part of the truth. You are quite correct in saying that we could in principle measure the position of the electron accurately by using light of very short wave length. We can generalise this statement, and say that if we consider any *one* of the quantities—position, momentum, kinetic energy, angular momentum, etc.—we can generally describe an experiment which would in principle enable us to measure the quantity concerned as accurately as we wish.

OM: What have you got to worry about then?

YS: Well, if you come to think of it, our description of the early theory of the hydrogen atom and your suggestion that we are concerned with a straightforward problem in dynamics imply a simultaneous knowledge of more than one of these quantities, position, velocity, etc. When we drew Fig. 2 (page 23) we implied that we could consider the electron to be exactly at the point marked, and that we could have an exact knowledge of its momentum, kinetic energy, etc.

OM: Why on earth shouldn't we?

YS: At the risk of boring you, I must repeat what I said before—namely, that if statements of this kind are to have real meaning, you must be able to describe an experiment which will enable you to measure the quantities concerned.

OM: Well, that's easy enough. We've simply got to carry out two experiments of the kind we have already discussed. You yourself have said that some one experiment can be found which will measure one of the quantities accurately, and so all we have to do is to make two experiments to measure the two quantities, and that's that!

YS: Ah! Would that it were so! But unfortunately you have failed to see that the first experiment may disturb the electron so much that you cannot carry out the second experiment accurately.

OM: Give me an example of what you mean.

YS: The usual illustration of the point concerned is an attempt to measure the position and momentum of an electron at a given instant. You have already suggested an experiment in which you measure the position of an electron by means of a microscope. See if you can adapt it so as to measure the position of an electron and its momentum at a given instant. You may take the momentum to be the mass multiplied by the velocity, so that an experiment which measures the velocity and the position of an electron at a given instant will be satisfactory.

OM: Well, I suppose I could set up two microscopes in the line of motion of the electron. I'd notice the time at which the electron was seen under the first microscope, and then the time at which it was seen under the second microscope, and in that way I could deduce its velocity, and, by focusing the microscope on points very close together I could get the velocity at the point half-way between them. As I explained before, I should use light of very short wave length, and objectives of high numerical aperture in order to get good resolution and accurate measurements of the positions.

YS: But you've forgotten the Compton effect of which I told you. Your observation of the electron through the first microscope means that the electron has scattered at least one photon, and so its motion will have been disturbed.

OM: But you said that the amount of the recoil could be calculated.

YS: I said it could be calculated if we knew the direction in which the photon was scattered.

OM: Well, measure the direction then.

YS: That's what you can't do, because you are using objectives of high numerical aperture, and so they receive light from a wide range of angles, and you can't get the direction from which the light comes.

OM: I'm sorry, I got it wrong there. I should have suggested using an objective of low numerical aperture.

YS: But then it will have a low resolving power, and you won't be able to measure the position accurately.

OM: You devil! You know, you are not treating me fairly. You've egged me on to use this method, and I agree that I've walked straight into a trap. On thinking it over, I can see now that the very conditions which are necessary to measure the position accurately will produce the greatest uncertainty in the velocity, and vice versa. The method won't work, and it's up to you to suggest one which will work. After all, it's you and not I who claim to know something about physics.

YS: You are being unfair to both of us. The method you have suggested is in principle a very good one, and I couldn't have suggested a better. The fact is that this difficulty is really fundamental, and nobody has been able to devise any method by which the simultaneous position and momentum of an electron can be measured exactly. However we set about it, the conditions necessary for the greatest accuracy in the measurement of the position produce the greatest uncertainty in the momentum, and vice versa. The phenomenon is called the Uncertainty Principle of Heisenberg, and a more careful analysis of the kind of process you suggested shows that if Δx is the uncertainty in the position of the electron, and Δp the uncertainty in its momentum, then the product $\Delta x \, \Delta p$ is of the order of h, where h is Planck's Constant. For particles of the order 1 gram, the value of h is relatively so small that the effect is negligible, and that was why the Uncertainty Principle was not discovered in the development of classical mechanics where the objects dealt with were enormously heavier than an electron. But for an electron, the Principle is of supreme importance.

OM: I understand the general idea, but you have not explained exactly what you mean by the term " uncertainty " for which you used the symbols Δx, Δp, etc.

YS: This is a rather difficult point and perhaps the most satisfactory thing is to say that by the uncertainty in position we mean the length outside which the probability of finding the electron becomes negligible. That is to say, we know the electron is in a certain region although we cannot say exactly where it is. We can say there is a certain probability of finding it at one place and another probability of finding it at a second place, and so on. These probabilities become smaller and smaller as we move away from the region of greatest probability until they become vanishingly small. This, of course, means that the " uncertainty " is not really exactly defined, and it is for this reason that we have expressed Heisenberg's Principle by saying that $\Delta x \Delta p$ is of the order h, which may be written $\Delta x \Delta p \sim h$.

Some authors use the term " effective uncertainty " to describe uncertainty in this sense. The point is rather important, because when we get farther into the theory we find that it is possible to define the quantity Δx in other ways, in which case Heisenberg's Principle assumes a slightly different form, although the general idea is unaltered. You will in some books find the principle expressed in the form $\Delta x \Delta p \sim \dfrac{h}{2\pi}$ and these differences simply depend on the exact way in which the uncertainties are defined. For our purpose it is sufficient to say that $\Delta x \Delta p$ is of the order h, where by the terms Δx and Δp we mean the ranges of distance and momentum outside which the probability of finding the electron is negligible.

OM: Does this sort of difficulty refer only to the simultaneous position and momentum?

YS: No. There are other cases too. For example, if you consider what experiments are necessary to justify the statement that an electron exists with energy E for a time t, you find that when t becomes very small, E becomes uncertain, and again

$$\Delta t \times \Delta E \sim h.$$

OM: Does that ever affect anything?

YS: Oh, certainly it does! If, for example, an electron is in a stationary state in an atom, then its energy can be specified exactly only if the time is left completely indeterminate. If the electron exists in the state only for a certain time t, then there will be a correspondingly uncertainty in its energy.

OM: But surely that is nonsense? If the energy were uncertain you wouldn't get sharp spectral lines when the electrons changed from one stationary state to another.

YS: You are forgetting the magnitude of Planck's Constant, h. If an atom remains in a stationary state for, say, 1 second, this period is so enormous compared with h that the uncertainty in the energy is negligible. Sometimes, however, an atom goes through a series of changes in which an electron passes through a series of stationary states $E_1 \rightarrow E_2 \rightarrow E_3 \rightarrow \ldots$ and then if one of the states has an exceedingly short life its energy is correspondingly uncertain, and the resulting spectral line is diffuse. It is only right to say that many other factors can also produce a broadening of spectral lines, but what we may call Heisenberg broadening is sometimes found. Incidentally, you may get the same effect with electrons in metals. Here some of the electrons are moving about rapidly between the atoms, and when the thermal vibrations disturb the perfect periodicity of the lattice, electrons begin to collide with the atoms[1] and this is what creates an electrical resistance. In this case, if the time between two collisions is very short, Heisenberg's Principle indicates that there is a corresponding uncertainty in the energy of the electron between the two collisions.

OM: This is all very mysterious.

YS: It is all very fundamental, because it is getting you to think whether expressions such as " the exact position and momentum of an electron at a given instant " have any real meaning.

---

[1] The Young Scientist should really have spoken of an interaction between the electron and the thermal vibrations of the lattice, but for a simplified description it is common to call this a collision with an atom, although the expression is rather misleading because the process must be thought of, not as a collision between two solid particles, but as the interaction between the wave system of the electron and the vibrations of the lattice.

8—How Wave Mechanics Arose

O LDER METALLURGIST: I've been thinking over what you said very carefully, and it seems to me that this sort of thing is all getting so mysterious that a totally different line of approach is needed. As far as I can see, the only way is to take back my statement (page 44) about a quantity having to be justified by some sort of an experiment. It's this continual reference to experiment which seems to cause all the trouble. I think now that I was really right in saying that quantities like momentum, position, kinetic energy, etc., are self-evident, and we ought to go back to that point of view.

YOUNG SCIENTIST: Well, to be honest, I think you are fundamentally wrong, and as you claim to be a practical man, I'm astonished that you will not listen to experimental evidence.

OM: It's not a question of experimental evidence. I'll gladly listen to any experimental evidence you have to offer, but what is worrying us is the question of how we are to think of quantities like momentum, position, kinetic energy, etc.

YS: But surely the expression " quantity " means something which we can measure? What I've been trying to show you is that when we consider an electron there is no way by which we can measure all these quantities accurately at a given instant. There are mutual uncertainties which are expressed by the Heisenberg relations.

OM: But that's only because our methods of measurement are imperfect. I can see no reason why I should not assume more perfect methods of measurement which do enable us to know the exact position and momentum, etc., at a given instant.

YS: Well, if you do assume that, how is one to imagine the electron to behave in your hypothetical world where position and momentum can be known accurately at the same instant? We have already seen that classical mechanics is unable to account for events on the atomic scale, and you yourself pointed out the arbitrary nature of the postulates of the Bohr theory.

OM: Oh, I can quite see that it isn't going to be easy! But surely we shall only make it more difficult if we go introducing all these mysterious Heisenberg relations? If you will do as I suggest, we shall at least keep our picture of the electron as something concrete and simple, whereas if once you add all this curious indeterminancy business, there seems to be no end to the difficulties.

YS: As a matter of fact that method of approach has been tried, but so far it has led to nothing very useful, and you must remember that there is no reason why our picture of the electron should be simple. The alternative method is to regard the Heisenberg Principle as an indication of something really fundamental underlying the ultimate nature of things, and then to try to build up a theory in which the Uncertainty Relations appear, not as something mysterious and confusing, but as the inevitable result of our theory of the electron. On the whole, this seems to be the more scientific course to follow—it means that we accept the Heisenberg Principle, and follow up the clues which it provides.

OM: Well, if you do adopt that course, do you obtain any useful picture, or anything which can be visualised?

YS: What you obtain is a new form of mechanics, the so-called *wave mechanics* which has led to a highly successful interpretation of atomic and electronic phenomena. Many of the conclusions can only be expressed in the form of mathematical equations, but it is the great advantage of wave mechanics that it does enable some of the results to be visualised.

OM: What do you mean by wave mechanics? The two words seem to me to be quite incompatible—waves are waves, whilst mechanics refers to the behaviour of particles or bodies.

YS: Well, if you feel like that perhaps one may ask what you would regard as a typical mechanical problem?

OM: Let us say a problem about the firing of a gun, and the forces produced, and the trajectory of the shell.

YS: The problem of the trajectory of a shell will do excellently for our discussion; it is a particular example of the general problem of the motion of a body in a field of force. Let us suppose that we have two points A and B, and that you wish to shoot a bullet or a shell from A to B. Then how would you aim your rifle or your gun, and what would be the trajectory of the bullet or shell?

OM: If it were not for the earth's attraction I should aim directly from A towards B, and the bullet would travel in a straight line. Actually, owing to the gravitational field, I should have to aim a little above B, and the trajectory of the bullet would be a parabola, except in so far as complications were introduced owing to the resistance of the air.

YS: That's right. In the absence of a field of force, the trajectory would be a straight line, whilst a uniform field would give rise to a parabola. In the same way a variable field of force would give rise to a more complicated trajectory.

OM: I remember working out that kind of problem at school, but I'm afraid that I've forgotten most of the formulae.

YS: Did you know that a great deal of that kind of work can be put into a simple generalised form from which you could work out the formulae yourself?

OM: No, I didn't do that kind of work. The formulae were quite simple as far as I remember.

YS: That was because you were dealing with relatively simple problems; if you had been dealing with more complicated problems

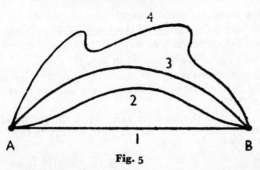

Fig. 5

you might have thought differently. Let us go back to the trajectory of the bullet, and consider a simplified case in which the total energy of the bullet remains constant, so that as it rises or falls in its trajectory it may exchange kinetic energy for potential energy or vice versa, but no energy is gained from, or lost to external sources. We might then imagine a large number of trajectories such as those in Fig. 5. If for each of these trajectories we work out the value of the integral

$$\int_A^B 2K dt$$

where K is the kinetic energy and t is the time, we find that the actual trajectory is characterised by a minimum value of this integral.[1] In other words, if we were to work out the value of the integral for all conceivable paths from A to B, we should find that in the absence of a field of force the straight line path would give the minimum value of the integral, whilst in the case of the gravitational field the minimum value of the integral would correspond with the correct parabolic path. In this way the equations of motion can be predicted from one general principle, which is known as the Principle of Least Action and was first discovered by Maupertuis as long ago as the early eighteenth century.

OM: What do you mean by " action "?

YS: Action is not a quantity which comes into what you may call schoolboy dynamics, and I'm afraid it isn't possible to give any very simple visualisation of what it implies. You may note, however, that it has the dimensions ML^2T^{-1}. Kinetic energy equals $\frac{1}{2}mu^2$, and has dimensions $\frac{ML^2}{T^2}$, so kinetic energy multiplied by time has dimensions ML^2T^{-1}.

OM: If the principle is as old as that, it surely can't have much connection with atomic theory?

YS: On the contrary, it is one of the more important foundation stones of the theory.

---

[1] Strictly speaking, we should describe the stationary value of the integral, but for a simplified description it is justifiable to use the minimum value.

OM: How does that come about?

YS: Well, now let us turn from the mechanical problem to an optical problem, and ask ourselves how a ray of light would travel from A to B.

OM: That's easy. Light travels in straight lines.

YS: Oh, not necessarily. If, for example, A were in air and B in water, the path of the ray of light would be bent or refracted at the air/water boundary.

OM: I'm sorry. I should have said that if the surrounding medium had the same refractive index throughout, the ray of light would travel from A to B in a straight line.

YS: That's right—so the trajectory of a ray of light in a uniform medium resembles the trajectory of the bullet in the absence of a field of force. Now what would happen if the refractive index of the medium between A and B varied, not discontinuously as in the case of an air/water interface, but continuously?

OM: The light would, I suppose, travel in a curved path.

YS: That's more or less right. Did you ever deal with that kind of problem?

OM: No, I don't think I ever dealt with problems involving a continuous variation of refractive index, although I did learn about the ordinary processes of reflection and refraction at surfaces.

YS: It's really all part of the same problem, and just as the equations of motion of a particle can be generalised by the Principle of Least Action, so the laws governing the paths of light rays can be expressed in a generalised form known as Fermat's Principle of Least Time. You will know that the velocity of light in a medium varies inversely as the refractive index. If now we consider the problem of the path of a ray of light from A to B, Fermat's Principle states that of all the conceivable optical paths from A to B, the actual optical path is characterised by a minimum[1] value of the integral

$$\int_A^B \frac{ds}{v}$$

where v is the velocity of light at an element of length ds on the trajectory. Since $\frac{ds}{v} = dt$, Fermat's Principle implies that light travels from A to B by the path which takes the least time, and the principle is therefore called the Principle of Least Time. If, therefore, we know how the refractive index varies in the region between A and B, we can evaluate the integral for different conceivable paths, and the path which gives the minimum value to the integral is the path actually followed by the light. This principle enables the laws of reflection and refraction to be predicted, and also applies to the more general case of a problem in which the refractive index varies continuously. If, for example, A and B are in a uniform medium, the integral has a minimum

[1] Strictly speaking, we should again refer to the stationary value of the integral.

value for the straight line path, whilst if the refractive index is variable the correct path is predicted.

OM: Has all this got any advantage over the simple laws of reflection and refraction?

YS: Well, it is always satisfying to be able to express a number of laws or equations as a direct consequence of one general principle. But, apart from this, there is clearly a very interesting correspondence between the principles governing the trajectory of a bullet in travelling from *A* to *B*, and those governing the trajectory or path of a ray of light. In each case the actual path followed is characterised by the minimum value of a very simple integral, and you will see that in the optical problem a variable refractive index has much the same effect as that of a field of force in the mechanical problem.

OM: You mean that a variable refractive index makes the ray of light travel in a curve, whilst the field of force makes a bullet travel in a curve?

YS: That's right. Further, this correspondence between what we may call the mechanical problem and the optical problem can be expressed in a precise mathematical form so that a problem concerning the trajectory of a bullet, or in the more general case the trajectory of a particle in a known field of force becomes, as far as the mathematics is concerned, identical with the problem of the path of a ray of light in a medium of varying refractive index.

OM: You mean that if we had a particular mechanical problem for which we know the trajectory in the field of force concerned, we could imagine a variation of refractive index in space which would make a ray of light travel in the same trajectory?

YS: That's right. The problem of the mechanical trajectory can be treated so that mathematically it is equivalent to the problem of a path of a light ray in a medium of variable refractive index.

OM: That's all very ingenious, but it seems to me to be a typical example of the way in which the mathematician wastes his time in being clever. The mechanical trajectory is a definite problem and, although it may be possible to manipulate the mathematical equations so that they resemble those of an optical problem, the whole thing seems a useless piece of mathematical juggling.

YS: On the other hand you were very impressed by the way in which the engineers manipulated the equations of their problem of torsional stress so that they were analogous to those for the curvature of a soap-bubble!

OM: Of course I was. That was a case where the manipulation enabled them to solve a problem which was otherwise too difficult.

YS: Exactly! And, strange to say, this manipulation of the equations of a mechanical problem to resemble those of an optical problem has led to the solution of a problem which was previously insoluble, namely, the behaviour of an electron in the field of an atom.

OM: But how can that possibly be? All that you seem to be doing is to manipulate your equations of mechanics so that they resemble those of optics. So surely what was insoluble before the manipulation will be insoluble afterwards—you are not producing anything like the curvature of a soap bubble which can be measured.

YS: You are in too much of a hurry. You may remember that I asked you how a ray of light would travel in a medium in which the refractive index varied continuously, and your reply was that it would travel in a curve. My comment (page 52) was then that you were more or less right, and not that your answer was the whole truth!

OM: How was I wrong?

YS: Your statement was not so much incorrect as incomplete. You should have said that the ray of light would travel in a curved path, provided that the variation of refractive index was not so extreme as to be appreciable over a distance of the order one wave length. But, if the conditions are such that the refractive index varies markedly over a distance of the order of a wave length, then curious new phenomena such as dispersion are encountered, and these cannot be explained in terms of simple paths of rays.

OM: What has that sort of effect to do with our problem?

YS: The answer to that question is that the mathematicians had the imagination and the courage to carry the analogy between the equations of what we have called the mechanical and the optical problems to its logical conclusion. The line of argument might be put roughly as follows:

First—In the optical problem a variable refractive index plays the same part as a field of force in the mechanical problem.

Second—In the optical problem strange effects are produced if the refractive index varies appreciably over the small distance of a wave length.

Third—Therefore, in the mechanical problem, we may expect strange effects if the force changes greatly over very small distances.

Fourth—Therefore let us carry the analogy further. So far we have considered large-scale trajectories only, for which the older geometrical optics was sufficient. We know, however, that the laws of geometrical optics can be expressed in terms of the wave theory of light, and that this theory is able to explain small-scale events which lie outside the older theory. Therefore, let us retain our analogy between field of force and variable refractive index, and re-write our equations for the motion of a particle in a form analogous to those which the wave theory of light gives for the path of a ray. This will mean that our equations for the motion of a particle will be mathematically similar to those of a wave motion, and our equations will contain terms which, if we were dealing with a wave motion, would be wave lengths, frequencies, etc. In this way our equations for the motion of a particle will contain terms which we may speak of as wave lengths, etc., although this will be nothing more than a convenient way of visualising our equations, and the " waves " will have no more physical reality than the soap bubble has reality in the problem of torsional stress (page 39).

If we adopt this course, we shall expect no new phenomena in cases where the field of force varies only slightly over a distance of the order of a wave length, but if the field of force varies appreciably over a wave length, we may find a host of new effects, just as the wave theory predicted new optical effects when distances of the order of a wave length were considered. The name " wave mechanics " is given to this new branch of mathematics in which the older equations of mechanics are re-written in a form analogous to the equations of the wave-theory of light.

OM: The mathematicians must have moved quickly if they got all this done since the discovery of electron diffraction in 1927.

YS: As a matter of fact, most of the theory was developed before there was any experimental evidence for the wave-like properties of the electron.

OM: But why on earth should people have worked out a wave theory of mechanics when there was no experimental evidence for the wave-like properties of the electron?

YS: The first steps were taken by Hamilton as long ago as 1824 to 1835, and at the time this was simply an example of the mathematical juggling which you so much despise. The later developments were due to de Broglie (1925) and Schrödinger (1926), and were the result of the most brilliant mathematical imagination.

OM: Now let us see if I have understood you rightly. You say that the mathematicians juggled the equations of mechanics about so that the equations for the problem of a particle in a field of force were mathematically similar to those of the wave theory of light for the path of a beam of light in a medium of varying refractive index. If there are to be wave theories mixed up with the motion of particles, there must, I suppose, be some relation between the waves and the mechanical properties of the particle such as its momentum, kinetic energy, etc. Can this be explained simply so that I can grasp it, or is it only expressible in complicated mathematical form?

YS: That can be expressed in quite a simple way. Do you know what is meant by the mass energy of a particle?

OM: That's got something to do with the Theory of Relativity, hasn't it?

YS: Yes, that's right. In the sense of the Theory of Relativity, as long as we are dealing with velocities which are small compared with that of light, the total energy of a particle is the sum of the potential energy W, the kinetic energy $\frac{1}{2}mu^2$, and the energy associated with the mass of the particle which is mc^2 where c is the velocity of light. If we call this total energy E_m, we have

$$E_m = mc^2 + \tfrac{1}{2}mu^2 + W$$

and the first term mc^2 is enormously greater than the others.

OM: But surely this sudden change in what you are calling the total energy must affect your previous arguments?

YS: No. As long as we are dealing with problems in which the velocities are much smaller than c, the change from E to E_m results merely in the addition of the constant term mc^2, and so it is equivalent to a shift in the zero from which the potential energy is measured. You must remember that the potential energy has always to be measured relatively to some arbitrary zero, and so the addition of the constant term mc^2 does not affect the Principle of Least Action. It is only right to warn you that some of the books are very confusing about the difference between the total energy

$$E_m = mc^2 + \tfrac{1}{2}mu^2 + W$$

and the ordinary total energy

$$E = \tfrac{1}{2}mu^2 + W.$$

Some books use the same symbol indiscriminately for E and E_m, and much confusion is caused in this way.

OM: What is the relation between E_m and the waves connected with the moving particle?

YS: Historically, it was first shown by de Broglie that if waves were associated with moving particles, then the Theory of Relativity necessitated the two relations:

$$\frac{\text{Energy, } E_m}{\text{Frequency, } \nu} = \frac{\text{Momentum}}{\text{Wave Number}} = \text{Constant.}$$

This constant was then intuitively identified with Planck's Constant, h, so that we have the two fundamental relations

$$E_m = h\nu, \text{ and}$$

$$\frac{mu}{\dfrac{1}{\lambda}} = h.$$

The second of these relations was then confirmed experimentally by the electron diffraction experiments, which showed that electrons behaved as though they were associated with a wave length λ given by the relation

$$\lambda = \frac{h}{mu}.$$

People then naturally assumed that the first relation would also be satisfied, and so these two relations are the ones for which you asked.

OM: But they don't seem to make sense!

YS: Why not?

OM: Well, if the frequency is equal to $\dfrac{E_m}{h}$, and the wave length is equal to $\dfrac{h}{mu}$, then the velocity of the waves will equal

$$\lambda \times \nu = \frac{h}{mu} \times \frac{E_m}{h} = \frac{E_m}{mu}$$

and since

$$E_m = mc^2 + \tfrac{1}{2}mu^2 + W$$

the velocity of the waves will be at least $\dfrac{c^2}{u}$. But the Theory of Relativity says that nothing can move faster than light, and so u must be less than c, and $\dfrac{c^2}{u}$ must be greater than c. So the velocity of the waves is greater than c, which is impossible.

YS: No! No! You are forgetting that the waves are not material waves. They are merely a convenient way of visualising the mathematical equations. They have no physical existence, and are not observable quantities.

OM: Then what are the observable quantities?

YS: In the general problem of the motion of an electron in a field of force, the observable quantities might be the probability of finding the electron in a given element of volume at a given time, or the probability of its having a given momentum at a particular place. You must remember that Heisenberg's Principle showed how some of the mutual uncertainties of these quantities were related, but the Uncertainty Principle does not conflict with the description of events in terms of probabilities, and it is these probabilities which are calculated by means of wave mechanics. As we shall learn later, our description of the behaviour of electrons in atoms is expressed mainly in terms of probabilities, and it is by means of wave mechanics that these probabilities are calculated.

9—More About Wave Mechanics

OLDER METALLURGIST: Let us begin by making sure that I have understood you rightly. You say that the object of this new wave mechanics is to re-write the equations of mechanics so that the problem of a particle in a field of force is mathematically similar to that of the path of a ray of light in a medium of varying refractive index. When this is done, you say that a particle of mass m is associated with probability waves so that the wave length λ is given by the relation

$$\lambda = \frac{h}{mu}$$

where u is the velocity of the particle and the frequency ν is given by

$$E_m = h\nu$$

where the total energy E_m is given by

$$E_m = mc^2 + \tfrac{1}{2}mu^2 + W$$

where W is the potential energy.

You then say that we shall have to learn to think in terms of probabilities, and that the amplitude of the waves at a given place is to be a measure of the probability of finding an electron at the place concerned.

YOUNG SCIENTIST: That's more or less right.

OM: In that case I suppose there will have to be some mathematical function which expresses the amplitude, and can you explain how this is done?

YS: This is the point at which I am afraid you will have to be prepared to lose the thread of the argument, and simply to take things on trust. It will be easiest if we consider first streams of electrons so that a continuous stream of electrons of velocity u is analogous to a homogeneous beam of light of wave length $\dfrac{h}{mu}$.

In the theory of light it is common to speak of the light waves as being waves in the ether although, as I have explained, the ether has no physical existence, but is merely a convenient mental image by means of which we visualise our mathematical equations. We therefore speak of vibrations in the ether, or of ether vibrations, although no physical ether exists.

In the theory of electrons the corresponding "something-which-vibrates" is called Ψ, and we may speak of Ψ vibrations, although as in the case of the ether, this is merely a convenient way of visualising our equations, and Ψ is not a physical vibrating medium.

In the theory of light the intensity of the light at a given place, or in other words the probability of finding a photon at a given place, is proportional to the square of the amplitude of the hypothetical ether vibrations at the place concerned.

In the theory of electrons, the amplitude of the vibrations is a measure of the probability of finding an electron at the place concerned. The mathematical form assumed for the Ψ waves is not the same as that assumed in the theory of light, and involves the use of complex numbers, that is to say expressions involving the use of $\sqrt{-1}$, which is written i. You said at the beginning (page 10) that you did not understand this branch of mathematics and, except for the one point referred to below, I think you had better take it on trust that just as in the wave theory of light the mathematician obtains an expression for the square of the amplitude, and assumes this to be proportional to the probability of finding a photon at the place concerned, so in the wave theory of electrons an appropriate function can be found which is proportional to the probability of finding an electron at the place concerned.

The point you should note is that if we use the symbol Ψ for the " quantity which vibrates," then from the very idea of a vibration Ψ will involve both space and time. When one is dealing with a stationary state, the form of waves used by the mathematicians in wave mechanics enables one to write Ψ in the form

$$\Psi = \psi\,(xyz)\,e^{2\pi i\nu t}$$

where the small ψ is called the amplitude factor or the space factor and involves only the space co-ordinates (x, y, z). The second term is called the time factor. In the general case the probability of finding an electron at the place concerned is given by a mathematical function which is written $\Psi\Psi^*$. The probability of finding an electron in an element of volume ΔV is equal to $\Psi\Psi^*\,\Delta V$, which equals $\psi\psi^*\,\Delta V$.

OM: What is the meaning of the * signs?

YS: Ψ and Ψ^* are what are called conjugate complexes. That is to say if Ψ is equal to $(f + ig)$ then Ψ^* is equal to $(f - ig)$.

OM: Can one understand what all these symbols mean?

YS: The general idea is that the Ψ vibrations are supposed to be the result of two vibratory processes which are one-quarter period apart—this is the significance of the term $e^{2\pi i\nu t}$—and which unite to give a resultant independent of time, and whose amplitude is a measure of the probability of finding an electron at the place concerned. But you need not let the mathematical details worry you, and fortunately it is possible to put things quite simply for many of the problems concerning stationary states of electrons in atoms, molecules, crystals, etc. In many of these problems ψ is real, and $\psi\psi^*$ is equal to ψ^2. In these problems the wave mechanics permits the calculation of a quantity ψ which has simply to be squared in order to give the probability of finding an electron at the place considered.

OM: I'm afraid that I find great difficulty over some of this. I can understand the general idea that the amplitude is to be a measure of the probability of finding an electron at the place concerned, and I can see how helpful this will be in problems of electron diffraction. But I can't see how it is going to help for ordinary mechanical problems.

YS: In the ordinary mechanical problem, we know the variation of the potential in space—in the problem of the hydrogen atom for example, the potential energy, W, is equal to $-\dfrac{e^2}{r}$, where r is the distance of the electron from the centre of the atom. When the equations of dynamics are transformed into wave-mechanical form it is found that there is a certain differential equation which expresses Ψ as a function of the total energy E of the particle, and the potential energy W. This equation is called the Schrödinger equation, and was obtained by assuming that the Ψ vibrations were of a sine form.

OM: Can you explain the equation to me?

YS: I'll write down the equation later on,[1] because you will come across it so often that you may as well know what it means. For the moment there is no need for you to bother about the form of the equations, or the way in which they are handled. The important thing is for you to realise that the problem of the motion of electrons in a known field of force is manipulated so that the appropriate differential equation is set up, and then if the equation can be solved the electron density (that is the probability of finding an electron in a particular element of volume) is proportional to the value of $\Psi\Psi*$ at the place concerned. You need not worry yourself about the mathematics, but you will meet the symbols so often in books and papers that you must know what they mean.

OM: You said that your remarks would refer first to a stream of electrons. How do you treat a problem where there is only one electron?

YS: In the case of one electron the same general method is used, and the solution of the wave equation gives the probabilities of finding the one electron at different places. The probability of finding the electron in an element of volume is proportional to the value of $\Psi\Psi*$ at the place concerned. The value of the constant of proportionality is obtained by a process known as the normalisation of the wave function—if for example we know that the electron is in an enclosure of volume V, then the integral $\int \Psi\Psi* dV$ over the volume V must equal 1, since the probability of finding the electron somewhere in the volume V is clearly unity.

You will see therefore that, just as in the diffraction experiment, when we passed one electron through the diffraction apparatus, the relative probabilities of finding it moving in different directions were calculated by the same wave equation which we used for a beam of electrons, so in the general mechanical problem of one electron the solution of the Schrödinger equation gives the probability of finding the one electron in different regions.

[1] See Appendix, page 66.

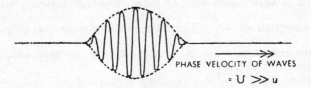

PHASE VELOCITY OF WAVES

$= U \gg u$

Fig. 6

velocity of wave-packet = group velocity

$$u = \frac{dv}{d\left(\frac{1}{\lambda}\right)}$$

OM: It seems to me that this continual calculation of probabilities leads to great difficulty. If we can only think in terms of probabilities, it seems that we can never really localise the electron. But in actual experiments the electron seems to be very definitely localised.

YS: In terms of probabilities that simply means that the value of $\Psi\Psi^*$ is appreciable only over a small region of space, and is vanishingly small elsewhere.

OM: How is one to express that in terms of Ψ waves, if the waves travel faster than light, while the electron travels relatively slowly?

YS: Well, suppose you ask yourself how you would cut out or isolate one electron from a beam.

OM: That's hardly my kind of work, but I suppose you could fit up some kind of shutter device so that if you opened it for a very short time only one electron passed through.

YS: In principle that is quite a suitable method. Do you know what happens when one uses a device of that kind to cut out a small group of waves from a regular stream of homogeneous material waves, that is a stream of waves of uniform frequency?

OM: No, I'm afraid that wasn't included in my training as a metallurgist.

YS: If one makes an experiment of that kind, one finds that the action of the shutter slightly disturbs the head and the tail of the little group of waves which is cut out of the beam, with the result that the small wave group is no longer completely homogeneous but consists of slightly different frequencies, and this produces very interesting effects. The slight difference in frequency means that the waves interfere with one another except over a small region where they reinforce one another. This results in the formation of a wave group or wave-packet such as I have drawn in Fig. 6, and this group moves with a group velocity given by the equation

$$u = \frac{dv}{d\left(\frac{1}{\lambda}\right)}$$

where u is very much smaller than the phase velocity, which for electrons equals $\nu\lambda \sim \dfrac{c^2}{u}$. The shape of the wave-packet may be very different from that of Fig. 6, but the packet as a whole always moves with the group velocity.

OM: But if u is smaller than the velocity of the waves, it would seem that the waves are, so to speak, continually overtaking the wave-packet.

YS: That's right. You may regard the waves as streaming on through the wave-packet, but as interfering with one another so that their resultant amplitude is negligibly small except in the region of the wave-packet itself. This small region moves with the velocity u given by $\dfrac{dv}{d\left(\dfrac{1}{\lambda}\right)}$ and this relation is a very fundamental one which you will need to remember on many occasions.

OM: Then does the wave-packet move on so that its shape remains unchanged?

YS: No. In the case of material waves, it is found that as the wave-packet travels along it gradually spreads out, so that a packet which starts with the shape shown in Fig. 6 spreads out into a packet extending over a larger region, but with a smaller amplitude. This spreading out of the wave-packet is more rapid the shorter the wave-packet is at the beginning, so that if you cut out a very small group of waves, the resulting wave-packet spreads out much more rapidly than if you cut out a larger group. This is another point which you will continually need to remember.

OM: But what has all this got to do with electrons and metals?

YS: Well, we have seen how we are to re-write the laws of mechanics in the form of a wave-theory, and we have used the symbol Ψ to denote the hypothetical quantity which vibrates. If, therefore, we take a stream of electrons of uniform velocity, and use some kind of a shutter device to cut out one electron, we may regard the process as equivalent to the cutting out of a small group of Ψ waves. The group of waves will not be the electron, but will be the region of space in which there is an appreciable chance of finding the electron. You must remember that the amplitude of the Ψ waves is a measure of the probability of finding the electron at the place concerned. Consequently if the waves interfere with one another except over the region of the wave packet, then the probability of finding the electron is negligible except in the region of the wave-packet.

OM: That would mean that the velocity of the electron was the same as the velocity of the wave-packet, and how much is this?

YS: You can work it out for yourself from the above equation.

OM: Let me see,

$$u = \frac{dv}{d\left(\dfrac{1}{\lambda}\right)}.$$

For electron waves of free electrons

$$\frac{1}{\lambda} = \frac{mu}{h}$$

whilst $v = \dfrac{E_m}{h} = \dfrac{mc^2 + \frac{1}{2}mu^2 + W}{h}.$

So that if W is constant as for free electrons, then omitting the constant terms,

$$\frac{dv}{d\left(\dfrac{1}{\lambda}\right)} = d\,\frac{\left(\frac{1}{2}u^2\right)}{du} = u$$

so the group velocity of the waves is the same as the velocity of the electron.

YS: That's right, and so now you have found the function of the Ψ waves which gives the velocity of the electron. The velocity of the electron is always the group velocity of the waves, and is always given by

$$\frac{dv}{d\left(\dfrac{1}{\lambda}\right)}.$$

OM: Now! Now! You are not being honest!

YS: Why not?

OM: You said that the wave-packet spread out as it went along. If the region of the wave-packet is the region in space where there is an appreciable probability of finding the electron, then the spreading out of the wave-packet means that the velocity is uncertain.

YS: Exactly! Further, this uncertainty is greater the smaller the wave-packet is at the beginning, and this is exactly what is required by Heisenberg's Principle. The smaller the group of waves cut out, the more we are localising the position of the electron, and hence the greater the uncertainty in its velocity.

OM: Then do you mean that this wave mechanics stuff is mixed up with the Heisenberg Principle?

YS: Yes. The concept of Probability Wave-Packets expresses the exact characteristics of the Heisenberg Principle. The wave-packet as a whole moves with the group velocity u, and there is always a greater probability of finding the electron in the region where the amplitude of the wave-packet is a maximum than of finding it elsewhere.[1] But the wave-packet extends over several wave lengths, and spreads out as it goes along, and so there is an uncertainty in the velocity, because there is always a probability of finding the electron a small distance on either side of the maximum of the wave-packet.

OM: But what does this all mean? Why does it go like this?

YS: It is not the province of Science to answer the question "Why?" if you use the word to imply purpose. But if you ask what happens, the answer is that the use of any shutter device to cut out one electron would produce fields of force near the electron, and these would disturb it slightly and so cause a slight uncertainty in its behaviour. The whole experiment is in fact but another attempt to measure the simultaneous position and velocity of an electron, and as with the method you yourself proposed, the conclusion is that there is an uncertainty, and it is easy to show that

$$\Delta p \times \Delta x \sim h.$$

You will see, therefore, that it is of great fascination to find that wave mechanics, which was developed purely theoretically, leads to the concept of a probability wave-group having the exact characteristics required by Heisenberg's Principle, although the latter was discovered by considering what experiments would be required in order to measure the quantities—position momentum, energy, etc. In spite of its purely theoretical background, wave mechanics is in close touch with what is indicated by experiment.

OM: Then do you mean that I have to learn to think of an electron as a wave-packet?

YS: When you try to visualise an electron as it moves about, you have to imagine a small region of space in which there is an appreciable probability of finding the electron. This region of space behaves like a wave-packet of Ψ waves, and moves with the group velocity. So long as you are dealing with large-scale events of free electrons this doesn't make much difference compared with the older view of the electron as a free particle. It simply means that there is some uncertainty and that one cannot give an exact description, because the electron may be anywhere within the region occupied by the wave-packet. The electron is most likely to be found where the amplitude of the wave-packet is greatest, but the electron may be found anywhere within the length of the wave-packet, the probability falling off gradually as the amplitude diminishes.

On the other hand, when you come to consider events on the scale of length of a wave-packet, that is, of a few wave lengths, the probability interpretation means that you can no longer follow the electron in its path.

OM: But why not?

[1] It should be noted that wave-packets are not always symmetrical in shape, so that the region of greatest amplitude is not necessarily in the centre of the packet.

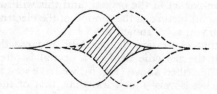

Fig. 7

In this diagram the full line indicates the envelope of a wave-packet at time t_1, and the dotted line its position a little later at time t_2. The wave-packet as a whole has moved to the right, and at the second instant of time the electron may be found farther to the right than at the first instant of time. The shaded region is common to both positions of the wave-packet and in this region we cannot say whether the electron has moved from left to right or from right to left, but only that there is a greater probability of its having moved from left to right. In this diagram the instants of time t_1 and t_2 are imagined to be so close together that the spreading out of the wave-packet between t_1 and t_2 is negligible.

YS: Because the whole wave-packet refers to one electron only, and so we cannot say what happens within the length of the wave packet. Suppose, for example, that the full line in Fig. 7 shows the wave-packet at time t_1, and the dotted line its position slightly later at time t_2. Then the wave-packet as a whole has moved to the right, and at the second instant of time the electron may be found farther to the right than it could be found at the first instant of time. But we cannot say what has happened in the region which is shaded. The electron may have moved from left to right or from right to left—all that we can say is that there is a greater probability of its having moved from left to right.

OM: This is all very curious, and I hope we shan't have to go into all these details in order to understand how electrons behave in atoms or metals.

YS: On the contrary. It's just what you will have to think about. You see, the size of an atom is of the same order as that of a wave-packet, and over this small distance we have to give up all attempts to follow the electron in its path. This is what I meant when I said before that we had to give up the idea of an electron in an orbit. You must no longer think of electrons as running round little orbits in atoms. This is a false picture and leads to wrong conclusions. You must just accept it that when you deal with events on the scale of an atom, you can describe the electron only in terms of probabilities, and it is these probabilities which are calculated by wave mechanics.

OM: Then do you mean that when I try to think of an electron moving about inside a metal crystal, I must not form any picture at all?

YS: If you try to localise the electron so precisely as to speak of its moving round one particular atom, or between two atoms, then you are dealing with events on the scale of the wave-packet, and you cannot form any precise mechanical picture. But if you are dealing with a crystal containing 10^{23} atoms, you can regard the electron as a probability wave-packet in the crystal, and this will sometimes enable you to form a useful picture of the motion of the electron in the crystal.

OM: Why do you say " sometimes "?

YS: I used that expression deliberately, because the behaviour of wave-packets in the periodic field of a crystal is often very curious. In the example described above (Fig. 6), we have seen how the velocity of the wave-packet is very much less than that of the waves, but in this particular case the direction of motion is the same for the waves and the wave-packet. On the other hand, when we deal with electrons in crystals we sometimes find that the waves move in one direction, but that they reinforce one another to build up a wave-packet which moves in another direction. In this case, the motion of the wave-packet gives the average or resultant motion of the electron, but we cannot say what happens within the length of the wave-packet. You will find that in the theory of electrons there is always a temptation to identify the waves with the electron, and to think that the electron moves in the direction of the waves. But this is often unjustified, and it may be quite possible to have the waves moving in one direction, and building up a wave-packet moving in another direction, and in such cases it is always the wave-packet which corresponds with the observable behaviour of the electron.

APPENDIX

The wave-equation expressing the magnitude of Ψ first proposed by Schrödinger is of the form:

$$\nabla^2\Psi + \frac{8\pi^2 m}{h^2}(E - W)\Psi = 0 \quad . \quad . \quad . \quad . \quad (1)$$

Here W is the potential energy and E the total energy, whilst the symbol $\nabla^2\Psi$ stands for

$\left(\dfrac{\partial^2\Psi}{\partial x^2} + \dfrac{\partial^2\Psi}{\partial y^2} + \dfrac{\partial^2\Psi}{\partial z^2}\right)$ and is sometimes written $\Delta\Psi$ by Continental writers. This equation is known as the first Schrödinger equation, or the time-free equation for ordinary (non-relativity) mechanics, and it represents a family of surfaces, each corresponding to one value of E. If Ψ is of the form

$$\Psi = \psi(xyz)\, e^{2\pi i v t} \quad . \quad . \quad . \quad . \quad (2)$$

the time factor may be cancelled out, and the amplitude equation

$$\nabla^2\psi + \frac{8\pi^2 m}{h^2}(E - W)\psi = 0 \quad . \quad . \quad . \quad (3)$$

is obtained, so that Ψ and ψ obey the same differential equation. If the time factor has the same form as in equation (2), the energy E may be eliminated to yield the second Schrödinger equation:

$$\nabla^2\Psi - \frac{8\pi^2 m}{h^2} W\Psi + \frac{4\pi m i}{h}\frac{\partial\Psi}{\partial t} = 0.$$

This is the more fundamental equation, and can be used for problems where W is an explicit function of the time. These equations are reproduced here merely because the reader will meet them frequently in books and papers, and it is desirable to recognise them, and to understand the meaning of the symbols. Those wishing for further information may consult the following books:

Elementary Quantum Mechanics. R. W. Gurney.

Elements of Quantum Mechanics. S. Dushman.

An Outline of Wave Mechanics. N. F. Mott. The elementary reader is advised to buy the first edition of this book, which is written at an elementary level and is most helpful. It has been replaced by N. F. Mott's *Elements of Wave Mechanics* which, although elementary, is much more mathematical in form and is intended for honours students in experimental physics.

Useful information will also be found in:
The Mathematics of Physics and Chemistry. H. Margenau and G. M. Murphy.

For more advanced reading reference may be made to:
Introduction to Quantum Mechanics. L. Pauling and E. B. Wilson.
Wave Mechanics: Elementary Theory. J. Frenkel.

For a general account (non-mathematical) on a slightly more advanced level than the present book, reference may be made to:
Atomic Theory for Students of Metallurgy, W. Hume-Rothery (Institute of Metals Monograph Series).

The following two books are of great interest as showing how the experimental evidence for the wave-like properties of electrons was accumulated:
The Wave Mechanics of Free Electrons, G. P. Thomson. McGraw-Hill Book Co., Inc.
Theory and Practice of Electron Diffraction, G. P. Thomson and W. Cochrane. Macmillan & Co. Ltd.

10—New Interpretation of the Hydrogen Atom

OLDER METALLURGIST: After all this discussion about $\Psi\Psi^*$ can we now get back again to the hydrogen atom, and can you explain what it looks like in wave mechanics?

YOUNG SCIENTIST: In the hydrogen atom the electron is moving round the nucleus in a field of force in which the potential energy varies as $-\dfrac{e^2}{r}$, and this variation of potential energy has to be substituted into the Schrödinger equation (page 66). The optical analogy would be a ray of light moving in a spherical bowl in which the refractive index varied so that the path of the ray was continually bent round, with the result that the light never escaped from the bowl.

OM: I don't see how that analogy will help, because there seem to be an infinite number of possible paths for the rays, and so an infinite number of types of motion will be possible, and we shall be back again among all the difficulties we discussed before. Or does the Schrödinger equation somehow give one single solution?

YS: The answer to that question is that the differential equation of Schrödinger is a very general kind of equation, and has innumerable solutions. You can readily see that by considering a very simple differential equation such as

$$\frac{dy}{dx} = a.$$

This has not got one single solution, but an infinite number of solutions of the general type

$$y = ax + C$$

where C is an arbitrary constant. The single differential equation $\dfrac{dy}{dx} = a$ thus corresponds to an infinite number of parallel straight lines of slope a. In the same way, a differential equation of the Schrödinger type is a very general kind of equation and contains innumerable solutions.

OM: What is the good of the equation then, if it is all as general as that?

YS: That is quite a fair question, and the answer is that the mathematician writes down the equation for his particular problem, and then if he is able to obtain solutions of many types, he inspects these and rejects those whose interpretations would not correspond to something physically possible. In this way he selects from the innumerable solutions those which may be called acceptable.

OM: I am afraid I find that is difficult to follow. Can you give me a simple example?

YS: If we are dealing with a single electron, the interpretation has always to be that $\Psi\Psi^* \Delta V$ gives the probability of finding the electron in the particular element of volume ΔV. It is found that some of the mathematical transformations can be carried out only if Ψ is continuous, and so the mathematician rejects solutions which would give a discontinuous value of Ψ. In the same way by examining the equation more critically the mathematician is able to show that only certain solutions can be regarded as physically acceptable.

OM: Then have these acceptable solutions any special characteristics?

YS: Yes. The interesting thing is that when one is dealing with problems of stationary states of electrons in atoms, molecules, crystals, etc., the acceptable solutions always involve the introduction of whole numbers. This means that the energies of the electron in the stationary states described by the different acceptable solutions, are related by functions involving *whole numbers*, and these whole numbers are naturally regarded as analogous to the quantum numbers which the older Bohr theory postulated as arbitrary assumptions. It is very necessary for you to understand this point clearly. In the older theory, as you yourself pointed out (page 34), the quantum numbers appeared as arbitrary assumptions which were made in order to obtain an agreement with empirically known facts. In wave mechanics whole numbers appear because it is only by their introduction that solutions to the equations can be found, which are physically possible.

OM: This seems very curious, because one would imagine that equations of a wave-like nature were essentially continuous. Can one obtain any physical analogy showing why whole numbers should appear?

YS: As I have emphasised before, the wave analogy is only a convenient way of visualising the equations but, as long as you don't forget this, it is quite justifiable to use simple physical waves to illustrate the point.

Suppose, for example, you take a piano wire of a definite length, and that you try to set this vibrating so that it sets up a steady vibration, that is, a stationary state of vibration. Then I suppose you know that it can only vibrate in certain tones and overtones?

OM: Yes, that's right.

YS: In this case the wave lengths of the different possible steady vibrations are related by simple whole numbers.

In the same way if you had some water in a rectangular bath with flexible sides, you might set up vibrations by regular displacement of the sides of the bath. The waves would then interfere with one another in some places, and reinforce one another in others, but you would find that a steady state of vibration would be set up only if there were certain whole-number relations between the wave lengths and the length and breadth of the bath.

OM: Then do you mean that the wave length of an electron in a stationary state has a whole number relation to some dimension of the problem?

YS: Yes, that's right. In problems of stationary states of electrons there is nearly always a simple relation between the wave lengths corresponding to the acceptable solutions and some length in the problem. If, for example, we consider an electron in a one-dimensional box of length L, then the only types of motion which will produce stationary states are those for which the wave length is equal to $\frac{2L}{n}$, where n is a whole number.

OM: Well, then, what are the characteristics of the stationary states of the hydrogen atom?

YS: The lowest energy state of the hydrogen atom can be described quite simply. I have explained how in wave mechanics the probability of finding an electron at a particular place is proportional to the value of $\Psi\Psi*$ at the place concerned. Since space is three-dimensional, we shall in general have to imagine a three-dimensional model, with the nucleus at its centre, and then to see how the value of $\Psi\Psi*$ varies in the surrounding space. A large value of $\Psi\Psi*$ implies a high probability of finding the electron at the place concerned. In this way we can represent the electron state of the atom by a probability pattern, and it is this kind of probability pattern which constitutes our " picture " of the atom. For the lowest state of the hydrogen atom, the probability pattern is spherically symmetrical, and so we can represent it by a single curve which is shown in Fig. 8 (a), where the abscissæ represent the distances from the nucleus, and the ordinates ρ are proportional to $\Psi\Psi*$ and hence to the probability of finding the electron in an element of volume at the distance concerned. It will be seen that the value of ρ becomes vanishingly small beyond about $2A$, and this means that there is a negligible chance of finding the electron at a greater distance from the nucleus. In other words the motion of the electron is confined to a region whose diameter is of the order $4A$. Within this region the probability of finding the electron in an element of volume ΔV increases as the nucleus is approached. At a distance r from the nucleus, the probability of finding an electron in an element of volume ΔV is proportional to $\rho(r)$, where $\rho(r)$ is the ordinate of the curve at the point r, and similarly for other distances. This curve, therefore, represents our " picture " of the hydrogen atom. This picture has to be interpreted in terms of probabilities, but the electron moves so rapidly round the nucleus that for many purposes it is justifiable to regard the negative charge as being smeared out into a cloud of negative electricity, the density of the cloud being greatest where the probability of finding the electron is greatest. In this way we may speak of the electron cloud patterns of atoms, and we may say that Fig. 8 (a) represents a spherically symmetrical electron cloud, the density of which is greatest near the centre of the atom,

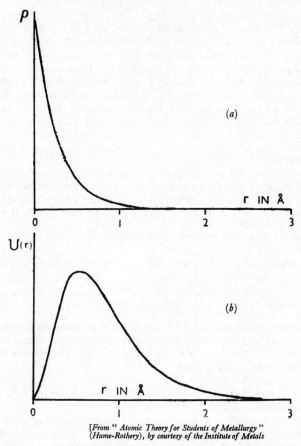

[From " Atomic Theory for Students of Metallurgy "
(Hume-Rothery), by courtesy of the Institute of Metals

Fig. 8—Electron distribution curves for the normal state of the hydrogen atom

(a) The curve in this figure shows the electron density for the normal state of the hydrogen atom as a function of the distance from the nucleus. The curve represents a spherically symmetrical electron cloud pattern, the density of which is greatest at the centre, and has almost vanished at a distance of 2A from the nucleus.

(b) The curve in this figure shows the U (r) curve for the normal state of the hydrogen atom. For the definition of the quantity U (r) see page 73. The curve rises to a maximum at r = 0.5292 A, and indicates that the electron spends a greater fraction of its time at this distance from the nucleus than at any other distance.

and which has practically faded away at distances greater than 2A from the nucleus. This concept of electron cloud patterns is exceedingly useful, and is often the best way of visualising the extra-nuclear electrons of an atom. You must not, of course, let this picture lead you to imagine that the electron occupies the whole region of the electron cloud pattern at any one instant. The correct interpretation is that of the relative probabilities of finding the electron at different places round the nucleus. But, as I said before, the electronic motion is so rapid that for many purposes it is quite justifiable to think in terms of an electron cloud. Attempts have been made to show this photographically by a method in which the intensity of illumination is proportional to the probability of finding an electron at the place concerned. Fig. 9 shows the electron cloud of the hydrogen atom in its normal state illustrated in this way. The figure is two-dimensional, and is thus more like a cross-section through the cloud—the actual electron cloud is, of course, three-dimensional, and is spherically symmetrical.

Fig. 8(a) thus represents the electron cloud pattern of the lowest electron state of the hydrogen atom. It corresponds with a quite definite energy, which is the energy of the first acceptable solution of the Schrödinger equation for the motion of an electron in the field of a point nucleus giving an attraction equal to $\frac{e^2}{r^2}$.

OM: This seems to me very confusing. If the pattern is spherically symmetrical, the electron can be found anywhere in the three-dimensional space immediately surrounding the nucleus. But all our previous talk has been about two-dimensional orbital motion.

YS: That's quite correct. The new view of the lowest state of the hydrogen atom is one of a spherically symmetrical electron cloud, and is quite different from the disc or ring type of motion which was postulated in the older theories.

OM: But if the Bohr theory was so utterly wrong, why did it give correct results at all?

YS: The Bohr theory was not really so far out as you might imagine. In the above figures $\Psi\Psi^*$ is proportional to the electron density or to the probability of finding an electron in an element of volume. $\Psi\Psi^*$ may thus be expressed in charge per unit volume, and the density of the electron cloud can be expressed in the same units. Electron density curves of this kind may be called $\rho\,(r)$ curves. Now suppose we consider a definite distance from the nucleus, say r. Then what will be the number of electrons at distances between r and $(r + dr)$ from the nucleus?

OM: You mean at a distance r irrespective of direction?

YS: Yes.

OM: Well, the points at a distance r from the nucleus lie on a sphere of radius r, whose surface is equal to $4\pi r^2$. So the volume between the spheres of radius r and $(r + dr)$ is $4\pi r^2 dr$, and if the number of electrons per unit volume is $\rho(r)$, the number of electrons in this spherical shell will be $4\pi r^2 \rho(r) dr$.

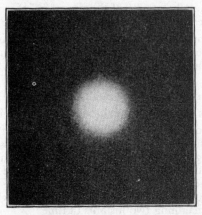

[*From " Atoms Molecules and Quanta "* (Ruark and Urey), by courtesy of McGraw Hill Book Company Inc.

Fig. 9—Photographic representation of the electron cloud pattern of the normal state of the hydrogen atom

In this figure the intensity of illumination is proportional to the value of $\Psi\Psi^*$ at the point concerned, and the figure may be regarded as a photographic representation of the $\rho\ (r)$ curve of Fig. 8 (a).

YS: That's right. It is customary to define the quantity $U(r)$ so that $U(r)dr$ is the number of electrons in a spherical shell of radius r and thickness dr. Consequently in atoms with spherically symmetrical electron clouds, we have from the relation you worked out above

$$U(r) = 4\pi r^2 \rho(r).$$

We may therefore plot $U(r)$ against r, and the $U(r)$ curves show the relative probabilities of finding the electron at different distances from the nucleus. The $U(r)$ curve for the lowest state of the hydrogen atom is shown in Fig. 8(b), and you will see that this rises to a maximum at $r = 0.5292$A. We may say therefore that there is a greater probability of finding the electron at a distance of 0.5292A from the nucleus than at any other distance, and this distance 0.5292A is the radius of the first Bohr orbit: it is this length which is the *atomic unit* of length to which you referred before (page 16). So the Bohr theory did express part of the truth, but the true picture is a three-dimensional electron cloud, and not a two-dimensional orbit.

OM: If the electron cloud is of the form of Fig. 8, then how does the electron move away from the inner part near the nucleus, to the outer part where it is farther from the nucleus?

YS: Oh! You've forgotten what I've told you. That is the kind of question you must not ask.

OM: But why not? I want to know how the electron moves about round the atom.

YS: Because the whole scale of the atom is of the order of a wave-packet, and you cannot say what happens within the wave-packet.

OM: That's not an answer to my question. I want to know how the electron moves about, and if the wave-packet model won't give an answer then the model is wrong.

YS: No! No! The model won't give an answer because Heisenberg's Principle prevents it. The model is right!

OM: What has Heisenberg's Principle got to do with it?

YS: I have told you that the diagram of Fig. 8(a) represents the lowest state of the hydrogen atom and corresponds with an exact value of the energy. Heisenberg's Principle states that if the energy is known exactly the time is completely indeterminate. Your question as to how the electron moves about implies that we can localise the electron at two definite instants—you can't speak of or imagine motion without imagining two instants of time.

OM: But what does it all mean? Why is this sort of complication always arising?

YS: The answer to that question is that in any experiment to determine how the electron moved about in the stationary state you would have to observe the electron twice, and your first observation could only be made by disturbing it, and so removing it from the stationary state concerned.

OM: I find it all most irritating.

YS: You're quite right. Heisenberg's Principle is one of the most irritating things known because it continually brings us up against the fact that so-called "common sense" is not enough. In all these electron cloud patterns you have to accept the pattern as a whole, and to recognise that the pattern itself is as far as we can go in providing a model or picture of what the electron does. We cannot expect to show how the electron moves within the pattern, because no experiment can be devised—even in principle—which would not disturb the electron so fundamentally as to make the experiment valueless for the question in hand. There are limits to what we can know, and it is by the recognition of these limits that modern theoretical physics has made such great advances. You may perhaps like the following quotations from the concluding pages of Born's *Atomic Physics*: " . . . Physicists of to-day have learnt that not every question about the motion of an electron or a light quantum can be answered, but only those questions which are compatible with Heisenberg's principle of uncertainty . . . This is a programme of modesty, but at the same time one of confident hope. For what lies within the limits is knowable; it is the world of experience, wide, rich enough in changing hues and patterns to allure us to explore it in all directions. What lies beyond, the dry tracts of metaphysics, we willingly leave to speculative philosophy."[1]

[1] Page 271, *Atomic Physics*. M. Born. (Blackie & Son.)

11—The s-States of the Hydrogen Atom

OLDER METALLURGIST: Now that we have got on to the hydrogen atom, I should like to know something about its higher energy states. Are the electron cloud patterns of these simply enlargements of the patterns for the lowest state?

YOUNG SCIENTIST: No. It is more complicated than that, I'm afraid. The electron cloud patterns of some of the higher electron states are not spherically symmetrical, and so we have to devise a method of showing how the electron cloud density varies in three dimensions. Do you understand the use of spherical polar co-ordinates?

OM: You mean co-ordinates involving r, θ, and ϕ.

YS: That's right. As you can see from Fig. 10, the position of the point P, which in rectangular co-ordinates is at (x, y, z) can be expressed in terms of the length OP, which is denoted r, the angle θ which OP makes with the z-axis, and the angle ϕ made by the x-axis with the projection of OP on the xy plane. All equations in terms of x, y and z can be transformed into equations involving r, θ, and ϕ.

OM: But won't it be more simple to stick to x, y and z?

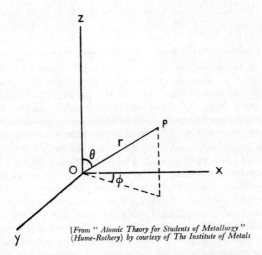

[From " Atomic Theory for Students of Metallurgy "
(Hume-Rothery) by courtesy of The Institute of Metals

Fig. 10—To illustrate spherical polar co-ordinates

The position of the point P which in rectangular co-ordinates is at (x, y, z) can be described by the length OP which is denoted r, the angle θ, and the angle ϕ.

YS: It is simply a question of mathematical convenience. For example, in spherical polar co-ordinates the equation for the surface of a sphere with its centre at the origin is simply $r = a$, where a is the radius of the sphere. This is much more simple than the expression $a^2 = x^2 + y^2 + z^2$, which is the corresponding equation in rectangular co-ordinates.

OM: Well, what is the advantage of the polar co-ordinates in the problem of the hydrogen atom?

YS: The advantage is that $\Psi\Psi*$, which you will remember is proportional to the electron cloud density at the place concerned, can be written as the product of three functions, the first depending only on the distance r from the nucleus, and the second depending only on θ, and the third depending only on ϕ. This means that we can write

$$\Psi\Psi* = R(r)\, R*(r) \times \Theta(\theta)\, \Theta*(\theta) \times \Phi(\phi)\, \Phi*(\phi)$$

or more shortly

$$\Psi\Psi* = R \times \vartheta \times \Phi$$

where the three terms each involve only one of the three co-ordinates r, θ, or ϕ, respectively.

This means that the electron cloud density in the space surrounding the nucleus can be written as the product of three factors, the first involving only the distance from the nucleus, the second involving only the angle θ, and the third only the angle ϕ. If the electron cloud is spherically symmetrical, then the Θ and Φ factors are constants, and the electron cloud density can be expressed by a single curve analogous to that of Fig. 8(a).

OM: But what has all this got to do with quantum numbers? I did understand that the Bohr theory of the hydrogen atom wasn't exactly correct, but I thought that quantum numbers were still used in order to describe the states of electrons in atoms.

YS: We have already seen how in problems of stationary states whole numbers have to be introduced in order to obtain acceptable solutions of the wave equations. In the problem of the hydrogen atom we have seen how the total electron density can be written as the product of the three factors R, Θ, and Φ given above. It is then found that the function for Φ will yield acceptable solutions only if a whole number is introduced. This whole number may be equal to 0, ± 1, ± 2, etc. This means that so far as the dependence of the electron density on the angle ϕ is concerned we have to introduce one whole number, and we may call this whole number m_l.

It is then found that for each value of m_l in the Φ function, the Θ function will yield acceptable solutions only if a second whole number is introduced, which may be called l. This second whole number is always positive, and must not be numerically less than m_l. In this way the dependence of $\Psi\Psi*$ on ϕ and θ involves the introduction of two whole numbers m_l and l.

It is then found that for each combination of m_l and l, the R function will yield acceptable solutions only if a third whole number n is introduced, which must not be less than l. In this way, by writing the wave equation in spherical polar co-ordinates, acceptable solutions for the problem of the hydrogen atom can be obtained only by the introduction of three whole numbers. Each combination of these whole numbers corresponds to a definite electron state, and these three whole numbers n, l, and m_l constitute the three main quantum numbers of the electron in the hydrogen atom. One can, for example, have an electron in a state characterised by

$$n = 3, l = 1, m_l = 0$$

or by

$$n = 2, l = 0, m_l = 0$$

and so on. Each of these states will have a definite energy, and a definite electron cloud pattern. It is in this way that wave mechanics introduces quantum numbers into the problem of the hydrogen atom, and they appear not as arbitrary assumptions, but as the inevitable conditions which must be satisfied if the equations are to yield acceptable solutions.

OM: Then have these numbers n, l, m_l any connection with the quantum numbers of the Bohr theory?

YS: The quantum number n is numerically equal to the n of the Bohr theory, and it is again a measure of the total energy of the electron in the state concerned. The larger the value of n, the greater is the energy, and in the hydrogen atom the total energy is proportional to $-\frac{1}{n^2}$. With infinitely large n, the total energy is zero, and this corresponds with an electron at an infinite distance from the nucleus.

OM: From what you said before, it would seem that the smallest possible value of n is 1, so is the lowest electron state of the hydrogen atom, that is, the state illustrated in Fig. 9, characterised by $n = 1$, $l = 0$, and $m_l = 0$?

YS: Yes, that's right.

OM: Is there no way by which one can avoid the very cumbersome method of description?

YS: Yes. It is customary to denote the electron states for which

$$l = 0, 1, 2, 3$$

by the small letters

$$s, p, d, f$$

whilst the value of n is indicated by a figure which is placed before the small letter. The symbol $3d$, for example, stands for the electron state for which $n = 3$, and $l = 2$, whilst $3s$ stands for the electron state for which $n = 3$ and $l = 0$. The lowest electron state of the hydrogen atom is thus $(1s)$.

OM: Then has the quantum number l any relation to the quantum number of the Bohr theory?

YS: The quantum number l is numerically equal to $(k - 1)$ of the Bohr theory.

OM: Then has l any relation to the angular momentum?

YS: Yes. The quantum number l is a measure of the angular momentum of the electron in the state concerned, and this angular momentum is of magnitude

$$\frac{h}{2\pi} \sqrt{l\,(l + 1)}$$

The postulate of the Bohr theory was that the angular momentum was equal to $\dfrac{kh}{2\pi}$, so that Bohr's guess was not exactly right.

OM: This is very puzzling because if the s-states are those for which $l = 0$, their angular momentum will be zero and this will mean a stationary electron, but surely the electron cannot be standing still?

YS: This is one of the cases where you just cannot visualise what is happening in terms of orbits. In the s-states the electron is not at rest, but its motion is as likely to be in one direction as another and does not give rise to an angular momentum.

OM: But has angular momentum any meaning if we are not to visualise the motion, and are not to think of orbits?

YS: Yes. We find that when a hydrogen atom undergoes a process such as a collision with another atom, it behaves as though the electron were associated with an angular momentum given by the above expression.

This angular momentum is often called the *orbital* angular momentum of the electron, because it corresponds with the angular momentum of the orbital motion in the older theories. On the whole it is rather an unfortunate expression because we must no longer think of the electron as being a little particle running round an orbit.

OM: If we are not to think of orbits, are there any characteristics of the s, p, d, f states which can be thought of or visualised?

YS: The s-states are relatively simple, and their first characteristic is that their electron clouds are spherically symmetrical. This means that the $\varTheta$ functions and the $\varPhi$ functions (page 76) are constants, and so the electron cloud density depends only on the R function, and can be represented by a single curve showing how $\varPsi\varPsi^*$ varies with the distance from the nucleus.

OM: Then are the curves of higher s-states simply enlargements of the curves for the $(1s)$ state which you have shown in Fig. 8a?

YS: Oh, no. The electron cloud patterns of the s-states are such that they posses $(n-1)$ spherical nodes round the centre of the atom, where n is the principal quantum number.

OM: What do you mean by a spherical node?

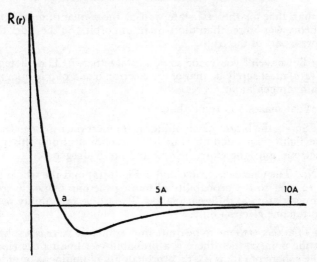

Fig. 11—The radial function $R(r)$ for the (2s) state of the hydrogen atom

YS: A node is a region where the amplitude of a vibration is zero, and a spherical node of the Ψ vibrations is thus a region where there is a zero probability of finding an electron. You will see that for the lowest or (1s) state of the electron in the hydrogen atom the above principle is obeyed. In the (1s) state $n = 1$, and so $n - 1 = 0$, and there are no spherical nodes—you will see by referring to Fig. 8a that the electron cloud density fades away gradually and continuously as one proceeds outwards from the centre of the atom. In the (2s) state, $n - 1 = 2 - 1 = 1$, and there will be one spherical node; Fig. 11 shows the radial function $R(r)$ for the (2s) state of the hydrogen atom, whilst Fig. 12 shows the corresponding $\rho(r)$ curve; $\rho(r)$ is proportional to $(R(r))^2$. In this case you will see that on proceeding outwards from the centre of the atom the electron cloud density first diminishes rapidly until it is zero at the distance $r = a$, and then rises to a maximum, after which it fades away gradually. The *s*-states are spherically symmetrical, and so the curve of Fig. 12 implies that the electron cloud of the (2s) state is a diffuse ball inside which there is a spherical shell where the electron cloud density is zero. There is thus one spherical node, since for the (2s) state $n = 2$ and $(n - 1) = 1$.

The electron cloud density of the (2s) state may be represented photographically by the same kind of photograph (Fig. 14(a)) which we used for the (1s) state, and Fig. 14(b) shows the pattern for the (2s) state. This, again, is of course really a two-dimensional cross-section through the electron cloud, and the real cloud is three-dimensional. The dark circle which you see in the photograph is the spherical node referred to above. When you compare Fig. 14(b) with Fig. 14(a) you will see that the electron cloud pattern for the (2s) state of the hydrogen atom is larger than that for the $(1s)$ state, just as the 2-quantum orbit of the older theory was larger than the 1-quantum orbit. So the older theory did express part of the truth.

OM: But haven't you made some mistake there? The photograph of Fig. $14(b)$ must surely be that of the electron cloud of a helium atom, not of a hydrogen atom.

YS. What makes you think that?

OM: Surely the bright patch of Fig. $14(b)$ must refer to one electron, and the lighter surrounding ring to a second electron—this means two electrons, and, therefore, helium and not hydrogen.

YS: No. The whole electron cloud of Fig. $14(b)$ and the whole curve of Fig. 12 refer to the probability of finding the one single electron of the hydrogen atom at different places. The whole probability pattern refers to the one electron only.

OM: That seems to me to be quite impossible. If there is a spherical node at the point a, then there is a probability of finding the electron inside the sphere of radius a, and a probability of finding it outside the sphere of radius a. But if the sphere of radius a is a node, and you say there is a zero probability of finding the electron at a distance a from the nucleus, then the electron can never travel from the inside to the outside of the atom or vice versa. I really believe I have caught you out this time!

YS: No. I'm afraid that all you have done is to forget Heisenberg's Principle once again.

OM: How can Heisenberg's Principle affect us here?

YS: You see, if you talk of the electron travelling about inside the atom, you are implying that you can observe the electron within the same electron state at two instants of time, and this means that the time is no longer completely indeterminate—it is the same point we dealt with before (page 74). The electron cloud pattern of a stationary state refers to an exact value of the energy, and so the time is completely indeterminate. However irritating you find it, you must accept it that these electron cloud probability patterns have to be taken as a whole; they give you all that you are entitled to visualise, and you must not ask how the electron moves about within the electron cloud. I know that you find this kind of difficulty very annoying, but it is just one of the cases in which the behaviour of the electron near an atom cannot be described in terms of so-called " common sense."

OM: You have said that the whole probability patterns of Figs. 12 and $14(b)$ for the $(2s)$ state refer to the probability of finding the one electron at different places, and that the pattern for the $(2s)$ state occupies a larger region of space than that for the $(1s)$ state. If the whole pattern refers to one electron, it would seem that the ordinates of Figs. $8(a)$ and 12, and the intensities of illumination of Figs. $14(a)$ and $14(b)$, must be very different.

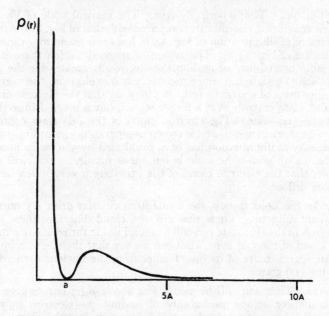

Fig. 12—The $\rho(r)$ curve for the (2s) state of the hydrogen atom

This represents a spherically symmetrical cloud of negative electricity with a spherical node at a distance $r = a$ from the centre. When compared with Fig. 8 it will be seen that the electron cloud of the (2s) state stretches out farther from the nucleus than that of the (1s) state. The whole curve in Fig. 12 refers to one electron only, and the vertical scale of the figure has been magnified greatly compared with that of Fig. 8.

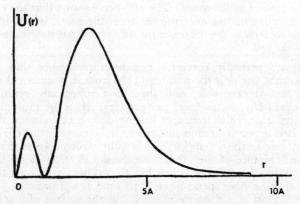

Fig. 13—The $U(r)$ curve corresponding to the $\rho(r)$ curve of Fig. 12

YS: Oh, yes. That's perfectly true. The vertical scale of Fig. 12 has been magnified enormously compared with that of Fig. 8(a), whilst the intensity of illumination of Fig. 14(b) has been made fifty times as great as that of Fig. 14(a). The region of space in which there is an appreciable probability of finding the electron is greater for the (2s) than for the (1s) state but, since there is only one electron, the average probability must of course be less. We may say that the electron cloud of the (2s) state extends over a larger region, but is more diffuse than that of the (1s) state. The electron cloud of the (3s) state contains $3 - 1 = 2$ spherical nodes, and is shown photographically in Fig. 14(c). The intensity of illumination has been multiplied by 500, as compared with Fig. 14(a), whilst the scale is ten times smaller. You will see, therefore, that the electron cloud of the (3s) state is very much larger and more diffuse.

OM: In the Bohr theory, the 2-quantum circular orbit lay outside the 1-quantum orbit. These new electron cloud diagrams show that the electron in the (2s) state can still be found inside the region occupied by the cloud of the (1s) state. But can we say that the electron in the (2s) state spends more of its time farther from the nucleus than when it is in the (1s) state?

YS: Yes. That can still be said. The above $\rho(r)$ curves give the electron density or the probability of finding the electron in unit volume. If you want to see the probability of finding the electron at a given distance from the nucleus irrespective of direction, you require the $U(r)$ curves to which we referred before (page 73). Fig. 13 shows the $U(r)$ curve for the (2s) state, and if you compare this with the $U(r)$ curve for the (1s) state (Fig. 8b), you will see that the electron in the (2s) state does spend most of its time farther away from the nucleus than when in the (1s) state.

OM: It seems to me that the $U(r)$ curve is very misleading if it is taken as a picture of the atom. The $\rho(r)$ curve shows that the electron cloud density is greatest near the centre of the atom, whilst the $U(r)$ curve goes to zero at the centre of the atom, and has its greatest value relatively far out.

YS: That's perfectly correct. You must remember that $U(r)$ is defined so that $U(r)dr$ is the number of electrons in a spherical shell of radius r and thickness dr, and that in a spherically symmetrical electron cloud $U(r) = 4\pi r^2.\rho(r)$ (see page 73). It is the multiplication by the term $4\pi r^2$ which accounts for the difference between the two curves. It is a very common mistake to imagine that the $U(r)$ curve gives a picture of the atom, but this is quite wrong. In so far as the expression " picture of the atom " means the electron cloud density, it is always the $\rho(r)$ curve which has to be considered. In the (2s) state the electron does spend more of its time at a distance $2.5A$ from the nucleus than at a distance of $0.5A$, but the surface of a sphere of radius $2.5A$ is so much greater than one of radius $0.5A$ that the electron density per unit volume is greater at $0.5A$.

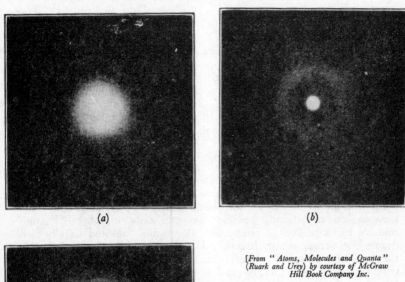

(*a*)   (*b*)

[*From " Atoms, Molecules and Quanta "
(Ruark and Urey) by courtesy of McGraw
Hill Book Company Inc.*

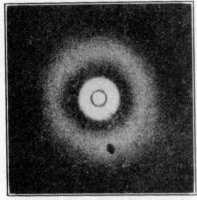

(*c*)

**Fig. 14 (a, b, c)—The electron
cloud patterns of the hydrogen
atom (1*s*), (2*s*) and (3*s*) states
respectively**

*In each case the whole pattern represents one electron, and the intensities of illumination of (b)
and (c) have been multiplied by 50 and 500 respectively compared with (a) in order to make the
outer rings visible. The scales of (b) and (c) are respectively 5 and 10 times smaller than that
of (a). Increasing value of the principal quantum number means, therefore, that the electron cloud
is spread over a larger region, and becomes more diffuse. Fig. 14 (b) is a photographic representation of the ρ(r) curve shown in Fig. 12.*

OM: Then does the same general principle apply to the higher
s-states?

YS: In the (3*s*), (4*s*) . . . states the electron cloud stretches farther
and farther from the nucleus, and as it refers to one electron it becomes
more and more diffuse. There are $(n - 1)$ spherical nodes, and with
increasing n the electron spends most of its time at an increasing
distance from the nucleus, although—for the reasons we have already
discussed—the electron cloud density $\rho(r)$ is always greatest near to
the nucleus.

12—The *p*- and *d*-States of the Hydrogen Atom

OLDER METALLURGIST: Before you describe the *p*- and *d*-electron states of the hydrogen atom, I should like to know something about the quantum number m_l. In the *s*-states $l = 0$, and so m_l can only be equal to zero, but in the *p*- and *d*-states m_l can have different values, and I should like to know what this means.

YOUNG SCIENTIST: In order to appreciate the meaning of m_l we have to consider what is meant by the shape and the orientation of an atom. I have already explained how from the modern viewpoint it is meaningless to speak of quantities unless we can decide how they are measured. From this point of view, " the shape of a perfectly free atom " is a meaningless expression, because we can only measure " shape " relative to some axes of reference. The policy adopted usually is to define the *z*-axis, as the direction of a very weak magnetic field. In this way the *z*-axis and hence the *xy* plane are defined. A second very weak field may then be used to define the direction of the *x*-axis. When a physicist speaks of the shape of a " free atom," he really means an atom defined by very weak fields.

Now we have already seen that the quantum number l is a measure of the orbital angular momentum which is of magnitude

$$\frac{h}{2\pi} \sqrt{l(l + 1)}.$$

If we define the *z*-axis by means of a very weak magnetic field, then the component of the angular momentum along the *z*-axis is equal to

$$\frac{h}{2\pi} \cdot m_l$$

and this is the significance of m_l. If $m_l = 0$, the component of the angular momentum along the *z*-axis is zero, whilst if $m_l = 1$ the component along the *z*-axis is $\frac{h}{2\pi}$, and so on.

OM: I seem to remember seeing m_l referred to as the magnetic quantum number. Has it any relation to magnetic properties?

YS: Yes. The angular momentum

$$\frac{h}{2\pi} \sqrt{l(l + 1)}$$

is associated with a magnetic moment of magnitude

$$\frac{e}{2mc} \cdot \frac{h}{2\pi} \sqrt{l(l + 1)}$$

where *m* is the mass of the electron, and *c* is the velocity of light.

The quantity $\frac{eh}{4\pi mc}$ is called a *Bohr Magneton*, and is equal to 0.927 × 10^{-20} erg gauss^{-1}. If magnetic moments are expressed in Bohr Magnetons, then an electron state is associated with a magnetic moment equal to $\sqrt{l(l+1)}$, and the component in the direction of the applied field is equal to m_l.

The Bohr Magneton is a very fundamental quantity, and we shall come across it again in connection with the magnetic properties of alloys.

OM: Then have the different values of m_l any effect on the shapes of the electron cloud patterns of the different electron states?

YS: Oh, yes. Very much so. The first thing to remember is that increasing values of m_l mean that the electron cloud is more and more concentrated in the direction of the *xy* plane.

OM: Then do you mean that we now have to deal with atoms whose shapes are no longer spherical?

YS: If by " shape " you mean the density distribution of the electron cloud, then the answer is " Yes."

OM: But if that is so, we shall have to have a four-dimensional model to illustrate the atom. There will be the three dimensions of space, and the electron cloud density will require a fourth variable.

YS: That is quite true, but the difficulty can be got over to some extent by means of what are known as polar diagrams. You will remember that we saw how, if spherical polar co-ordinates are used, the electron cloud density can be written as the product of three factors R, θ, and Φ where R depends only on the distance from the nucleus, whilst θ and Φ depend only on the angles θ and ϕ respectively. This means that the electron cloud density can be expressed as the product of one term, the radial factor, which depends on the distance from the nucleus, and of two other terms which depend only on the *direction* relative to the axes, so that we may write $\Psi\Psi^* = R(\theta\,\Phi)$ where the term in the bracket refers only to the direction, and is the same at all distances from the nucleus. It is thus possible to show the value of $(\theta\,\Phi)$ by means of a three-dimensional polar model, of such a nature that if a line is drawn from the origin in a given direction and cuts the surface of the model at a point P, then the length of OP is equal to the value of $(\theta\,\Phi)$ for the direction concerned.

Let us consider, for example, the three-dimensional polar diagram of Fig. 15. Suppose we proceed from the origin in the direction of the *z*-axis. The *z*-axis cuts the surface of the model at P and the length OP gives the value of $(\theta\,\Phi)$ for the direction of the *z*-axis, that is the direction $\theta = 0$. If we proceed in the direction of the straight line OA, this cuts the model at P_2, and the length of OP_2 gives the value of $(\theta\,\Phi)$ for this direction.

You will see, therefore, that for this example $(\theta\,\Phi)$ has a maximum value along the *z*-axis, and is equal to zero for all directions in the *xy* plane.

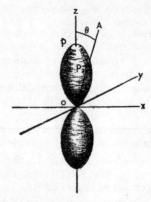

Fig. 15—To illustrate a three-dimensional polar diagram

OM: Then do you mean that a picture like that of Fig. 15 is the picture of an atom? It looks just as hard and concrete as the old billiard-ball atom.

YS: You haven't understood it fully yet. Fig. 15 shows the way in which the electron cloud density varies as far as *direction* is concerned, that is, it gives the $(\Theta\ \Phi)$ term. But to get the electron cloud density, you have to multiply the values of OP, OP_2, etc., in Fig. 15 by the values of the radial factor R at the different distances.

OM: Can one possibly visualise this kind of thing?

YS: Oh, it's not so difficult if you are prepared to think a little. Let us start now by considering the electron cloud patterns of the $2p$-states. There will be three of these corresponding with $m_l = 0$, and $m_l = \pm 1$ respectively.

Now we have seen that for s-states, the electron cloud is spherically symmetrical and possesses $(n - 1)$ spherical nodes. In the p-states the radial factor is characterised by the possession of a node at the centre, and by $(n - 2)$ spherical nodes.

Fig. 16, for example, shows the radial factor R for the $2p$-state. Since $n = 2$, $n - 2 = 0$, and there are no spherical nodes, and you will see that the curve has a zero value at $r = 0$, rises to a maximum, and then dies away gradually. This radial curve is the same for the three states $2p$, $m_l = 0$; $2p$, $m_l = \pm 1$ but the polar diagrams for the three states are different, and are shown in Fig. 17.

Now if you combine the radial curve of Fig. 16 with the polar diagram of Fig. 17(a), you begin to get your picture of the electron cloud distribution. In the state $2p$, $m = 0$, at the centre of the atom, the electron cloud density is zero; because the radial factor R (Fig. 16) is zero at $r = 0$. At other distances the electron density is greatest in the direction of the z-axis, because the length OP in the polar diagram Fig. 17(a) is a maximum in the direction of the z-axis, and the electron density is given by the product of the radial factor and the length from the polar diagram in the direction concerned. At all distances the electron density is zero in the xy plane, because the lengths in the

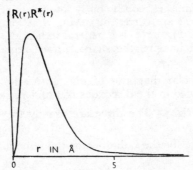

Fig. 16—The radial factor for the $2p$-state of the hydrogen atom

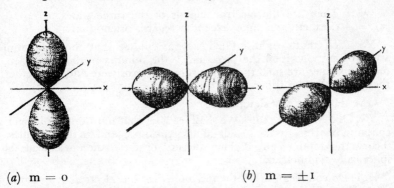

(a) m = 0   (b) m = ±1

Fig. 17—Three-dimensional polar diagrams for the three p-states

Figs. 17 (a), (b), and (c) are identical in shape and differ only in orientation relative to the x, y and z axes. It will be seen that an increase in the value of m from 0 to ± 1 results in the electron cloud becoming more concentrated in the xy plane. If the above three patterns are added together, they produce an electron cloud of spherical symmetry.

polar diagram are zero in this plane. You will see, therefore, that if we consider any direction outside the xy plane, the electron density starts by being zero at the centre of the atom, and then rises to a maximum and gradually fades away in accordance with the form of the radial curve of Fig. 16. If we compare the different directions, the polar diagram of Fig. 17(a) shows that the electron cloud stretches out farthest in the direction of the z-axis.

OM: Do you mean, therefore, that if we are dealing with the outside part of the electron cloud, Fig. 17(a) is a general "picture" of the atom, provided we imagine that the sharp boundary surface is replaced by a diffuse cloud?

YS: Yes, that is more or less right. Fig. 17(a) shows that, at a given distance from the nucleus, the electron cloud density is greatest in the direction of the z-axis. The radial curve of Fig. 16 shows that the radial factor diminishes continuously after about 1.5A from the nucleus, and so you are correct in saying that for the outer part of the electron cloud, Fig. 17(a) is a general indication of the "shape of the atom," if you imagine the sharp surface replaced by a diffuse cloud.

OM: Are the polar diagrams of Fig. 17(b) the same as that of Fig. 17(a), but turned in the directions of x and y axes respectively?

YS: Yes, that's right. The three are exactly the same, and differ only in orientation.

OM: Is the curve for the radial factor the same for the three polar diagrams?

YS: For a given value of l, the radial factor depends on the quantum number n, and is the same for the three states $m_l = 0$, $m_l = \pm 1$.

OM: Then are the electron clouds of the three states, $m_l = 0$, $m_l = \pm 1$, exactly the same, except as regards orientation?

YS: Yes, that's right. Further you will see that the maximum value of any one is in the direction of the minima of the other two, and the shapes are such that if the three patterns were added together they would form a sphere.

OM: Has that any significance?

YS: Oh, very much so! We shall see later that the atom of nitrogen contains one electron in each of the $2p$-states, and in the simplest theory the total electron cloud density of these three electrons is spherically symmetrical.

OM: Do you mean that if there is more than one electron in an atom, you can add their electron clouds together?

YS: Yes. You must remember that the electron clouds are only ways of visualising the probabilities of finding an electron in different regions of space. Since electrons are identical, it is quite legitimate to add together the electron clouds of the individual electrons in order to obtain the total electron cloud density.

OM: But surely the different electrons interfere with each other's motions?

YS: Most certainly, yes. That's why I said "in the simplest theory." In a complete theory one would have to consider how the different electrons affected one another, and that problem is too difficult for a complete solution.

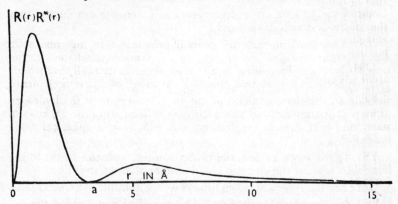

Fig. 18—The radial factor for the 3*p*-state of the hydrogen atom

This has a node at the centre and one spherical node at $r = a$, since $n - 2 = 1$

OM: Then do you mean that the diagrams of Figs. 16 and 17 enable one to read off the electron cloud density of the nitrogen atom?

YS: Oh, no! The radial factor, R, for the 2*p*-state of the nitrogen atom will be different from that of the 2*p*-state of the hydrogen atom. You must remember that nitrogen has atomic number $Z = 7$, and so each electron is moving in the field resulting from a nucleus of charge $+ 7e$, and the six other electrons. For an electron in a *p*-state the radial factor still shows $(n-2)$ spherical nodes, but the details depend on the atom concerned. The polar diagrams for the three 2*p*-states of the atom of nitrogen although not identical with those of Fig. 17, are of the same general form, and in the simplest theory when they are added together they produce an electron cloud with spherical symmetry. In this approximation, therefore, the nitrogen atom is spherically symmetrical because it contains one electron in each of the three 2*p*-states ($2p$, $m_l = 0$; $2p$, $m_l = +1$; $2p$, $m_l = -1$).

OM: I see. And then if we have an electron in a 3*p*-state of the hydrogen atom do the same polar figures still apply?

YS: Yes. The polar diagrams for the *p*-states always apply for hydrogen. The difference between the electron cloud pattern of an electron in a 3*p*-state of the hydrogen atom and of an electron in a 2*p*-state lies in the radial factor. For the 3*p*-state, $n-2 = 3-2 = 1$, and so the radial factor for the 3*p*-state has one spherical node, as well as the node at the centre. Fig. 18 shows the radial factor $R(r)R^*(r)$ for the 3*p*-state of the hydrogen atom, and you will see that this has a node at the point $r = 0$, and another node at the point $r = a$. The vertical scale of Fig. 18 has been greatly magnified compared with that of Fig. 16.

OM: If one compares Figs. 16 and 18, it seems that the electron cloud of the $3p$-state of the hydrogen atom stretches out farther than that of the $2p$-state. Is that right?

YS: Yes; that's a perfectly general principle. In any one atom the electron clouds of the $2p$, $3p$, $4p$ . . . states stretch out farther and farther with increasing n, although there is naturally no simple relation between the electron clouds of the atoms of different elements.

OM: So the electron cloud of the $3p$, $m = 0$ state of the hydrogen atom will be stretched out along the z-axis, like that of the $2p$, $m = 0$, state, and will stretch out farther, but will have a spherical node inside it?

YS: That's more or less right. So you see, you can begin to get some idea of what the electron cloud picture of an atom is like.

OM: Are the spherical nodes always well within the electron cloud?

YS: Yes, that's perfectly right. The spherical nodes affect the interior rather than the exterior of the electron cloud.

OM: It would seem, therefore, that if we consider only the outside of the electron cloud, Fig. 17 will still give more or less the " shape " of the atom, if we imagine the sharp surface replaced by a diffuse cloud.

YS: That's quite right.

OM: Well, now what about the d-patterns?

YS: If you have understood the general principle underlying the p-states, we can describe the d-states very simply. We have seen that in the s-states the radial factor $R(r) R^*(r)$ has $(n - 1)$ spherical nodes, and no node at the centre. In the p-states, the radial factor has $(n - 2)$ spherical nodes, and a node at the centre. In the d-states the process is carried a stage farther, and the radial factor has $(n - 3)$ spherical nodes together with a node at the centre. So there is a regular sequence of $(n - 1)$, $(n - 2)$, and $(n - 3)$ spherical nodes for the s-, p-, and d-states respectively.

OM: Then do you mean that for the $3d$-state the radial curve has no spherical nodes?

YS: That's right. For the $3d$-state, $n = 3$ and so $n - 3 = 0$, and there are no spherical nodes. The radial factor for the $3d$-state of the hydrogen atom is thus of the general form[1] of that of the $2p$-state; it is zero at $r = 0$, rises to a maximum, and then gradually fades away. The radial factor for the $4d$-state has a node at the centre, and $n - 3 = 4 - 3 = 1$ spherical node as well.

OM: Then when you have fixed the radial factor, the polar factors of the p- and d-states will I suppose be different?

YS: Yes. They are quite different. From what we said before you will see that there are five d-states for a given value of l, namely those for which $m_l = 0$, ± 1, and ± 2 respectively. The polar

---

[1] The details are not exactly the same. For the $2p$-state $R(r)R^*(r)$ varies as r^2e^{-r}, whereas for the $3d$-state $R(r)R^*(r)$ varies as r^4e^{-r}.

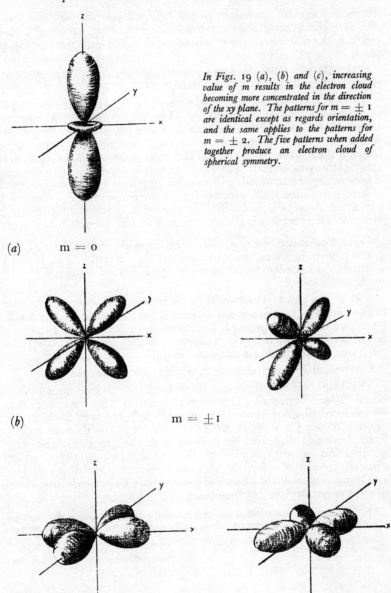

In Figs. 19 (a), (b) and (c), increasing value of m results in the electron cloud becoming more concentrated in the direction of the xy plane. The patterns for m = ± 1 are identical except as regards orientation, and the same applies to the patterns for m = ± 2. The five patterns when added together produce an electron cloud of spherical symmetry.

(a)   m = 0

(b)   m = ± 1

(c)   m = ± 2

Figs. 19 (a), (b) and (c)—Three-dimensional polar diagrams for the five *d*-states

diagrams for these are shown in Fig. 19, and you will see how these illustrate the general principle that with increasing value of m_l the electron cloud becomes more concentrated in the directions of the xy plane.

OM: Do the different d-patterns fit together so as to produce an electron cloud of spherical symmetry?

YS: Yes. If you add together the polar diagrams of the five types of the d-state, you obtain a sphere. This means that if you have an atom with one electron in each of the five d-states, or with two electrons in each of the five d-states of a given quantum number n, then, in the simplest theory, the electron cloud of the group of 5 or of 10 electrons is spherically symmetrical, because the electron cloud for each s electron is spherically symmetrical, whereas the $(3p)^6$ and $(3d)^{10}$ sub-groups of electrons are spherically symmetrical in the simple theory. But, as I explained above, the complete theory must consider how the different electrons affect each other's motions, and that problem is too difficult.

OM: You mean, do you, that these three-dimensional polar diagrams have to be combined with the curve for the radial factor in order to obtain the complete variation of the electron cloud density round the nucleus?

YS: That's right. They are to be interpreted exactly as in the case of the diagrams for the p-states which we have just discussed in detail. As in the case of the p-states, the radial curve for a given value of n is the same for all the polar diagrams of Fig. 19, whilst the polar diagrams are the same for all values of n.

OM: Shall I find these polar diagrams in other books?

YS: There are not at present many books which give three-dimensional polar diagrams. The general practice is to give one two-dimensional diagram showing how $\Theta(\theta)$ $\Theta^*(\theta)$ varies with θ, and another showing how $\Phi(\phi)$ $\Phi^*(\phi)$ varies with ϕ, and then the lengths from these two diagrams have to be multiplied together, and their product has to be multiplied by the radial factor $R(r)R^*(r)$ at the distance concerned. But the three-dimensional polar diagrams give you a much more vivid picture of the way in which the electron cloud density varies in different directions.

[1] In this notation the small numbers outside the brackets denote the numbers of electrons in the state concerned. Thus $(3s)^2$ means 2 electrons in the $(3s)$ state.

NOTE.—The illustrations used in this chapter are from " Atomic Theory for Students of Metallurgy " (W. Hume-Rothery), published by The Institute of Metals.

13—Hydrogen, Helium and Lithium: Electron Spin and Pauli's Principle

OLDER METALLURGIST: Now that we have dealt with the three quantum numbers of the electron in the hydrogen atom, can we begin to get on to the elements of higher atomic number?

YOUNG SCIENTIST: Before we do that, you must understand the meaning of the fourth quantum number which characterises an electron state, and is called the spin quantum number.

OM: But is it really necessary for me to go into questions like electron spin when all I'm wanting to do is to understand metals?

YS: Most certainly it is. Ferromagnetism is the result of electron spin, and even you can't call magnetism an unpractical subject!

OM: Then if a spin quantum number has to be considered, do you mean that an electron state is not fully defined by the three quantum numbers n, l and m_l?

YS: Yes. A detailed examination showed that all the facts could not be accounted for by three quantum numbers. The solution was found by Uhlenbeck and Goudsmit, who suggested that, apart from their translatory motion, electrons in atoms were associated with a spin and could set themselves either parallel or anti-parallel to an applied field. The angular momentum associated with the spin is of magnitude

$$\frac{h}{2\pi} \sqrt{s(s+1)}$$

where $s = \frac{1}{2}$. The component of the spin momentum in the direction of the z-axis, which you will remember is defined by a weak magnetic field, is

$$\frac{h}{2\pi} m_s$$

where the spin quantum numbers m_s may equal $+\frac{1}{2}$ or $-\frac{1}{2}$. In this way an electron state is completely defined by the four quantum numbers n, l, m_l, and m_s.

OM: Then is the magnetic moment of the spin equal to the angular momentum multiplied by $\frac{e}{2mc}$ as was the case for the orbital angular momentum?

YS: No. The magnetic moment associated with the spin is

$$\frac{e}{mc} \times \frac{h}{2\pi} \sqrt{s(s+1)}$$

The factor for the spin is $\dfrac{e}{mc}$ as compared with $\dfrac{e}{2mc}$ for the orbital angular momentum.

OM: Then is the component of the spin magnetic moment in the direction of the field

$$\frac{e}{mc} \times \frac{h}{2\pi} \times m_s?$$

YS: Yes. That's right.

OM: So if $m_s = \pm\frac{1}{2}$, the component is $\dfrac{eh}{4\pi mc}$, which is what you called a Bohr Magneton?

YS: That's right.

OM: Does the spin make any very great difference to the energy of an electron state?

YS: No. There is only a very small difference between the energies of states with a given n, l, and m_l, and with $m_s = +\frac{1}{2}$ and $m_s = -\frac{1}{2}$. The difference does, however, become greater with increasing atomic number.

OM: Then do these same quantum numbers come into the electron states of elements of higher atomic number?

YS: The problem of an atom with more than one electron is immensely difficult, and an accurate solution exists only for helium with 2 electrons. The main cause of the trouble is that it becomes difficult or impossible to calculate the way in which the different electrons affect each other's motions. Apart from this, when the atomic number becomes larger, the charge on the nucleus increases, and electrons when very near to the nucleus may move so rapidly that relativity corrections have to be made. For the lighter elements, it is often a reasonable approximation to assume that any one electron may be regarded as moving in the field of the nucleus and that the remaining electrons are smeared out and produce a field which is spherically symmetrical. In this approximation each electron moves in a central field of force, and quantum numbers analogous to those of the hydrogen atom are again introduced. The same is assumed to apply to the heavier elements, and the spectroscopical evidence suggests that this is not unreasonable.

OM: I can see how difficult the problem will become, but can you explain how one comes to get stable groups of electrons. I cannot see why one should not have any number of electrons in the lowest energy state.

YS: The answer to that question is summarised in what is called Pauli's Principle. According to this principle, in any one atom one cannot have more than one electron in a given quantum state as defined by all four quantum numbers n, l, m_l and m_s. There may for example be one electron in the $3p$-state, $m_l = 0$, $m_s = +\frac{1}{2}$, and one electron in the $3p$-state, $m_l = 0$, $m_s = -\frac{1}{2}$, but one cannot have two electrons in the same state as defined by all four quantum numbers.

OM: Does that come out of wave mechanics?

YS: The principle was discovered empirically, but it can readily be fitted into the framework of wave mechanics if an additional assumption is introduced, but this would lead us into the mathematics which you want to avoid.

OM: How does Pauli's Principle lead to stable groups?

YS: The principle does not predict *stable* groups, but a little thought will show you that it renders impossible your suggestion that any number of electrons could enter the lowest energy state. From the relation between the quantum numbers described before, you will readily see that if m_s can only equal $+\frac{1}{2}$ or $-\frac{1}{2}$, the maximum possible number of electrons in states with a principal quantum number n is $2n^2$, if there can only be one electron in each state as defined by all four quantum numbers.

OM: Before we go on, there is one thing I don't understand. I've seen references to Pauli's Principle which say that there can be two electrons in a given state—not one as you have stated above.

YS: That's a common difficulty at first, and it simply depends on whether you regard the quantum number m_s as defining a state. If you prefer to leave out m_s, then you may say that each energy state defined by a given combination of n, l and m_l can contain not more than two electrons—when the state is fully occupied one electron will correspond to $m_s = +\frac{1}{2}$ and the other to $m_s = -\frac{1}{2}$. If, on the other hand, you include m_s in your definition of a state, then a state defined by a given combination of n, l, m_l, and m_s can contain not more than one electron.

OM: Then does this principle mean that there cannot be more than two electrons in the $(1s)$ state?

YS: Yes. We can now pass on from hydrogen to helium; in the latter element the atomic number is equal to 2, and so the nucleus of charge $+2e$ is surrounded by two electrons. As in the case of hydrogen, the lowest energy state is the $(1s)$ state, and since Pauli's Principle allows this to contain 2 electrons, both the electrons of the helium atom are in the $(1s)$ state. We may write the electronic structure of the atom $(1s)^2$, and Fig. 21 is a photographic reproduction of the electron density of the normal state of the helium atom, and you should compare this with the corresponding photograph (Fig. 20) for the $(1s)^1$ state of the hydrogen atom.

OM: The electron cloud of helium seems to be much more dense round the nucleus. Is that because the increased nuclear charge is pulling the electrons more strongly towards the nucleus?

YS: That's right. With increasing atomic number a $(1s)$ electron is drawn towards the nucleus more and more firmly, and as the atomic number increases the electron cloud of the (1s) group occupies a continually smaller region of space, and is bound more firmly to the nucleus.

OM: Is there any way of measuring the firmness of the binding?

YS: The work required to remove an electron from an atom is often called the *ionisation potential* of the electron in the state concerned. In the case of hydrogen the ionisation potential of the (1s) electron is 13.53 volts, whereas in helium it is 24.47 volts. So a (1s) electron is held more firmly in helium than in hydrogen.

OM: But if the atomic numbers of hydrogen and helium are 1 and 2, should not the ionisation potentials be simple multiples of one another?

YS: Oh, no! That doesn't follow at all. In the hydrogen atom the single electron moves in the field of the single nucleus. In the helium atom each electron moves in the field resulting from the nucleus and

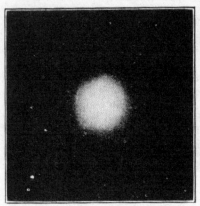
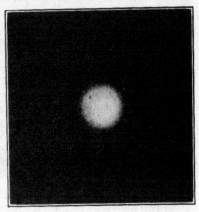

From " Atoms, Molecules and Quanta " (Ruark and Urey), by courtesy of McGraw Hill Book Company Inc.

Fig. 20—Photographic representation of the electron cloud pattern of the normal state of the hydrogen atom

In this figure the intensity of illumination is proportional to the value of $\Psi\Psi^*$ at the point concerned, and the figure may be regarded as a photographic representation of the $\rho(r)$ curve of Fig. 8 (a).

Fig. 21—To illustrate the electron cloud of the normal $(1s)^2$ helium atom

This is on the same scale as the photograph (Fig. 20) of the $(1s)^1$ normal hydrogen atom, but the intensity of illumination has been divided by a factor of 100. The electron cloud of the helium atom is thus very much more dense than that of the hydrogen atom.

from the motion of the other electron—it's a horribly difficult problem.

OM: Well, in that case can one get a singly charged helium ion He^+, in which there will be only one electron moving round a charge of $+2e$, and, if so, will the ionisation potential of that electron be simply related to the ionisation potential of hydrogen?

YS: Yes. Under some conditions it is possible to study the energy relations of the He^+ ion, and the ionisation potential of this ion is 54.14 volts, which you will see is almost exactly four ($= 2^2$) times that of hydrogen.

OM: It would seem that the He^+ ion is a very interesting thing to study.

YS: That's quite right—it enables one to examine the behaviour of one electron round a nucleus of charge $+ 2e$.

OM: Now suppose we proceed from helium to the next element, lithium. This has atomic number 3, and 3 electrons. So am I right in thinking that if the $(1s)^2$ group can hold only two electrons, the third electron will have to go into a state of higher quantum number?

YS: That's right. Pauli's Principle says that the $(1s)^2$ group can hold not more than two electrons, and so the third electron goes into the next highest energy state, which is the $(2s)$ state. We may write the electronic configuration of the lithium atom in its *normal* or lowest energy state

$$(1s)^2 \ (2s)^1.$$

OM: Then what does the electron cloud of that atom look like? Is the $(1s)^2$ group held more firmly than in an atom of helium?

YS: The $(1s)^2$ group of electrons is held more firmly in lithium than in helium, and it occupies a smaller region of space, because the atomic number of lithium is greater than that of helium. But the electron cloud of the $(2s)$ electron in lithium is much larger and more diffuse than that of the $(1s)$ electron, just as the electron cloud of the $(2s)$ state of the hydrogen atom occupies a larger region of space than that of the $(1s)$ state. So you may say roughly that the inside of the electron cloud of the lithium atom is due mainly to the $(1s)^2$ group of electrons, whilst the outside of the electron cloud is due mainly to the valency or $(2s)$ electron. Of course the electron cloud of the $(2s)$ electron does extend to the interior, as was the case for the $(2s)$ state of the hydrogen atom, but its density is so small relatively to that of the $(1s)^2$ group that we are justified in saying that the inside of the electron cloud is due to the $(1s)^2$ group, and the outside to the $(2s)$ valency electron.

OM: Can one show this kind of thing diagrammatically?

YS: Fig. 22 may help you to understand the way in which the electron cloud of the atom is built up. In this diagram the ordinates are proportional to the electron cloud density, while the abscissæ give the distances from the nucleus. The one curve refers to the $(1s)^2$ group of the electrons, and the other curve to the $(2s)^1$ or valency electron of the free atom of lithium in its normal state. You will see that beyond about 1.2A the electron density of the $(1s)^2$ group becomes vanishingly small, and that the electron cloud of the $(2s)$ electron projects farther. The electron cloud density of the atom as a whole is obtained by the summation of the ordinates of the two curves, and you will see therefore that at large distances from the nucleus the electron cloud is due entirely to the $(2s)$ or valency electron. On the other hand, at very small distances from the nucleus the electron cloud density of the $(1s)^2$ group is enormously greater than that of the $(2s)$ electron, so that we are justified in saying that the inside of the atom is due mainly to the $(1s)^2$ group.

OM: If the electron cloud of the $(2s)$ electron extends outside that of the $(1s)$ electrons, is it more easy to remove a $(2s)$ electron from the atom?

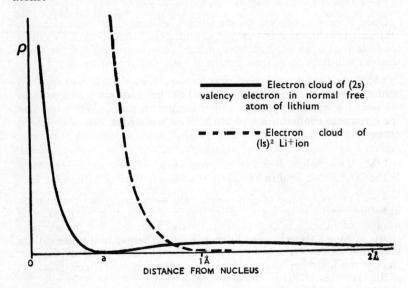

Fig. 22—To illustrate the electron cloud density distribution in the normal free atom of lithium

In this diagram the horizontal axis represents the distance from the nucleus in A. On the vertical axis the co-ordinates are proportional to the electron density ρ. The one curve refers to the electron cloud of the $(1s)^2$ group of electrons; it will be seen that the electron cloud density of this group of electrons has become vanishingly small at distances greater than about 1.2A. The second curve refers to the $(2s)^1$ valency electron, and shows one spherical node at the point (a) in agreement with the principle that an electron in an ns state possesses an electron cloud with $(n-1)$ spherical nodes. The electron cloud density of the atom as a whole is obtained by adding the ordinates of the two curves. At distances nearer to the nucleus than 0.5A, the electron cloud density of the $(1s)^2$ group becomes too great to be shown on the scale of the figure.

YS: Yes. The ionisation potential of the $(2s)$ valency electron of a lithum atom is only 5.47 volts, so it is more easy to remove a $(2s)$ electron from a lithium atom than to remove a $(1s)$ electron from an atom of helium. We may say that the atom of lithium has one comparatively loosely-bound electron outside a stable group, and you will now notice that lithium is a metal.

OM: Do you mean that atoms of metals have always got loosely-bound electrons outside stable groups?

YS: The transition elements form a rather complicated class, but if we omit them we may say that the atoms of normal metals are characterised by a comparatively small number of loosely-bound electrons outside a stable group.

OM: Then do the above figures give me the work necessary to remove an electron from solid metallic lithium?

YS: Oh, no! The ionisation potentials given above indicate the work required to remove an electron from a free neutral atom of lithium. When the atoms of lithium unite to form a solid crystal, the energy characteristics of the valency electrons are greatly altered, although the $(1s)^2$ electrons are not much affected. The problem of a metal is much more complicated than that of a free atom, and for the present you may merely note that Pauli's Principle prevents the $(1s)^2$ group from containing more than two electrons, and it is this prohibition which causes the valency electron of lithium to enter the $(2s)$ state, and so results in the production of a metallic element. Pauli's Principle, which is also known as the Exclusion Principle, is of the very greatest importance because it applies not only to free atoms, but also to molecules and to any system (for example, a crystal) in which the electrons occupy energy states—in all such cases a given energy state can contain not more than two electrons, one of each spin.

Suggestions for further reading. For a more detailed account of the electron groupings in atoms, and their bearing on the chemical properties of the elements, the following books may be consulted:

The Electronic Theory of Valency, N. V. Sidgwick (Clarendon Press, Oxford);
The Nature of the Chemical Bond, L. Pauling (Cornell University Press).

14—The Elements Lithium to Potassium

OLDER METALLURGIST: You have explained why the atom of lithium has one $(2s)$ electron outside a stable $(1s)^2$ group. Now what happens when we pass on to beryllium, whose atom has four electrons and a nucleus of charge $+ 4e$?

YOUNG SCIENTIST: The energies of the lower electron states of these elements increase in the order

$$1s < 2s < 2p < 3s < 3p.$$

We have seen that the $(1s)$ state can hold only two electrons, and you will readily see that Pauli's Principle allows the $(2s)$ state to contain two electrons, one of each spin. Consequently, the atom of beryllium will have its lowest energy if two electrons are in the $(1s)$ state, and two in the $(2s)$ state; we may write the electron grouping in the form

$$(1s)^2 (2s)^2$$

OM: But if that is the case, why is beryllium not a gas like helium?

YS: The $(1s)^2$ group in helium is a complete 1-quantum group. The ionisation potential of helium is 24.465 volts, and so it requires a lot of work to extract an electron from the $(1s)^2$ group. The $(1s)^2$ group is thus very stable, and it is for this reason that helium is an inert gas—the electrons are so firmly bound that they cannot interact with other atoms to give rise to stable chemical compounds.

In contrast to this, the $(2s)^2$ grouping in beryllium is not a complete quantum group, although it is a complete sub-group. You will remember that Pauli's Principle allows the 2-quantum group—we may call it the 2-quantum shell—to contain $2 \times 2^2 = 8$ electrons, and it is only when the complete group is filled that we obtain an inert gas, neon, which is analogous to helium.

OM: Then how firmly is a valency electron held in the beryllium atom?

YS: The ionisation potential of beryllium is 9.28 volts, so it requires about twice as much energy to remove an electron from an atom of beryllium as from an atom of lithium.

OM: Now suppose you have removed one electron, how much work is required to remove another electron?

YS: The work required to remove the remaining valency electron from the Be$^+$ ion is 18.12 volts.

OM: And now how much to remove another electron?

YS: 153.1 volts.

OM: Oh! I see! The large increase is I suppose the result of the fact that when you have removed two electrons from the $(1s)^2 (2s)^2$

atom of beryllium, you are left with the $(1s)^2$ Be^{++} ion, and this is the stable helium grouping to which you referred before.

YS: Exactly!

OM: Then do you mean that the $(1s)^2$ or helium group is to be looked on as existing as a stable group inside the beryllium atom?

YS: That's more or less right. If you consider the electron cloud of the beryllium atom as a whole, the $(1s)^2$ electrons are deep down in the atom, and so are concentrated round the nucleus. The outer part of the electron cloud is due to the $(2s)^2$ electrons and, as these are not held very firmly, the atoms give rise to a metal.

OM: The atom of beryllium has two valency or $(2s)$ electrons, whilst the atom of lithium has only one. Does this mean that the electron cloud of the beryllium atom is larger than that of the lithium atom?

YS: No. The increase in the nuclear charge from $+ 3e$ for lithium to $+ 4e$ for beryllium means that the valency electrons of beryllium are bound more firmly than those of lithium, and so the electron cloud of the beryllium atom is smaller than that of the lithium atom. This is a general principle, and the electron clouds of the atoms of each alkaline earth metal are smaller than those of the atoms of the preceding alkali metal.

OM: You mean that when you pass from lithium to beryllium, not only does the electron cloud of the $(1s)^2$ group of electrons contract, but the electron cloud of the valency electrons also contracts?

YS: That's right.

OM: Then which shell of electrons contracts the more?

YS: In passing from an alkali to an alkaline earth metal, the electron cloud of the valency electrons contracts relatively much more than the electron cloud of the underlying ion or core. This is a general principle, and as we shall see later it is very important in connection with the structure of some alloys.

OM: Well, suppose we now go on from beryllium to boron. If the $(2s)$ sub-group can contain not more than two electrons, the extra electron, will, I suppose, have to enter the $(2p)$ sub-group. So is the electronic arrangement in the boron atom

$$(1s)^2 (2s)^2 (2p)^1?$$

YS: That's correct. For convenience I have summarised the electronic structures of the different elements in Tables I to VI and you will see that on passing from boron to neon the electrons enter the $(2p)$ sub-group until this has attained its full complement of 6 electrons. The structure of neon is

$$(1s)^2 \underbrace{(2s)^2 (2p)}_{}{}^6$$

so that there are now 8 electrons in the 2-quantum shell, and this is the maximum ($2 \times 2^2 = 8$) allowed by Pauli's Principle. This group of 8 electrons is very stable, and so neon is an inert gas like helium.

OM: When the electrons enter the $2p$ shell do they pair off with opposite spins? In carbon, for example, are the two $2p$ electrons of opposite spin?

YS: No. That's a very important point. As you pass along the series of elements in which the $(2p)^6$ sub-group is gradually built up, you find that the $2p$ electrons avoid forming pairs with opposite spins as long as this is possible. In carbon, for example, each of the two $2p$ electrons has the same spin, and in nitrogen the three $2p$ electrons have the same spin.

OM: You mean that in the atom of nitrogen there is one electron in the $2p$, $m = 0$ state, and one in each of the $2p$, $m = +1$ and $2p$, $m = -1$ states and these all have the same spin?

YS: That's right, and as we saw before (p. 89) this means that in the simplest theory the atom of nitrogen is spherically symmetrical.

OM: Then what happens when you get to oxygen with one more electron?

YS: In the atom of oxygen the electronic arrangement is
$$(1s)^2 (2s)^2 (2p)^4.$$
There will then be two unpaired p electrons with the same spin, whilst the remaining two p electrons will form a pair with opposite spins. You can understand the whole thing if you remember that there are only *three* p-states of a given quantum number n, namely those with $m = 0$, $m = +1$, and $m = -1$. Each of these can contain only one electron of a given spin. With not more than three electrons to distribute among the p-states, the electrons can all have the same spin, but with more than three electrons, some will have to pair off and so form pairs of opposite spin.

OM: Then by the time you have got to neon, the structure of the atom is
$$(1s)^2 (2s)^2 (2p)^6.$$
Does that mean that the six $2p$ electrons consist of three pairs, each pair containing two electrons of opposite spin?

YS: Yes. The $(2p)^6$ sub-group is a completely filled sub-group, in which each of the three states $2p$, $m = 0$; $2p$, $m = +1$, and $2p$, $m = -1$, contains two electrons, one of each spin.

OM: So this completed $(2p)^6$ sub-group will have spherical symmetry, and the neon atom will be spherically symmetrical because the $(1s)^2$, $(2s)^2$, and $(2p)^6$ groups or sub-groups are all spherically symmetrical?

YS: That's right in the simplest theory, but, as I have emphasised, the full story is not yet known.

OM: When you pass along the series
$$Li \to Be \to B \to C \to N \to O \to F \to Ne$$

Tables I, II, and III

ATOMIC STRUCTURES

Element and Atomic Number	Principal and Secondary Quantum Numbers									
$n =$ / $l =$	1 / 0	2 / 0	1	3 / 0	1	2	4 / 0	1	2	3
1 H ..	1									
2 He ..	2									
3 Li ..	2	1								
4 Be ..	2	2								
5 B ..	2	2	1							
6 C ..	2	2	2							
7 N ..	2	2	3							
8 O ..	2	2	4							
9 F ..	2	2	5							
10 Ne ..	2	2	6							
11 Na ..	2	2	6	1						
12 Mg ..	2	2	6	2						
13 Al ..	2	2	6	2	1					
14 Si ..	2	2	6	2	2					
15 P ..	2	2	6	2	3					
16 S ..	2	2	6	2	4					
17 Cl ..	2	2	6	2	5					
18 A ..	2	2	6	2	6					
19 K ..	2	2	6	2	6		1			
20 Ca ..	2	2	6	2	6		2			
21 Sc ..	2	2	6	2	6	1	2			
22 Ti ..	2	2	6	2	6	2	2			
23 V ..	2	2	6	2	6	3	2			
24 Cr ..	2	2	6	2	6	5	1			
25 Mn ..	2	2	6	2	6	5	2			
26 Fe ..	2	2	6	2	6	6	2			
27 Co ..	2	2	6	2	6	7	2			
28 Ni ..	2	2	6	2	6	8	2			
29 Cu ..	2	2	6	2	6	10	1			
30 Zn ..	2	2	6	2	6	10	2			
31 Ga ..	2	2	6	2	6	10	2	1		
32 Ge ..	2	2	6	2	6	10	2	2		
33 As ..	2	2	6	2	6	10	2	3		
34 Se ..	2	2	6	2	6	10	2	4		
35 Br ..	2	2	6	2	6	10	2	5		
36 Kr ..	2	2	6	2	6	10	2	6		

do the electron clouds become continually smaller?

YS: As you pass along the series, the electron cloud of the $(1s)^2$ underlying group becomes continually smaller. The electron cloud of

Tables IV and V

ATOMIC STRUCTURES

Element and Atomic Number	Principal and Secondary Quantum Numbers										
$n =$	1	2	3	4				5			6
$l =$	—	—	—	0	1	2	3	0	1	2	0
37 Rb ..	2	8	18	2	6			1			
38 Sr ..	2	8	18	2	6			2			
39 Y ..	2	8	18	2	6	1		2			
40 Zr ..	2	8	18	2	6	2		2			
41 Nb ..	2	8	18	2	6	4		1			
42 Mo ..	2	8	18	2	6	5		1			
43 Tc ..	2	8	18	2	6	6		1			
44 Ru ..	2	8	18	2	6	7		1			
45 Rh ..	2	8	18	2	6	8		1			
46 Pd ..	2	8	18	2	6	10		—			
47 Ag ..	2	8	18	2	6	10		1			
48 Cd ..	2	8	18	2	6	10		2			
49 In ..	2	8	18	2	6	10		2	1		
50 Sn ..	2	8	18	2	6	10		2	2		
51 Sb ..	2	8	18	2	6	10		2	3		
52 Te ..	2	8	18	2	6	10		2	4		
53 I ..	2	8	18	2	6	10		2	5		
54 Xe ..	2	8	18	2	6	10		2	6		
55 Cs ..	2	8	18	2	6	10		2	6		1
56 Ba ..	2	8	18	2	6	10		2	6		2
57 La ..	2	8	18	2	6	10		2	6	1	2
58 Ce ..	2	8	18	2	6	10	2	2	6		2
59 Pr ..	2	8	18	2	6	10	3	2	6		2
60 Nd ..	2	8	18	2	6	10	4	2	6		2
61 Pm ..	2	8	18	2	6	10	5	2	6		2
62 Sm ..	2	8	18	2	6	10	6	2	6		2
63 Eu ..	2	8	18	2	6	10	7	2	6		2
64 Gd ..	2	8	18	2	6	10	7	2	6	1	2
65 Tb ..	2	8	18	2	6	10	8	2	6	1	2
66 Dy ..	2	8	18	2	6	10	10	2	6		2
67 Ho ..	2	8	18	2	6	10	11	2	6		2
68 Er ..	2	8	18	2	6	10	12	2	6		2
69 Tm ..	2	8	18	2	6	10	13	2	6		2
70 Yb ..	2	8	18	2	6	10	14	2	6		2
71 Lu ..	2	8	18	2	6	10	14	2	6	1	2
72 Hf ..	2	8	18	2	6	10	14	2	6	2	2

$(2s)^2$ sub-group of the beryllium atom is smaller than the electron cloud of the $(2s)^1$ electron in the atom of lithium, and the $(2s)^2$ group continues to contract as we go along the series Be→B→C . . . As regards the $(2p)$ electron clouds, the same general principle applies, but you must remember that there are the three sub-sub-groups, the electron clouds of which are in different directions, so you must be

Table VI

ATOMIC STRUCTURES

Element and Atomic Number	Principal and Secondary Quantum Numbers										
$n =$ $l =$	1 —	2	3	4	5 0	 1	 2	6 0	 1	 2	7 0
73 Ta ..	2	8	18	32	2	6	3	2			
74 W ..	2	8	18	32	2	6	4	2			
75 Re ..	2	8	18	32	2	6	5	2			
76 Os ..	2	8	18	32	2	6	6	2			
77 Ir ..	2	8	18	32	2	6	7	2			
78 Pt ..	2	8	18	32	2	6	8	2			
79 Au ..	2	8	18	32	2	6	10	1			
80 Hg ..	2	8	18	32	2	6	10	2			
81 Tl ..	2	8	18	32	2	6	10	2	1		
82 Pb ..	2	8	18	32	2	6	10	2	2		
83 Bi ..	2	8	18	32	2	6	10	2	3		
84 Po ..	2	8	18	32	2	6	10	2	4		
85 At ..	2	8	32	32	2	6	10	2	5		
86 Rn ..	2	8	18	32	2	6	10	2	6		
87 Fr ..	2	8	18	32	2	6	10	2	6		1
88 Ra ..	2	8	18	32	2	6	10	2	6		2
89 Ac ..	2	8	18	32	2	6	10	2	6	1	2

The exact electronic configuration of the later elements is uncertain, but according to Seaborg, Katz, and Manning* the most probable arrangements of the outer electrons are:

90 Th ..	$(6d)^2 (7s)^2$		97 Bk ..	$(5f)^8 (6d)^1 (7s)^2$
91 Pa ..	$(5f)^1 (6d)^2 (7s)^2$ or $(5f)^2 (6d)^1 (7s)^2$		98 Cf ..	$(5f)^{10} (7s)^2$
92 U ..	$(5f)^3 (6d)^1 (7s)^2$		99 Es ..	$(5f)^{11} (7s)^2$
93 Np ..	$(5f)^4 (6d)^1 (7s)^2$ or $(5f)^5 (7s)^2$		100 Fm ..	$(5f)^{12} (7s)^2$
94 Pu ..	$(5f)^6 (7s)^2$ or $(5f)^5 (6d)^1 (7s)^2$		101 Md ..	$(5f)^{13} (7s)^2$
95 Am ..	$(5f)^7 (7s)^2$		102 No ..	$(5f)^{14} (7s)^2$
96 Cm ..	$(5f)^7 (6d)^1 (7s)^2$		103 ..	$(5f)^{14} (6d)^1 (7s)^2$

* G. T. Seaborg, J. J. Katz, and W. M. Manning, *The Transuranic Elements: Research Papers*. Part II, p. 1,509. 1950. New York (McGraw Hill Book Co. Inc.); London (McGraw Hill Publishing Co., Ltd.).

careful to define exactly what you mean by " size." In the atom of boron there is only one electron in a p-state, and so its electron cloud sticks out in one direction, whereas in an atom of carbon there are two p electrons whose clouds are in different directions.

OM: You mean that in the atom of carbon, the fact that there are two directions concerned may make the electron cloud as a whole larger, even though it is smaller in any one direction?

YS: That's right. But once you get a pair of $2p$ electrons occupied, then the electron cloud of that pair becomes continually smaller with increasing atomic number.

OM: You have said that at neon the 2-quantum group is completely filled, so on passing to sodium does the extra electron enter the 3-quantum group?

YS: Yes. The valency electron of sodium is in the $3s$-state, that is, the lowest state of the 3-quantum shell.

OM: Oh! I see! So that means there is now one loosely-bound electron outside a completely filled group, and that is why you get a repetition of properties, and sodium is a metal like lithium!

YS: Exactly!

OM: And in passing from sodium to argon, the changes in electronic structure are similar to those found on passing from lithium to neon, and the periodicity is explained.

YS: Yes. As you will see from Table I, the passage from sodium to argon results in a building up of a group of 8 electrons in the 3-quantum shell, and the process takes place step by step just as in the building up of the group of 8 electrons in the 2-quantum shell which takes place between lithium and neon.

OM: Are the electron clouds of the atoms Na→Mg→Al→Si . . . larger than those of the corresponding elements Li→Be→B→C . . . in the preceding period?

YS: Yes. The electron cloud of the $3s$ electron in the atom of sodium occupies a larger region of space than that of the $(2s)$ valency electron in the atom of lithium. It is a quite general principle that the atoms of the elements of the second period (Na, Mg, Al . . .) are larger than corresponding elements in the first period (Li, Be, B . . .).

OM: I suppose that in second period, the electron clouds tend to contract with increasing atomic numbers as they do in the first period?

YS: That's a quite general principle. The electron cloud of the $(3s)^2$ sub-group of electrons in magnesium is smaller than that of the $(3s)^1$ electron in sodium, and then on passing down the series Na→Mg→Al→Si . . . the $(3s)^2$ group contracts more and more. The process is exactly like that in the preceding period.

OM: If we write the electronic structure of the magnesium atom
$$(1s)^2 \, (2s)^2 \, (2p)^6 \, (3s)^2$$
can we say that the outside of the electron cloud of the atom as a whole is due mainly to the $(3s)^2$ electrons?

YS: That's more or less right. At the outside of the atom the electron clouds of the $(1s)^2$ and $(2s)^2$ and $(2p)^6$ groups or sub-groups have practically vanished, so that the electron cloud at the outside of the atom is due almost entirely to the $(3s)^2$ sub-group. But you will understand that the electron cloud of the $(3s)^2$ electron does extend right into the centre of the atom—you will remember the radial curves for the hydrogen atom. But broadly speaking it is correct to say that the outside of the Mg atom is due to the $(3s)^2$ electrons, whilst inside the atom the electron cloud results mainly from the 1-quantum and 2-quantum shells.

OM: The radial curves for the $(3s)$ electrons in magnesium will, I suppose, be different from those for the $(3s)$ electrons in hydrogen?

YS: Yes. Each element has its own radial curve, but the radial curve for a $(3s)$ electron still has $3 - 1 = 2$ spherical nodes. The details must obviously be different in the different atoms because an electron moves in the field of force resulting from the nucleus and the motion of all the other electrons.

OM: Can the radial curve be calculated—if so can you show me some of these?

YS: The electron cloud distribution in a great many atoms can be calculated approximately, but it is not worth your while to bother about the results, because they refer to free atoms whereas you as a metallurgist are concerned with the atoms in a crystal.

OM: How does that affect things? Do you mean that all this theory is useless to me as a metallurgist?

YS: When the atoms are brought together to distances of the order 10^{-7} cm, the inner electrons are not greatly affected, because these electrons are so predominantly under the effect of one nucleus that they are only slightly affected by the presence of other atoms. But the electrons in the outermost parts of the electron clouds are greatly affected or perturbed, and it is just this disturbance or interaction which produces cohesion, and is responsible for the characteristic properties of metals. But, however anxious you are to get on to the theory of metals, you must first understand the main electronic structures of the free atoms.

Note.—The tables of atomic structures are based on those in " Atomic Theory for Students of Metallurgy " (Hume-Rothery) by courtesy of the Institute of Metals.

15—The Elements Potassium to Krypton, and Rubidium to Xenon

OLDER METALLURGIST: I have been thinking over what you said about Pauli's Principle and the number of electrons in completed quantum groups, and it seems to me that there must be some mistake in it.

YOUNG SCIENTIST: What makes you think that?

OM: Well, you said that the number of electrons in a completed quantum group is $2n^2$, where n is the principal quantum number. This means that the numbers of electrons in the completed groups are 2, 8, 18, 32 . . . This agrees with the fact that helium (atomic number $= 2$), and neon (atomic number $= 10$) are inert gases corresponding with completely filled groups. But the atom with three completely filled groups would contain $2 + 8 + 18 = 28$ electrons, and would therefore have atomic number 28. This is the atomic number of nickel, and so we should expect nickel to be an inert gas, which it certainly is not—the next inert gas after neon is argon, and its atomic number is only 18.

YS: What you say is not altogether unreasonable, but you've jumped to conclusions too quickly. When we reach the 3-quantum shell, the total number of electrons which it can contain is $2 \times 3^2 = 18$. These electrons divide themselves up into three sub-groups

$$(3s)^2 \ (3p)^6 \ (3d)^{10}.$$

You will see, therefore, that the first two sub-groups

$$(3s)^2 \ (3p)^6$$

contain 8 electrons, just as was the case for the

$$(2s)^2 \ (2p)^6$$

sub-groups of the 2-quantum shell. The solution to your difficulty lies in the fact that the octet of electrons formed by the two sub-groups of the general form

$$(ns)^2 \ (np)^6$$

forms a very stable arrangement. This means that when you reach argon, whose electronic structure is

$$(1s)^2 \ (2s)^2 \ (2p)^6 \ (3s)^2 \ (3p)^6,$$

the outer shell of electrons is a stable octet, and it is the stability of this arrangement of 8 electrons which gives argon the properties of an inert gas. The 3-quantum shell can eventually contain 18 electrons, but the $(3s)^2 \ (3p)^6$ octet has, as it were, a kind of provisional stability.

OM: Then when you pass from argon to potassium, does the extra electron go into the $3d$-state, and so begin to fill up the $(3d)$ sub-group?

YS: This is the point at which the process becomes a bit complicated. If we consider the outermost electrons in the atoms of the elements immediately following potassium we find that the energies of the different states increase in the following order:

$$3s < 3p < 4s < 3d < 4p$$

This means that when the $(3s)^2 (3p)^6$ sub-groups are filled, the next lowest energy state is the $4s$-state and so the outermost electrons of the atoms of potassium and calcium have the arrangements

| K | .. | .. | $(3s)^2 (3p)^6 (4s)^1$ |
| Ca | .. | .. | $(3s)^2 (3p)^6 (4s)^2$ |

The electrons enter the $4s$ sub-group, and potassium and calcium have electronic structures analogous to those of sodium and magnesium.

OM: You mean that the $(4s)^1$ electron of potassium is relatively loosely bound outside a stable group, and that is why it is an alkali?

YS: That's right.

OM: Then what happens when you go on to scandium?

YS: Look at the above order of the different energy states and answer the question yourself.

OM: You mean that as the energy increases in the order

$$3s < 3p < 4s < 3d < 4p$$

the last electron in scandium must enter the $3d$ sub-group?

YS: Yes. The electronic structure of scandium is

$$\ldots \; (3s)^2 (3p)^6 (3d)^1 (4s)^2$$

and so the 3-quantum shell has now begun to expand from the provisionally stable octet into the complete group of 18 electrons. If you examine Table III, you will see that the elements from scandium to copper are those in which the $(3d)$ sub-group gradually fills up until it holds its full complement of 10 electrons, and then the 3-quantum shell contains its completed

$$(3s)^2 (3p)^6 (3d)^{10}$$

sub-groups, giving a total of 18 electrons. The elements in which the group of 8 electrons expands into one of 18 electrons are known as transition elements.

OM: I can see from Table III that in the atom of copper there is one $(4s)$ electron outside the completed group of 18 3-quantum electrons. If this is so, why is copper not an alkali metal?

YS: You will remember that copper does give rise to univalent salts, so that in some ways it does resemble an alkali metal. The difference in properties arises to some extent from the fact that the group of 18 electrons in copper is not yet very stable, with the result that some of the $(3d)$ electrons can still interact with the electrons of other atoms. It is customary to use the letters $K, L,$ and $M,$ to denote the electrons whose principal quantum numbers are 1, 2, and 3 respectively, and as you pass along the series

$$Cu \rightarrow Zn \rightarrow Ga \rightarrow Ge \ldots$$

the group of 18 M electrons becomes more and more firmly bound.

OM: You say that in the atom of copper, the $3d$ electrons are not yet very firmly bound. Does this mean that they still concern the outside of the electron cloud of the copper atom?

YS: In a general way, yes. The extreme outside of the electron cloud of the copper atom is due to the $4s$ or valency electron. If you compare the atom of copper with that of an alkali metal, you find that in copper the electron cloud of the *ion* extends relatively much nearer to the outside of the atom. The outermost part of the electron cloud of the Cu^+ *ion* is due mainly to the $(3d)$ electrons. You may say that in copper the electron cloud of the Cu^+ *ion* extends over a much greater fraction of the volume of the atom than is the case with the atom of an alkali metal.

OM: Does the same apply to the elements immediately preceding copper?

YS: Yes. As soon as the $(3d)$ sub-group of electrons begins to fill up, its electron cloud is relatively much nearer to the outside of the atom than is the electron cloud of the underlying $(3s)^2 (3p)^6$ group.

OM: Then, when you pass on from copper to zinc, what happens?

YS: On passing from copper to krypton, the electronic changes are exactly analogous to those occurring between sodium and argon. The 4-quantum shell builds up an octet, and as you will see from Tables I, II and III the $4s$ and $4p$ sub-groups build up in exactly the same way as in the case of the $3s$ and $3p$ sub-groups in the pervious period. When we reach krypton, there is an octet of 4-quantum electrons, and so krypton is an inert gas like neon and argon. Then when we go on to rubidium, the extra electron enters the $(5s)$ state, and so there is one relatively loosely-bound electron outside a stable octet, and the result is again an alkali metal.

On passing from rubidium to xenon, the general changes in electronic structure are similar to those in the passage from potassium to krypton, although, as you can see from Tables I and IV, the exact details round about Groups VI–VIII are not exactly the same. Rubidium and strontium are typical alkali and alkaline earth elements, and the outermost of the electrons in their free atoms are in the $(5s)$ sub-group. Then on passing to yttrium the transition process sets in and the $(4d)^{10}$ group begins to fill up, and on reaching silver we have, as in copper, one electron outside a completed group of 18. Finally, on passing from silver to xenon, the $(5s)^2 (5p)^6$ octet is built up, and xenon is an inert gas. In general, therefore, the electronic processes occurring in the first two long periods are very similar.

OM: There is one point about these tables on which I am not clear. I understand the general process by which the electron groups and sub-groups are built up, but you said something about the outermost electrons being affected when atoms approached one another as closely as they do in crystals, and I am not certain how this affects the use of the tables in connection with solid metals. If the outermost electrons

Table VII

INTERNATIONAL ATOMIC WEIGHTS, 1957

	Symbol	At. No.	At. Wt.*
Actinium	Ac	89	[227]
Aluminium	Al	13	26·98
Americium	Am	95	[243]
Antimony	Sb	51	121·76
Argon	A	18	39·944
Arsenic	As	33	74·91
Astatine	At	85	[210]
Barium	Ba	56	137·36
Berkelium	Bk	97	[245]
Beryllium	Be	4	9·013
Bismuth	Bi	83	209·00
Boron	B	5	10·82
Bromine	Br	35	79·916
Cadmium	Cd	48	112·41
Cæsium	Cs	55	132·91
Calcium	Ca	20	40·08
Californium	Cf	98	[248]
Carbon	C	6	12·011
Cerium	Ce	58	140·13
Chlorine	Cl	17	35·457
Chromium	Cr	24	52·01
Cobalt	Co	27	58·94
Copper	Cu	29	63·54
Curium	Cm	96	[245]
Dysprosium	Dy	66	162·51
Einsteinium	Es	99	—
Erbium	Er	68	167·27
Europium	Eu	63	152·0
Fermium	Fm	100	—
Fluorine	F	9	19·00
Francium	Fr	87	[223]
Gadolinium	Gd	64	157·26
Gallium	Ga	31	69·72
Germanium	Ge	32	72·60
Gold	Au	79	197·0
Hafnium	Hf	72	178·50
Helium	He	2	4·003
Holmium	Ho	67	164·94
Hydrogen	H	1	1·0080
Indium	In	49	114·82
Iodine	I	53	126·91
Iridium	Ir	77	192·2
Iron	Fe	26	55·85
Krypton	Kr	36	83·80
Lanthanum	La	57	138·92
Lead	Pb	82	207·21
Lithium	Li	3	6·940
Lutecium	Lu	71	174·99
Magnesium	Mg	12	24·32
Manganese	Mn	25	54·94
Mendelevium	Md	101	—
Mercury	Hg	80	200·61

	Symbol	At. No.	At. Wt.*
Molybdenum	Mo	42	95·95
Neodymium	Nd	60	144·27
Neon	Ne	10	20·183
Neptunium	Np	93	[237]
Nickel	Ni	28	58·71
Niobium	Nb		
(Columbium)	(Cb)	41	92·91
Nitrogen	N	7	14·008
Nobelium	No	102	—
Osmium	Os	76	190·2
Oxygen	O	8	16·0000
Palladium	Pd	46	106·4
Phosphorus	P	15	30·975
Platinum	Pt	78	195·09
Plutonium	Pu	94	[242]
Polonium	Po	84	[210]
Potassium	K	19	39·100
Praseodymium	Pr	59	140·92
Promethium	Pm	61	[145]
Protactinium	Pa	91	[231]
Radium	Ra	88	[226·05]
Radon	Rn	86	[222]
Rhenium	Re	75	186·22
Rhodium	Rh	45	102·91
Rubidium	Rb	37	85·48
Ruthenium	Ru	44	101·1
Samarium	Sm	62	150·35
Scandium	Sc	21	44·96
Selenium	Se	34	78·96
Silicon	Si	14	28·09
Silver	Ag	47	107·880
Sodium	Na	11	22·991
Strontium	Sr	38	87·63
Sulphur	S	16	32·066†
Tantalum	Ta	73	180·95
Technetium	Tc	43	[99]
Tellurium	Te	52	127·61
Terbium	Tb	65	158·93
Thallium	Tl	81	204·30
Thorium	Th	90	232·05
Thulium	Tm	69	168·94
Tin	Sn	50	118·70
Titanium	Ti	22	47·90
Tungsten	W	74	183·86
Uranium	U	92	238·07
Vanadium	V	23	50·95
Xenon	Xe	54	131·30
Ytterbium	Yb	70	173·04
Yttrium	Y	39	88·92
Zinc	Zn	30	65·38
Zirconium	Zr	40	91·22

[*Reprinted from* Atomic Theory for Students of Metallurgy *by William Hume-Rothery published by The Institute of Metals, London*, 1961.]

* A value given in brackets denotes the mass number of the isotope of longest known half-life, which is not necessarily the most important isotope in atomic-energy work. These values are not included in the International Table for 1957.

† Because of natural variations in the relative abundance of its isotopes, the atomic weight of sulphur has a range of ±0.003.

were very much affected by the presence of neighbouring atoms, it would seem probable that for these electrons the details of the tables might be different for the free atoms, and for the solid metal.

YS: That is quite true, and you must understand plainly that the electronic structures of the tables refer to *free atoms*, and that the details of the outermost electrons are often quite different in solid metals. As we shall see later, the electrons in solid metals can often be regarded as in states derived from those of the free atoms, but the details of the distribution of the outer electrons are often quite different. For example, as you can see from Table IV the free atom of palladium has no electrons in the 5s-state, but in solid palladium there are electrons in states resembling those of the 5s-state of the free atom. You must understand very clearly that the tables refer to free atoms, and not to solid metals, although you can appreciate the structures of the solid metals only when you have grasped those of the free atoms.

16—The Elements Caesium to Uranium

OLDER METALLURGIST: It seems to me that if the Pauli Principle is carried to its logical conclusion, there must be a further complication later on in the Periodic Table. You have explained how, in the first two long periods, the 3- and 4-quantum shells build up groups of 18 electrons. In the case of the 3-quantum shell, a group of 18 electrons is the maximum possible, since $2 \times 3^2 = 18$. But according to Pauli's Principle the 4-quantum shell can hold up to $2 \times 4^2 = 32$ electrons, and so the $(4s)^2 (4p)^6 (4d)^{10}$ arrangement of 18 electrons is not a completely filled quantum shell. It needs a further 14 electrons before a complete group of 32 electrons is filled.

YOUNG SCIENTIST: What you say is perfectly correct, and the process to which you refer actually occurs in the periodic table at the place occupied by the so-called *Rare Earth Elements*. If you look at Table V you will see that on passing from caesium to barium to lanthanum, the electrons enter the 6s and 5d sub-groups, and the process is analogous to that in the preceding long periods. But on passing to cerium the additional electron enters the 4f sub-group, and in the succeeding elements, as you will see from the table, the 4f sub-group fills up until it holds its full complement of 14 electrons. By the time we reach lutecium the $(4f)^{14}$ sub-group is full, and there is a complete group of 32 electrons in the 4-quantum shell. Then on passing to hafnium the normal transition process continues and the 5d sub-group fills up, and this process continues more or less—you will see from the table that the details are not exactly the same—as in the preceding periods, and gold has its (6s) or valency electron outside a group of 18.

OM: Then is the process from gold to emanation similar to that from silver to xenon, and from copper to krypton?

YS: Yes. On passing from gold to emanation, first of all the $(6s)^2$, and then the $(6p)^6$ sub-groups are filled up.

OM: But that does not explain why thallium and lead often behave as univalent and divalent elements respectively, and not as trivalent and tetravalent elements as one would expect from their places in the periodic table. This would suggest some difference in the electronic structures.

YS: That is a very important point, and one which concerns the structures of some alloys. As we have already seen, the general process in the seven elements preceding each inert gas is for the $(ns)^2$ sub-group to be built up first, followed by the $(np)^6$ sub-group. The valency of a metal is determined essentially by the number of loosely-bound electrons outside a relatively stable group—the alkali metals are univalent because they have one electron outside a stable group.

The answer to your question lies in the fact that the stability of the $(ns)^2$ sub-group increases greatly with increasing n. When one reaches thallium the $(6s)^2$ sub-group is so stable that it can persist unchanged in many chemical reactions, and so the atom of thallium has one relatively weakly-bound $6p$ electron outside a fairly stable $(6s)^2$ sub-group, and therefore behaves as the atom of a univalent element. Similarly, the atom of lead can behave like that of a divalent element. In the preceding period the $(5s)^2$ group is not so stable, although there are some univalent indium compounds. In the earlier periods the $(ns)^2$ sub-group is much less stable, and in aluminium, for example, there are no univalent compounds. The increasing stability of the $(ns)^2$ sub-group in the later periods is of very great importance because the $(6s)^2$ sub-group—and sometimes also the $(5s)^2$ sub-group—are so stable that they may persist unchanged in certain alloys, although in other alloys the sub-group may break down.

OM: In this description you have dealt with the electronic arrangement in the atoms of the transition elements. Can you say anything about the sizes of the electron clouds of the different elements? Do the electron clouds of the atoms of any one group become larger as one passes from the first to the second to the third long period?

YS: In any one group of the periodic table, the atom of an element of the second long period has a larger electron cloud than the corresponding element in the first long period—the electron cloud of an atom of palladium, for example, is larger than that of an atom of nickel. In the third long period caesium and barium have larger electron clouds than rubidium and strontium respectively. But once the $(4f)^{14}$ sub-group has been built up, the electron clouds of the remaining elements of the third long period are little if any larger than those of the corresponding elements in the second long period. The electron cloud of the atom of hafnium, for example, is about the same size as that of zirconium, and the electron clouds of gold and silver are not very different, although both are larger than that of copper.

OM: But why should the building up of the $(4f)^{14}$ sub-group have this effect? Surely the fact that one has put a new sub-group into the atom should make it larger and not smaller?

YS: You are forgetting that the size of an atom is determined mainly by its most loosely-bound electrons, since it is these which move farthest from the nucleus, and so produce the outer part of the electron cloud. When you pass from lanthanum to lutecium you increase the nuclear charge by 14, and this tends to attract the $(6s)$ valency electron more closely. At the same time you add 14 more electrons to the 4-quantum shell, and these electrons neutralise or screen off part of the nuclear charge. But the net effect of the whole process is that the outermost electrons of the atoms of the elements from hafnium to gold are bound more firmly than they would be if the $4(f)^{14}$ sub-group had not been built up. Consequently the normal expansion of the electron cloud expected on passing from one period to the next is to a great extent neutralised by the stronger attraction of the nucleus for the outermost electrons. This effect is sometimes called the "lanthanide contraction," because it results from the changes taking place in the elements which follow lanthanum in the periodic table.

OM: You said before (page 110) that if one compared the electron clouds of the atoms of potassium and copper, one of the main differences was that in the copper atom the electron cloud of the underlying Cu^+ ion extended relatively much nearer to the edge of the electron cloud of the atom as a whole. Does the same apply to silver and gold?

YS: Yes. In atoms of copper, silver and gold the outermost parts of the electron cloud are due almost entirely to the $(4s)^1$, $(5s)^1$ and $(6s)^1$ valency electrons respectively. But the electron clouds of the underlying $(3d)^{10}$, $(4d)^{10}$, and $(5d)^{10}$ sub-groups push out relatively much farther than is the case for the electron clouds of the ions of the alkali metals.

OM: When you say that the outermost parts of the electron clouds of atoms of copper, silver and gold are due mainly to the $(4s)^1$, $(5s)^1$ and $(6s)^1$ valency electrons respectively, I presume that the valency electron clouds do still extend towards the centres of the atoms, so that a valency electron is sometimes found relatively near to the nucleus.

YS: Oh, certainly! Just as in Fig. 12, the $\rho(r)$ curve for the $(2s)$ state of hydrogen atom has its greatest value near to the nucleus, so the corresponding curves for the $(4s)$, $(5s)$ and $(6s)$ valency electrons of copper, silver and gold rise as the nucleus is approached after the innermost node. But in this region of the atom, the electron cloud density of the inner electron groups is so enormously greater than that of the valency electron that it is a reasonable approximation to say that the electron cloud near to the centre of an atom of copper, silver or gold is due to the inner electrons.

OM: Then when you proceed along the series

$$Cu \rightarrow Zn \rightarrow Ga \rightarrow Ge$$
$$Ag \rightarrow Cd \rightarrow In \rightarrow Sn$$
$$Au \rightarrow Hg \rightarrow Tl \rightarrow Pb$$

do the electron clouds of the $(3d)^{10}$, $(4d)^{10}$, and $(5d)^{10}$ sub-groups contract on account of the increased nuclear charge?

YS: Yes, that's quite right. They contract very rapidly, and what is more they contract more rapidly than the electron clouds of the valency electrons. This is one of the differences between the elements following an alkali metal and those following copper, silver, and gold, and, as we shall see later, the point is of great importance in some alloy structures. In the elements following the alkali metals, increasing atomic number results in the electron cloud of the valency electrons contracting much more rapidly than the electron cloud of the underlying ion, so that at each step the ion occupies a greater fraction of the atom. But in the elements following copper, silver, or gold, each step results in the electron cloud of the ion contracting more rapidly than that of the valency electrons, so that the ions occupy a smaller fraction of the atom.

OM: In the Rare Earth Group, you say that the 4-quantum shell is completed by the building up of the $(4f)^{14}$ sub-group, and this gives a complete 4-quantum shell of $(4s)^2$ $(4p)^6$ $(4d)^{10}$ $(4f)^{14}$ electrons, making a total of 32, which equals 2×4^2. It would seem, therefore, that when we go to the next Long Period there will be a similar tendency to build up a $(5f)^{14}$ sub-group.

YS: That's quite true, and it is now known that this process begins in the region of actinium in the Periodic Table.

OM: That would mean that uranium and all the trans-uranic elements formed a kind of Rare Earth Group.

YS: In a sense that is so, but the details are not the same. From Tables V and VI you will see that, once the filling up of the $(4f)$ sub-group has begun, it tends to go straight on, with one $(4f)$ electron being added at each step. There is a slight variation in gadolium and terbium where the $(4f)^7$ grouping persists over two places, and this is owing to the fact that an exactly half-filled group acquires an increased stability. In general, however, once the process starts, it rushes through to completion. In contrast to this the corresponding elements in the Fourth Long Period—they are called the *actinons* or *actinides*, show much more variable valencies, and the energies of the $(5f)$ and $(6d)$ electrons are more nearly equal, and at the moment (1954) the electronic structures of these elements are not known with certainty.

PART II—THE NATURE OF A METAL

17—The Metal as a Crystal

OLDER METALLURGIST: Now that we have dealt with the structure of the free atom, I hope we can begin to consider the structures of some actual metals.

YOUNG SCIENTIST: It will be simplest if we begin first with pure elements. I suppose you know that although pieces of metal do not often show well-defined crystal faces, the structure of a metal is essentially crystalline, in the sense that the atoms are arranged in a regular pattern?

OM: Yes. That fact has already found its way into the metallurgical textbooks and journals. Is there something in the nature of a metal which prevents the crystals from ever possessing properly developed crystal faces?

YS: Oh, certainly not! Under some conditions it is quite possible to obtain metal crystals with beautifully developed plane faces. Fig. 23 shows crystals of magnesium formed by sublimation, and you will see that the plane faces are well developed. I have also been shown crystals of titanium and zirconium in the form of very regular hexagons. These crystals were deposited on hot tungsten filaments suspended in a dilute vapour of the iodide of the metal. Under these conditions the hot filament decomposes the iodide, and the metal crystallises out on

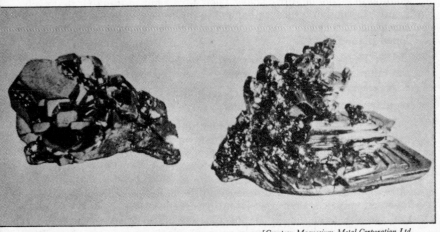

[Courtesy Magnesium Metal Corporation Ltd.

Fig. 23—Crystals of magnesium formed by sublimation and showing well-developed plane faces (natural size)

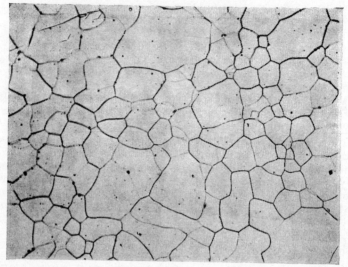

[*Courtesy F. A. Hughes & Co., Ltd.*

Fig. 24—Etched section of pure cast magnesium (× 25)

the tungsten wire. In fact it is quite a common thing to obtain well-developed crystal faces when a metal is deposited from the vapour phase.

OM: Suppose now we consider an ordinary casting of a metal—Fig. 24, for example, shows the microstructure of cast magnesium after etching in alcoholic nitric acid. Then am I right in thinking that each grain is a single crystal, and that the internal atomic arrangement is the same as that of a single crystal of the same metal with well-developed plane faces?

YS: That's right. The essential thing is not the external form but the internal atomic arrangement.

OM: Then am I to regard each grain in Fig. 24 as having a perfectly regular arrangement of its atoms?

YS: That's not quite correct. The grains in Fig. 24 are commonly called single crystals, and the atomic arrangement is more or less regular throughout. But a number of facts have indicated that the atomic arrangement is not absolutely regular. For many years the evidence was mostly indirect, and the whole subject remained in a rather confused state because several different effects might be present together, and were not always distinguished. With some substances, such as the diamond, it is possible to obtain crystals the internal structure of which is extremely perfect. Such crystals may be called *perfect crystals*, but it must be understood that the word "perfect" refers to the regular internal arrangement, and does not necessarily imply the existence of plane faces. Some writers use the term *ideal crystals* but, as we shall see later, this term is better avoided.

In contrast to the diamond, many other crystals, including those of nearly all metals, do not possess an ideally regular structure. In some cases one encounters what is called a " lineage structure." You will know that in nearly all cases the solidification of a metallic crystal from the liquid state takes place by the growth of dendrites, and the way in which the dendrites grow is of great importance because in many cases the metal does not join up to form a perfect crystal. You may regard the process of solidification as involving first the formation of very small dendritic crystals, the branches of which grow outwards. Fig. 25, for example, shows some dendritic crystals of zinc which were found in a contraction cavity in a slowly-cooled ingot. As the cooling proceeds, the different branches may come into contact with one another, and with those of an adjacent dendrite, and slight deformation may occur so that the branches of a dendrite are no longer exactly parallel. In the final stages of solidification, the metal crystallises by filling in the skeleton frameworks. In this way each dendritic crystal gives rise to a grain which has solidified from one centre but, as the different dendritic branches are not exactly parallel, there will be slight irregularities at the places where the growths from two branches meet. This kind of structure was called a lineage structure by M. J. Buerger, and Figs. 26 *A* and *B* show the difference between a perfect crystal and one with a lineage structure. You will see that there are no large empty spaces in the grain, but there is a great difference between this structure and that of a perfect crystal, and there is no doubt that this difference affects the mechanical properties.

OM: One might overcome that difficulty by using recrystallised metal.

[From *Zeits. für Kristallographie*

Fig. 25—Dendritic zinc crystals in a contraction cavity of a polycrystalline zinc rod ($\times$ 7)

[1]In the first printing of this book the term "ideal crystal" was preferred.

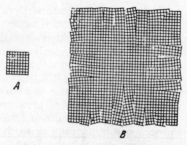

[From Zeits. für Physik. Chem.

Fig. 26—To illustrate the formation of a lineage structure

A shows a perfect structure. In B the whole grain has grown from one centre, but slight accidents of growth have deformed the branches of growing denrites so that the orientation is not exactly the same throughout

YS: You are right in saying that the grains of recrystallised metal are sometimes more nearly ideal than those in cast metal, but one then finds that so-called mosaic structures are formed, and these are often present in crystals obtained by solidification from the liquid or vapour state. Until recently it was thought that, in a mosaic structure, each crystal grain is divided up into small blocks or mosaics whose dimensions are of the order 10^{-4} to 10^{-6} cm. Each block possesses a perfect or very nearly perfect structure, but the different blocks are slightly out of alignment, the divergence from exact alignment varying from a few minutes to several degrees of arc.

OM: Do you mean that I am to regard each grain of a recrystallised metal as involving a regular structure of mosaic blocks of equal size?

YS: No: At one time it was suggested that crystals possessed a *regular* mosaic structure, but the conclusion was shown to be fallacious.

OM: But do you still mean that real crystals consist of small irregular blocks which are slightly out of alignment?

YS: That's a difficult question to answer. Until about 1945 the existence of some kind of irregular mosaic structure was regarded as almost certainly established, but in the years from 1950 onwards there has been a great development of what are known as the dislocation theories of crystals, and these suggest that the problem may be more complex. We shall discuss these later,[1] and for the meantime you should just note that the X-ray work indicates conclusively that a real crystal contains regions of slightly differing orientation, or misfit. The term mosaic structure is still used, but sometimes without any very precise definition of exactly what is meant.

OM: If lineage structures and mosaic structures are accepted, I can imagine many other kinds of imperfection in crystals.

YS: Oh, certainly! Under some conditions one gets a lamellar or plate-like structure. Fig. 27 shows examples of cadmium and zinc

[1]See Chapter 32

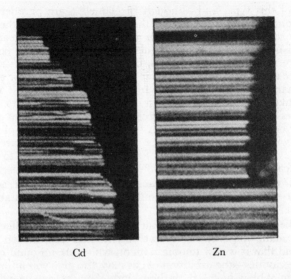

Cd   Zn

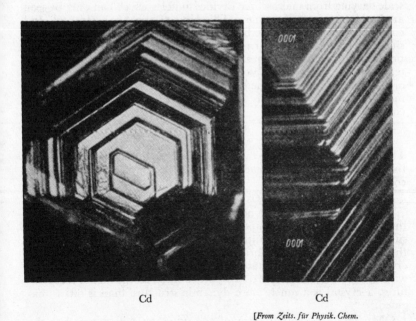

Cd   Cd

[From Zeits. für Physik. Chem.

Fig. 27—To show plate-like structures sometimes found when zinc and cadmium crystals are formed from condensation of the vapour

crystals of this type, and although the lamellae are parallel there is clearly some kind of difference at the boundaries between them.

Under some conditions one finds a structure in which the atoms are arranged in what is clearly a regular pattern from which occasional atoms are missing. These defects, or " holes " or " vacant sites," in the lattice are of great importance in many connections. For example, many characteristics of diffusion in the solid state suggest that the process takes place by a mechanism in which an atom next to a vacant site moves into that site, and thereby creates a new vacant site. In a perfect crystal it is often difficult to see how interchange of atoms is possible without a large excitation energy, but if there are vacant sites it may be comparatively easy for a neighbouring atom to migrate to the vacant site.

OM: Do you mean that these vacant sites are, so to speak, accidents in the crystal structure which could be removed by suitable heat treatment?

YS: There you have to distinguish between two distinct effects. As a practical man, you will know that most metals contract on solidification, and that it is easy to obtain ingots which are unsound owing to shrinkage cavities—the evolution of gas may also give you unsoundness in the form of blow-holes. Both these kinds of defect may be found on a scale varying from microscopic cavities to holes which can only be seen at the highest magnifications. This kind of effect is accidental, and could be removed by suitable treatment. Apart from this, vacant sites may be created by thermal excitation. If, for example, the formation of a vacant site requires a given amount of energy E, then at all temperatures above the absolute zero there is a certain probability of a vacant site being formed. In the simplest thermodynamic treatment of the subject, if n is the number of vacant sites in a crystal containing N atoms,

$$\frac{n}{N} = e^{\frac{-E}{RT}}$$

This equation means that the number of vacant sites increases with the temperature, and at each temperature there is an equilibrium concentration of vacancies.

OM: You mean that there are so many fixed holes in the lattice?

YS: The vacant sites are not fixed, but are in continual circulation through the crystal. The important thing to realise is that these vacant sites are not accidents resulting from faulty preparation. They are the result of the lattice vibrations, and the most stable state of the crystal, that is to say the state with the lowest free energy, is the one with the equilibrium proportion of lattice sites. At the higher temperatures, a crystal is a much more dynamic structure than is often imagined.

OM: The exponential form of the equation will mean that the number of vacancies increases rapidly with temperature, but what sort of magnitudes are involved?

YS: For copper the valves of n/N are of the order 10^{-19} at room temperature, and 10^{-5} at 900°C. We shall discuss the details of the process later.

OM: But if a metal crystal is really as imperfect as all this, why do the books and papers talk of regular crystal structures, and show diagrams of unit cells which they say are repeated in regular array throughout the crystal?

YS: The answer to that question is that the structures of the actual or " *real* crystals " are often reasonably regular over distances which are large compared with that between two adjacent atoms. Under these conditions what one may call the ordinary methods of X-ray crystal analysis reveal the perfect or ideal structure within the mosaic blocks, and this is what you will find described in the ordinary textbooks and papers. It is only by looking into the X-ray diffraction effects more closely that the existence of the secondary structure is revealed. In the same way occasional vacant sites in the lattice will be revealed only by very subtle X-ray diffraction effects, or slight differences in density, and the ordinary crystal analysis reveals the underlying regular structure.

OM: This is all most disturbing. Do you mean that the ordinary crystal structure work is worthless to me as a practical metallurgist?

YS: Oh, no! The actual structures are always based on or derived from the ideal structure, and so the latter must be understood thoroughly before there is any chance of appreciating the structure of the real crystal. Apart from this, an understanding of the ideal structures when combined with empirical methods may lead you a long way. You may, for example, know that a phase of a particular structure leads to an alloy with unsatisfactory properties, and if you understand what factors lead to the production of the phase concerned you may be able to avoid its formation in complex alloys containing five or six metals. At present one must admit that the electron theory is concerned almost entirely with the ideal structures, and as you will soon realise, this problem is quite complicated enough. But in dealing with the theory you must always remember that the whole story will involve the structure of the real crystal as well as that of the ideal crystal.

18—Electrons in Crystals: Soft X-ray Spectroscopy

YOUNG SCIENTIST: In Part I of this discussion we saw how the free atoms of the elements are to be regarded in the light of the new theories, and in our last discussion I explained how the electron theories deal only with the structure of the ideal crystal, and not with the dislocations and other imperfections of real crystals. The next stage is clearly to see what are the characteristics of the electrons when the atoms of a given metal assemble together to form a crystal in which the atomic arrangement is perfectly regular throughout. It will probably be convenient if we begin by considering some of the new work on the soft X-ray spectroscopy of crystals.

OLDER METALLURGIST: Is it really necessary for us to bother about spectroscopy when all I am wanting is an account of cohesion in solid metals?

YS: Oh, very much so! You have always prided yourself on being a practical man, and it is the soft X-ray spectroscopy which provides a direct proof of the correctness of some of the theory. Suppose we consider first the emission spectrum of the free atoms of a metallic element, that is, the emission from a hot metallic vapour—say that of sodium. In Chapter 14 we have seen that the electronic structure of a normal atom of sodium is

$$(1s)^2 \, (2s)^2 \, (2p)^6 \, (3s)^1.$$

We might represent the energies of the different possible sub-groups by a vertical scale such as I have drawn in Fig. 28(a)—this is purely diagrammatic and not in any way an accurate scale. If the figure were drawn to scale, the distance between the $(1s)$ and $(2s)$ levels would be very much greater than that shown in Fig. 28(a), whilst the distance between the $(3s)$ and the $(3p)$ levels would be much less, and so it would not be possible to show the whole thing clearly on one page.

OM: Then in the actual free atom of sodium there will in the normal state be two electrons in the $(1s)$ group, two in the $(2s)$ sub-group, six in the $(2p)$ sub-group, whilst the one valency electron will be in the $(3s)$ level, and the $(3p)$ and $(3d)$ levels will be unoccupied—is that right?

YS: That's right. In the normal state the $(1s)^2 \, (2s)^2$ and $(2p)^6$ groups or sub-groups are completely filled, and the single valency electron is in the $(3s)$ sub-group, whilst the higher levels such as the $3p$, $3d$ or $4s$ are unoccupied. Under suitable conditions such as the high temperatures of flames or of electric discharges, it is possible to excite an electron into a higher state, so that an excited atom with an electronic configuration such as

$$(1s)^2 \, (2s)^2 \, (2p)^6 \, (3p)^1$$

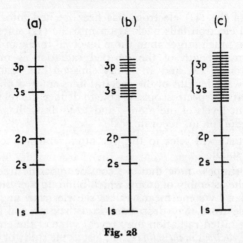

Fig. 28

(a) *Is a diagrammatic representation of the energy levels of a free atom of sodium.*

(b) *Shows the corresponding energy levels of an assembly of sodium atoms forming a body-centred cubic lattice of side 6 kX. The lower energy levels are still sharp, whilst the 3s and 3p levels have broadened into bands.*

(c) *Shows diagrammatically the energy levels in the actual crystal of sodium where the side of the unit cell is 4.28 kX. The 3s and 3p bands have broadened so much that they overlap.*

is formed. This will have a higher energy than the atom in its normal state, because the $(3p)$ level has a higher energy than the $(3s)$ level.

OM: Then if the excited electron drops back from the $(3p)$ state to the $(3s)$ state, the atom will, I suppose, emit a quantum of light.

YS: That's right. If the excited electron drops back from the $(3p)$ to the $(3s)$ state, the atom emits a quantum of radiation whose frequency is given by the equation

$$h\nu = E_1 - E_2 \qquad \ldots \qquad \text{XVIII (1)}.$$

where E_1 is the energy of the atom in the excited state, and E_2 that in the normal state. The human eye could not detect the one single quantum, but if one had a large number of atoms all undergoing this kind of transition then the light would be visible. It is electronic transitions of this kind which give rise to the characteristic spectra of the elements, each line in the spectrum corresponding to a definite electronic change.

OM: Then are all the electrons concerned in optical spectra?

YS: The wave lengths of visible light lie in the range 3,000–7,000A, and in general it is only the outermost one or two shells of electrons which are concerned in the visible optical spectra. But under some conditions it is possible to excite one of the inner electrons of the atom. In the case of sodium, for example, one might obtain an excited atom with an electronic configuration such as

$$(1s)^1 (2s)^2 (2p)^6 (3s)^1 (3p)^1$$

Here one of the $(1s)$ electrons has been excited into the $3p$ state. If the excited electron falls back again into the $(1s)$ state, the energy change is very much larger than those involved in the optical spectra; hence the wave length of the emitted radiation is much shorter, being of the order $1A$, and an X-ray emission line results. It is by studying the wave lengths of the spectral lines emitted under different conditions that the spectroscopist is able to deduce the relative energies of the different levels of the atoms, and so to draw diagrams such as that of Fig. 28(a) on an accurate scale.

OM: But that will refer to the free atom, and not to the state of affairs in the solid.

YS: Well, suppose now that we consider not the free atoms of a vapour, but the assembly of atoms which build up a crystal of sodium. Then if we can by some means excite the electrons in solid sodium, the excited electrons may drop back into their normal states, and a study of the emitted radiation may reveal some of the energy characteristics of the *electrons in the solid crystal*, just as the study of the radiation from hot metallic vapours revealed the electronic energy levels of the free atoms.

OM: Do you mean that the electrons in solid crystals occupy definite energy levels?

YS: Yes. You may, if you like, regard the assembly of atoms in a metallic crystal as forming a gigantic molecule. This molecule has a series of electronic states or energy levels, and at the absolute zero of temperature the electrons occupy the lowest energy levels, subject to the Pauli Restriction Principle that a given state can contain not more than two electrons—one of each spin. At the absolute zero an assembly of N electrons thus occupies the $N/2$ lowest energy levels.

OM: Then are the electronic energy levels in a solid metal the same as those in free atoms, so that one can, in the case of sodium for example, speak of $(1s)$ $(2s)$ . . . etc., electrons?

YS: It is not quite as simple as that. Suppose we return to Fig. 28, in which, as I have already explained, Fig. 28(a) represents the electron levels in a free atom of sodium. Sodium crystallises in the body-centred cubic structure, the unit cell of which is shown in Fig. 29. We shall consider the details of this structure later, and for the moment we may note that there is one atom at each corner of the unit cell, and one at the centre. The side of the unit cell is $4.28\ kX$, and the closest distance between two atoms is $4.28 \times \dfrac{\sqrt{3}}{2} = 3.71\ kX$. Now let us suppose that we start with sodium vapour, and gradually compress this so that the atoms assemble to form a body-centred cubic structure, and let us suppose that we imagine this process stopped at a stage at which the side of the unit cell is $6kX$. In this case we should find a condition of affairs represented by Fig. 28(b). Here you will see that the $(1s)$, $(2s)$ and $(2p)$ levels are practically the same as those in the free atom, but that the $(3s)$ and $(3p)$ levels have broadened slightly

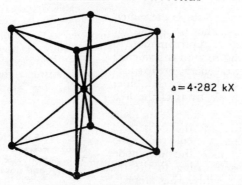

Fig. 29—The unit cell of the body-centred cubic structure of sodium

There is one atom at the centre, and one at each corner of the unit cell, and the crystal structure is formed by the repetition of this unit in three dimensions

into *ranges or bands* of energies. At this stage in the process the assembly of sodium atoms would have two, two and six electrons per atom respectively, in states almost the same as those of the $(1s)^2$, $(2s)^2$ and $(2p)^6$ sub-groups of the free atoms, but the valency electrons would have energies spread over a range.

OM: Would the valency electrons still be in $(3s)$ states?

YS: At the stage shown in Fig. 28(b), yes.

OM: Then would their energies be spread over the whole range of energy you have marked in Fig. 28(b)?

YS: The single energy level of the free atoms broadens into a band as the atoms approach one another, but the number of electron states per atom remains unaltered. So if the crystal contains N atoms the range of energy shown for the $(3s)$ electrons in Fig. 28(b) contains $2N$ electron states. Since there is one valency electron per atom, the valency electrons will, at the absolute zero, occupy the lower half of the $(3s)$ band shown in Fig. 28(b).

OM: It would seem that if the atoms were squeezed together sufficiently closely, the $(3s)$ and $(3p)$ bands might overlap.

YS: Exactly! Fig. 28(b) represents the condition of affairs when the atoms form a hypothetical body-centred cubic crystal in which the side of the unit cell is 6 kX. To get the condition of affairs in sodium itself we have to squeeze the atoms closer together until the side of the unit cell is 4.28 kX. In this case the condition of affairs is as shown in Fig. 28(c). Here you will see that the $(1s)$, $(2s)$, and $(2p)$ levels are still sharp, but the $(3s)$ and $(3p)$ levels have now broadened so much that they overlap and form a continuous band. Under these conditions the valency electrons are said to occupy *hybridized orbitals*, and their condition is described by the superposition of the two wave functions. Strictly speaking we should no longer speak of electrons as being in s-states, or p-states, etc., when this hybridization has occurred, but it is a reasonable approximation to say that in solid sodium the valency electrons of lowest energy are in states derived from and closely resembling those of the 3s electrons of the free atom.

OM: In this case they will have $3 - 1 = 2$ spherical nodes round the nuclei, but I suppose the outer node will be distorted owing to the influence of the neighbouring atoms.

Fig. 30—Soft X-ray emission band spectrum of solid sodium. This part of the spectrum is a band and not a sharp line

YS: Yes. They are two nodes round each nucleus, and the inner of the two nodes will be approximately spherical, although the outer node will be distorted. The remarks refer to the valency electrons of lowest energy in the solid crystal and, as the energy increases, the p-fraction of the hybrid becomes more and more pronounced. You will see therefore that the difference between the solid metal and the free atom is that in the latter the energy levels are all sharp, whereas in the solid metal the valency electrons have energies extending over a band or range of energies.

OM: It seems to me that what you say is quite impossible.

YS: Why do you think that?

OM: If the valency electrons are distributed over a range of energy, there will no longer be a constant difference of energy between a valency electron and an electron in a lower shell. This will mean, according to your equation above, that the spectrum should no longer consist of sharp lines. Or does the equation not apply to solids?

YS: The equation always applies, and what you say is perfectly correct, and is, in fact, borne out by experiment. Fig. 30 shows part of the soft X-ray spectrum of sodium, and you will see that the emission is now in the form of a band and not of a sharp line. So what you thought was an objection turns out to be a direct confirmation of what I have explained to you in connection with Fig. 28.

OM: Can you show me a spectrum of sodium vapour to compare with the above?

YS: I've not found a film of the spectrum of sodium vapour for direct comparison with Fig. 30, but I have photographs of the X-ray spectra of aluminium, and these are shown in Fig. 31. Here, again, you will see that this part of the emission is in the form of a band, although other parts of the X-ray emission spectra contain lines.

OM: Why is it not all in the form of bands?

YS: Look at Fig. 28(c), and think for yourself. Consider the different possible transitions.

OM: Oh, I see. You mean that if a transition were to occur between

Wave-length (A)

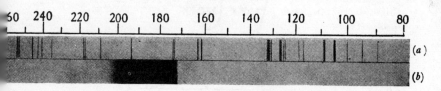

[From Reports on Progress in Physics, 1938, V, 258

Fig. 31—Soft X-ray spectra of aluminium (a from vapour and (b) from solid metal

The spectrum of the vapour consists of lines, and this indicates that the electronic energy levels of the free atoms are sharp. The spectrum from the solid shows a diffuse band which indicates that one of the electronic energy levels concerned is not sharp but extends over a range of energies

two levels which are sharp in Fig. 28(c), there would be a single characteristic energy difference, and consequently a sharp line would be produced. Whereas if the transition involved one of the levels which has broadened appreciably, then there would be a range of energies in equation (XVIII) (1), and consequently an emission band will be found.

YS: That's right. It is in this way that the spectroscopist is beginning to explore the energy characteristics of electrons in solids, just as the earlier spectroscopy investigated the energy levels of the electrons in free atoms.

OM: When you say that the energies of the valency electrons are spread over a range or band, what sort of magnitudes are involved?

YS: The widths of the bands of the valency electrons in different metals are of the order 1—10 electron volts.

OM: What sort of excitation process is used to obtain the soft X-ray spectra of solids?

YS: The usual procedure is to bombard the metal with a stream of electrons. Under these conditions the atoms of the metal receive an intense stimulus, as a result of which an electron may be jerked out of one of the inner electron shells—say the (1s) or K shell—and then if an electron drops back from the valency band into the (1s) level, a quantum of radiation is emitted whose frequency is proportional to the energy change involved. If a large number of such transitions occurs, the distribution of frequency in the emission band will clearly be related to the distribution of the valency electrons over the range of energy in the solid.

OM: Is it not very difficult to prevent the metal from overheating if electron bombardment is used?

YS: Very much so. It is necessary to cool the target, more or less as in the water-cooled targets used in some X-ray sets. What is more, it has been found possible to cool the target with a stream of

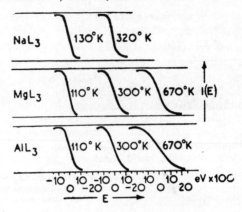

[From Phil. Trans. Royal Soc., 1940, 801, 114

**Fig. 32—To illustrate the effect of temperature on the high energy
end of the soft X-ray emission bands of metal**

*The lines show how the intensity falls off at the high energy end of the emission band, and it will
be seen that the lines become more nearly vertical as the temperature falls. At the absolute zero
of temperature the line would be exactly vertical, and the head of the band would terminate
abruptly*

liquid air, and so to investigate the effect of temperature on the
energy distribution of the electrons in metals. Very beautiful work
of this kind was done by R. W. B. Skinner at Bristol.

OM: Am I right in thinking that if you were to cool the metal
down to the absolute zero of temperature, the valency electrons would
be at rest and the emission band would become a sharp line?

YS: That is what was thought until about 1920, but the new
theories which are supported by the soft X-ray spectroscopy show that
the real position is very different. From what I have just said you
will realise that by studying the intensity distribution across the
emission bands, the spectroscopist is able to deduce some of the energy
characteristics of the valency electrons in metals. As the temperature
is lowered it is found that the high energy end of the band terminates
more and more sharply. This effect is shown in Fig. 32, which is
taken from the work of Skinner. Without going into details we may
say that, although the actual experimental work has not been carried
below −183°C (liquid air temperature), it is quite certain that at the
absolute zero the energies of the valency electrons are spread over a
band or range (of the order 1–10 electron volts), and that this range
of energies terminates sharply at a limiting value which we may call
E_{max}. As the temperature is raised some of the electrons of highest
energy are excited into higher states, and the head of the band becomes
diffuse. You will see, therefore, that the previous view of the condition
of the electrons at the absolute zero was quite wrong. At the absolute

zero the energies of the valency electrons are still spread over a range or band, and the valency electrons as a whole have quite a high energy.

OM: Is what you are describing a theoretical conclusion or an experimental fact?

YS: It was first a theoretical conclusion, but the work of Skinner has confirmed it down to $-183°C$, and a large amount of experimental work has confirmed the general conclusion. You may take it as quite definitely established that at the absolute zero the energies of the valency electrons are distributed over a band or range which terminates sharply at the high energy end, and that on raising the temperature the high energy end of the band becomes more and more diffuse.

OM: All this is very interesting and I suppose the soft X-ray spectroscopy is important because it gives a method of investigating the energies of electrons in solid metals?

YS: Exactly! And these energies are clearly related to the properties of the solid concerned. At the present the theory of electrons in solids is a long way ahead of the experiments, but as a practical man you will like to know that the general conclusions of the theory are being confirmed.

19—Electron Distribution Curves

OLDER METALLURGIST: You suggested last time that the soft X-ray spectroscopy was of interest to metallurgists because it gave an indication of the energy relations of the electrons in a metal. If this is so, there must, I suppose, be some way of showing how the electrons are divided over the different ranges of energy.

YOUNG SCIENTIST: That's quite right, and in many problems you will come across what are called $N(E)$ curves. Let us suppose for a simple example that we know the valency electrons to have energies extending over the range XY shown in Fig. 33. Then clearly the

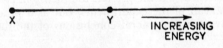

Fig. 33

properties of the assembly will depend on whether the electrons nearly all have high energies, or nearly all have low energies, or are more or less uniformly distributed over the whole range of energy. For this purpose we may define a quantity $n(E)$ in such a way that $n(E)dE$ is the number of electrons per unit volume of metal with energies between the limits E and $E + dE$. We may then plot $n(E)$ against E, and the resulting curve will indicate the distribution of the electrons among the different energies. An $n(E)$ curve of the form shown in Fig. 34 would, for example, imply that the electrons had energies extending over the range OD, and that most of them had energies in the region of B where the curve rises to a maximum. The vertical end of the curve at CD means that no electrons have energies exceeding this value, and one may say that the head of the band is sharp.

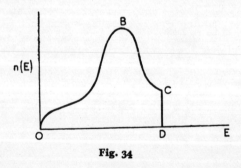

Fig. 34

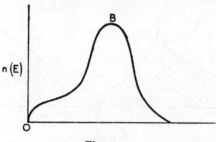

Fig. 35

OM: Do you mean that that is the way in which an $n(E)$ curve terminates for electrons at the absolute zero?

YS: That's right. As I explained last time, at the absolute zero the electronic energies extend over a band or range which terminates sharply at the high energy end, and this is what is shown by the vertical portion CD in Fig. 34. At a higher temperature some of the electrons are excited into higher energy states, and the $n(E)$ curve might be as in Fig. 35. In this case the curve again means that most of the electrons have energies in the region of B, where the curve rises to a maximum, but the head of the band will be diffuse.

OM: If Figs. 34 and 35 refer to the same number of electrons, it would seem from the definition of $n(E)$ that the areas under the curve must be the same.

YS: That's right. The area under the $n(E)$ curve is proportional to the number of electrons.

OM: I notice, by the way, that you have written $n(E)$, whereas most of the books write $N(E)$.

YS: I've done that intentionally to avoid confusion. As I have explained above, the $n(E)$ curves show the way in which the electrons are distributed over the ranges of energy concerned. Now in a metallic crystal there is a large number of possible electron states, and we shall deal with some of these later on. At the absolute zero an assembly of N electrons will then occupy the $N/2$ lowest electron states, each occupied state containing two electrons—one of each spin. For many purposes it is therefore of importance to know how the *electron states* are distributed over the various energy ranges.

OM: But don't the electron states just go up regularly with increasing energy?

YS: Oh, no! That doesn't follow at all. There may be certain ranges of energy for which energy states are not possible.

OM: We seem to want a curve corresponding to that of Fig. 35, but referring to electron states.

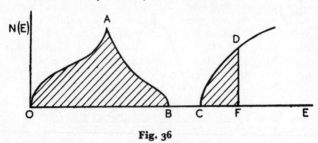

Fig. 36

YS: You're right, and for this purpose we may define $N(E)dE$ as the number of electronic energy states with energies in the range E and $(E + dE)$, and we may then plot $N(E)$ against E. In this way we obtain a curve showing how the *electron states* are distributed over the various ranges of energy, just as the $n(E)$ curves showed how the actual *electrons* were distributed over the various ranges of energy. The condition of affairs at the absolute zero may then be represented by shading the area of the occupied states. For example, the $N(E)$ curve of Fig. 36 would show that on increasing the energy, the number of energy states per unit volume of the metal at first increased with increasing energy, rose to a maximum at the point A, and then sank to zero between B and C, and finally increased again. This would mean that there were no states with energies in the range BC, but that there were energy states on either side of this range. The shaded areas which terminate in the vertical line DF mean that the number of electrons present is at the absolute zero sufficient to fill all the energy states up to the limit $E = F$.

OM: If the occupied states each contain two electrons, then except for a factor of 2 in the vertical axis, the $n(E)$ curve at the absolute zero will be the same as the $N(E)$ curve up to the point D and terminated by the vertical line DF. Is that right?

YS: That's right.

OM: Then how does the $N(E)$ curve show the condition of things at higher temperatures?

YS: The $N(E)$ curve shows the distribution of electron states over

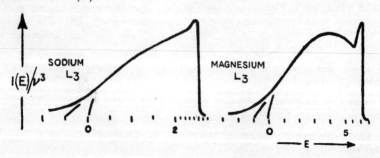

134

the energy ranges concerned. It is only at the absolute zero that there is a sharp division between the occupied and the unoccupied states, and so it is only at the absolute zero that the $N(E)$ curve can indicate the occupied states by means of a shaded area terminated by a vertical line. At higher temperatures the condition of affairs is represented by the $n(E)$ curve. Many of the books used the symbol $N(E)$ indiscriminately for what I have called $n(E)$ and $N(E)$, and that is why I deliberately distinguished between the two.

OM: Is there any simple relation between the form of the $N(E)$ and $n(E)$ curves and the energy of the electrons?

YS: Most of the theories of metals were developed first for conditions at the absolute zero. We may adopt this policy ourselves, and can therefore deal with the $N(E)$ curves, and shade the area of the occupied states.

OM: So far you have drawn sketches of the $N(E)$ curves, but are these purely theoretical or have they any experimental basis?

YS: Speaking generally, each crystal structure gives its own characteristic $N(E)$ curve. Some of these have been calculated approximately, but in most cases the calculations are too approximate for the results to be of much critical value—this point has often not been appreciated. On the experimental side, the $n(E)$ curves for many metals have been determined by the methods of soft X-ray spectroscopy. In general, theory and experiment are in good agreement, and what may be called the science of $N(E)$ curves is on a satisfactory foundation.

OM: I'm afraid I don't see how the form of the $N(E)$ curve will come from the soft X-ray spectrum. Can you give an example?

YS: Let us suppose we have a metal for which the $n(E)$ curve of the valency electrons has the form shown in Fig. 34. Then most of the valency electrons will have energies in the region of the maximum at B. Now suppose the metal to be excited by electron bombardment, so that electrons are expelled from one of the inner electron shells of the atoms. Then an emission spectrum will result if electrons drop back from the valency band to the inner shell. This, as you pointed out before, (page 127) will mean that there is an *emission band*, because the valency electrons have not one constant energy but energies extending over a range. You can readily see that since most of the

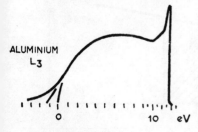

ALUMINIUM
L₃

0   10   eV

Fig. 37—Electron distribution curves deduced by Skinner from the soft X-ray spectra of sodium, magnesium and aluminium

In this figure the abscissæ represents energies and are analogous to the abscissæ of Figs. 34–35. The quantity $I(E)/v^3$ on the vertical axis of Fig. 37 may to a rough approximation be regarded as the equivalent of $n(E)$ in Figs. 34 and 35

[From Phil. Trans. Royal Soc., 1940, 801, 12

valency electrons have energies in the region of B, there will be a greater probability of an electron with this energy falling back into the inner shell than there will be for a valency electron with an energy in the region where the $n(E)$ curve is low. Now the frequency of the emitted radiation is always given by the equation

$$h\nu = \Delta E$$

where ΔE is the change in energy. So you can see that by studying the variation of intensity over the different frequencies of the emission band, it is possible to arrive at the form of the $n(E)$ curve.

OM: Do you mean that the $N(E)$ curve is simply a repetition of the intensity distribution across the emission band?

YS: In a rough way, yes, but there are a lot of complications in unravelling the experimental data, so that it isn't a simple question of a direct proportionality. But you need not bother about these details, and Fig. 37 shows some of the $n(E)$ curves deduced by Skinner. You will see that for the univalent alkali metals the $n(E)$ curves are

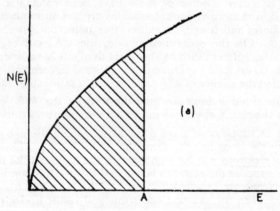

Fig. 38(a)

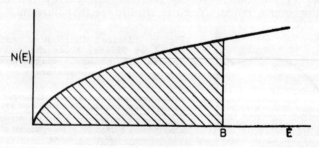

Fig. 38(b)

relatively simple, but that the curves for the elements of higher valency contain peaks and valleys, and are clearly more complicated.

OM: From what you said before the width of the $n(E)$ curve is of the order 1–10 electron volts, as this was the width of the band (page 129). Now if the temperature is raised, by how much does the head of the $n(E)$ curve depart from a vertical line?

YS: At room temperatures the diffuse head of the band is of the order of a few tenths of an electron volt. Fig. 32, which is due to Skinner, shows how the head of the band becomes more and more diffuse as the temperature is raised.

OM: From the definition of $\mathcal{N}(E)$ it seems that if all the electron states are fully occupied up to a limiting value E_{max}, the total energy of the assembly will be equal to

$$2 \int_{0}^{E_{max}} E. \quad \mathcal{N}(E) \, dE$$

whilst the total number of electrons will be equal to twice the shaded area in Fig. 36, that is

$$2 \int_{0}^{E_{max}} \mathcal{N}(E) \quad dE.$$

YS: That is quite right and it follows that the more steeply the $\mathcal{N}(E)$ curve rises, the lower the energy of a given number of electrons. This is really only commonsense, as you can see from Fig. 38, where I have drawn two $\mathcal{N}(E)$ curves, one steep and the other flat. The shaded areas are equal to one another, and so they correspond with an equal number of electrons. You can readily see that the condition of affairs represented by Fig. 38(a) will correspond with a much lower energy than that represented by Fig. 38(b). In Fig. 38(a) no electron has an energy greater than $E = A$, whereas in Fig. 38(b) the occupied states go all the way up to $E = B$.

OM: This is very interesting, but I'm afraid I find it all rather confusing. What has it all got to do with practical things like alloy structures?

YS: I've already told you that each type of crystal structure gives rise to a characteristic $\mathcal{N}(E)$ curve. Now suppose for the sake of argument that we could calculate the $\mathcal{N}(E)$ curves for two particular crystal structures A and B, and could show that A gave the $\mathcal{N}(E)$ curve of Fig. 38(a), and B the curve of Fig. 38(b). Then so far as the energies of the electrons were concerned, we could say that structure A could accommodate a given number of electrons with a lower energy than structure B. We could then argue that as far as the electronic energy was concerned A would be a more stable structure than B.

OM: Do you mean that from a knowledge of the $N(E)$ curves we can predict which structures are stable?

YS: From a knowledge of the $N(E)$ curves we can estimate how the type of crystal structure affects the energies of a given number of electrons. The total energy of the crystal may involve other factors, but in some cases the electronic factor is predominant and the $N(E)$ curves lead to a quite straightforward explanation of why particular structures are stable in some alloys and not in others.

OM: This all sounds most exciting.

YS: You're right. It's one of the triumphs of the electron theories that they do lead to calculations of this kind.

20—Free Electron Theory: Electrons in A Box

OLDER METALLURGIST: The work on soft X-ray spectroscopy is certainly most interesting, but it doesn't seem to tell us anything about the way in which the atoms are held together in metallic crystals.

YOUNG SCIENTIST: If we deal with the metals of Groups I and II—the alkali and alkaline earth metals, copper, silver, gold, zinc, cadmium and mercury—the general picture of the cohesion process is fairly simple, and we may look upon the metallic crystal as an array of positively charged ions held together by the valency electrons.

OM: Do you mean that the positive ions occupy the points of one lattice, and the electrons the points of an interpenetrating lattice, so that there is a lattice of electrons?

YS: No. An electron lattice theory was at one time advanced, but it is now realised that the concept was wrong. The valency electrons are continuously moving about within the crystal, and so serve to hold the ions together. You may if you like regard the metal crystal as an immense molecule in which the valency electrons are in continuous circulation, and so bind the atoms or ions together. The problem of metallic structure is thus a problem of how the electrons will behave under these conditions.

OM: It must be very complicated, and I hope you can simplify it as much as possible.

YS: That is the way in which the problem was actually approached, and the first theory which we shall consider is the so-called free electron theory. In this theory, the structure of the crystal is ignored completely, and we regard the metal as an assembly of electrons in an empty box, surrounded by potential walls which prevent the electron from escaping.

OM: That seems to me to be entire nonsense. A crystal of a metal has a definite regular arrangement of its atoms, and any theory which ignores this must surely be so far removed from the truth as to be worthless.

YS: What you say is only partly correct. The electron-box, or free electron theory, is by its very nature quite unable to deal with any properties which involve direction relative to crystal axes. As we shall learn later it is, however, quite a good approximation to the state of affairs in the alkali metals, although it cannot legitimately be applied to other metals. But quite apart from applications to actual metals, the free electron theory is of great importance in two ways. In the first place it shows us that, according to the new theories, an assembly of electrons in an empty box, at concentrations equal to those in a solid metal, will have some properties entirely different from those predicted by the older theories. Some of these differences apply also to the behaviour of electrons in an actual crystal lattice, and the free electron theory is the easiest way by which these characteristics can be appreciated.

In the second place, even in cases where the free electron theory cannot really be applied, it often provides a convenient approximation against which the complexities of the more complete theories can be viewed. As we shall see later, the behaviour of electrons in an actual crystal lattice is often very difficult to visualise, and in many cases a comparison with their behaviour in an empty box is the easiest way to appreciate what is happening.

OM: I must say I think it all sounds very suspicious, but let's see how you begin.

YS: What is done is to assume that the electrons are contained in a cubical enclosure, of side L, and volume $V = L^3$, surrounded by high potential walls which prevent the electrons from escaping. If one then takes a cross-section parallel to the side of the cube, the condition

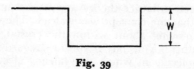

W

Fig. 39

of affairs can be represented by a potential diagram of the type shown in Fig. 39.

OM: You said before (page 130) that the energy of the valency electrons in a metal was of the order 1 to 10 electron volts, so that W in Fig. 39 must, I suppose, be of this order, because metals emit electrons fairly easily.

YS: Yes. If we call the potential of an electron in free space zero, then the potential inside a metal is of the order -5 to -10 volts, so that W in Fig. 39 is of this magnitude.

OM: Then do you mean that in the free electron theory we are to regard a number of electrons as being introduced into the cube of side L whose potential boundaries are shown in Fig. 39, and that this process is to be continued until the number of electrons per unit volume is the same as the number of electrons per unit volume in sodium?

YS: That's right.

OM: It seems to me that the whole thing is absurd because, as you introduce more and more electrons, you will build up an enormous negative charge.

YS: I'm sorry. I should have said that when you introduce the electrons into the box you must imagine that you add a corresponding amount of positive electricity, so that the whole assembly is electrically neutral like the assembly of electrons and ions in a crystal. The free electron theory really imagines the electrons to move in a field of uniform potential with positive electricity distributed uniformly throughout the box to just the density required in order to keep the whole electrically neutral. We have now to consider how to describe an assembly of electrons of this kind.

OM: The description must surely be impossibly complicated if there are 10^{23} electrons in the assembly.

YS: That is perfectly true, and so we have to learn to think in terms of the assembly as a whole, that is, to think statistically. We may begin by considering the older viewpoint, and imagine that we have an electron in the box. Then in the older theory we could at any instant describe the condition of the one electron by stating that it was at a position (x, y, z) relative to axes parallel to the sides of the cube, and that the components of its momentum parallel to these axes were (p_x, p_y, p_z). In this way the six co-ordinates (x, y, z, p_x, p_y, p_z) would describe the conditions of the one electron, and we could say that the condition of the electron was described by one point in a *six-dimensional space*, the so-called *molecular phase space*. The term six-dimensional space need not worry you. It is only a convenient way of saying that six quantities have to be specified in order to describe the condition of the electron at any instant.

OM: Even so, you have so far described the condition of only one electron whereas actually there is something like 10^{23} of them.

YS: In the older theory the condition of the assembly of N electrons could then be described by stating the values of x, y, z, p_x, p_y, and p_z for each electron, and we could say that at any instant the condition of affairs was represented by the distribution of N points in the six-dimensional molecular phase space.

OM: I'm afraid I find this continual reference to six dimensions very confusing. Can't you simplify it somehow?

YS: For some of our purposes we can reduce it to three dimensions by dealing with what is called a *momentum diagram*. Let us suppose that we have an assembly of N electrons in a cubical box of side L, and volume $V = L^3$. We may now construct a diagram such as that

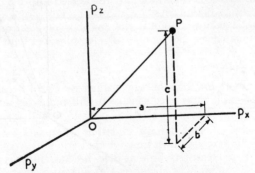

Fig. 40—To illustrate momentum space

of Fig. 40, in which the axes are parallel to the sides of the cube, and may use this diagram to indicate the components of the momentum (p_x, p_y, p_z) parallel to the three directions. Thus a point such as P in Fig. 40 would indicate that the electron concerned had components of momentum $p_x = a, p_y = b, p_z = c$, and a total momentum equal to the length OP, and in the direction of OP. In this way one point in the so-called momentum diagram would indicate the magnitude and direction of the momentum of the electron concerned. Similarly, for an assembly of N electrons, an assembly of N points—one might call it a dust of points—would indicate the momentum of the N electrons.

OM: That kind of diagram doesn't seem to tell the whole story. It only gives the momentum of each electron, and not its position in the box.

YS: That's perfectly true. The momentum diagram by its very nature describes only the momenta. If you want to describe the positions of the electrons as well as the momenta, you must go into six dimensions. If we use the momentum diagram, and introduce N electrons into our box of volume $V = L^3$, then the momentum of the assembly at any instant can be indicated by the distribution of N points in the momentum diagram. Let us look at the matter from the older viewpoint, and suppose that we have six electrons in the box, and that at a given instant their momenta are represented by the six points in Fig. 41(a). This would indicate a state of affairs in which the total energy was low because the points are near to the origin, and the momenta are small. The state of affairs represented by Fig. 41(b) would represent a higher energy because the points are farther from the origin, and the momenta and hence also the velocities and the kinetic energies of the electrons are higher. In a piece of metal of ordinary size, say 1 c.c., there will be something like 10^{23} electrons, and you must imagine a cloud or dust of 10^{23} points in the momentum diagram, and the distribution of this dust as a whole will indicate some of the characteristics of the assembly.

OM: Does the representative point of any one electron always stay at the same place in the momentum diagram?

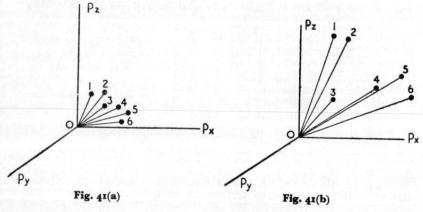

Fig. 41(a)　　　　　　　　　Fig. 41(b)

YS: Oh no! Each time the motion of an electron changes (for example, by its hitting the walls of the box or by its coming under the influence of another electron) the representative point in the momentum diagram undergoes a corresponding change. But if you consider the equilibrium distribution of the dust of points *as a whole*, it will not be appreciably affected by these individual changes. The statistical method means that you think in terms of the assembly as a whole, and ignore the individual changes.

OM: Well, if you do use momentum diagram like this, I suppose the dust of points will move continually towards the origin as the temperature falls.

YS: That was what happened in the older theories which were based on the classical gas laws. In these theories the energy of the assembly was proportional to the absolute temperature, and if the temperature were gradually lowered, the dust of points crowded towards the origin, so that at the absolute zero the dust of points was congregated with infinite density at the origin, that is the momentum of each electron was zero, and the total energy was zero.

OM: Why do you keep on saying " the older theories "? Surely this is all straightforward and general?

YS: There I am afraid you are wrong, and you have forgotten what I said before when we discussed Heisenberg's Principle.

OM: You don't mean to say that Heisenberg is going to bother us here!

YS: Most certainly I do. You can never escape from Heisenberg's Principle.

OM: But how can it affect the way in which we describe a dust of points in a momentum diagram?

YS: You have forgotten that we are dealing with a theory in which we assume that we introduce electrons into a cubical box, of side L and volume $V = L^3$. Since the electron is confined to the box, there will be an uncertainty in the momentum of at least $\frac{h}{L}$ for each of the three components of momentum. We are no longer entitled to think of a *point* in the momentum diagram—this would be justifiable only if the position of the electron were completely indeterminate, and in this case it would not be confined to the box.

Fortunately, this does not mean that the idea of a momentum diagram has to be discarded. If we look on the matter in a very simple way—it is not quite the whole story but it is a justifiable simplification for our purpose—we may say that the momentum diagram may be regarded as divided up into a number of little cells each of side $\frac{h}{L}$, and volume $\frac{h^3}{L^3} = \frac{h^3}{V}$. You will readily see how the size of the cells is related to Heisenberg's Principle—if the electron is known to be

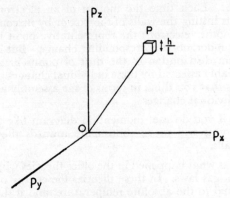

Fig. 42—To illustrate the momentum diagram of the quantum theories

The momentum space is divided into little cells of side $\frac{h}{L}$, and volume $\frac{h^3}{L^3}$

within the cube of side L, there must be an uncertainty of at least $\frac{h}{L}$ in each component of the momentum, and we cannot define the momentum more precisely than by saying it is associated with a cell of volume $\frac{h^3}{V}$ in the momentum diagram. The whole of the momentum diagram is to be regarded as built of adjacent cells of volume $\frac{h^3}{V}$, and each of these little cells represents an energy state (Fig. 42).

OM: In view of the small value of h, the difference between adjacent cells must surely be exceedingly minute unless the box is only of the order of a few atomic diameters?

YS: That's perfectly true. For a piece of metal of ordinary size the cells in the momentum diagram are so small that they may be treated as a *continuum*—this is really not quite the whole story, but it will do for our purpose.

OM: In that case I don't see that there is much difference between the old and new views. There will be just a little uncertainty as to exactly where the representative point of the electron is in the momentum diagram, but otherwise we can go on as before.

YS: What you say is more or less correct at very high temperatures, but you haven't yet thought out what will happen as you cool the metal down to the absolute zero.

OM: That seems easy enough—the dust of points will just contract towards the origin as in the older theory.

YS: There I am afraid you are wrong, and you have forgotten what I said before about Pauli's Principle (page 94).

OM: What has Pauli's Principle to do with us here? We are not dealing with a single atom or a molecule, but with a whole assembly of electrons.

YS: The assembly of electrons in the box constitutes a system, and this system has a number of possible energy states which are represented by the little cells, each of volume $\frac{h^3}{V}$, in the momentum diagram. Pauli's Principle applies to this system just as it applies to the system of electrons in an atom or molecule. Consequently each electronic energy state of the system of electrons in the box can contain at the most two electrons—one of each spin.

OM: That will mean that in the momentum diagram there cannot be more than two representative points in each little cell of volume $\frac{h^3}{V}$.

YS: Yes. And now see what happens when you cool the assembly down to the absolute zero!

OM: Oh! I see! You mean that as there cannot be more than two representative points in any one cell, the dust of representative points will no longer be able to contract to the origin of the momentum diagram because this would mean more than two points in each of the cells near the origin?

YS: That's right.

OM: Surely that's absurd; because the energy of the electrons must be zero at the absolute zero?

YS: That is the great difference between the old and the new theories. In the old theory of electrons, the energy of the assembly at the absolute zero was zero. In the new theories Pauli's Principle means that at the absolute zero, an assembly of N electrons occupies the $\frac{N}{2}$ lowest energy states, that is, 2 electrons per occupied state. The assembly thus possesses kinetic energy at the absolute zero, and this energy is considerable and can be calculated quite easily. Let us return to the momentum diagram, built up of little cells of volume $\frac{h^3}{V}$. Then at the absolute zero the dust of representative points for an assembly of N electrons will occupy the $\frac{N}{2}$ lowest energy cells, and all the remaining cells will be unoccupied. You can readily see that the volume of momentum space containing occupied cells will be

$$\frac{N}{2} \times \frac{h^3}{V} = \frac{Nh^3}{2V}.$$

Now we have to think which part of momentum space will contain the occupied cells.

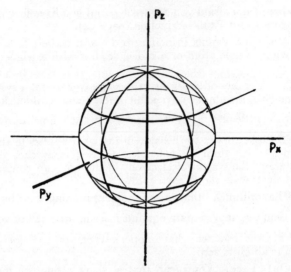

Fig. 43—To illustrate the Fermi surface of occupied states

At the absolute zero, an assembly of N electrons occupies the $\dfrac{N}{2}$ lowest electron states. The occupied states thus form a sphere round the origin of the momentum diagram. At the absolute zero every state within this sphere is fully occupied, and contains two electrons, one of each spin, whilst the states of higher energy are unoccupied. There is thus a sharp surface, the Fermi surface, in the momentum diagram, and this surface separates the unoccupied and occupied states

OM: Oh, well, that's easy—the occupied cells will be those of lowest energy, that is, those nearest the origin.

YS: That's right. The lowest energy will clearly correspond with a symmetrical filling up of the states round the origin of the momentum diagram, and the occupied states will form a sphere round the origin of the diagram. The surface which bounds the occupied states is often called the Fermi surface. I've drawn this sphere in Fig. 43 and if we use the symbol p_{max} for the momentum of the highest occupied state, the radius of the sphere will be equal to p_{max}, and the volume of the sphere will be given by the usual equation $\dfrac{4}{3}\pi r^3 = \dfrac{4}{3}\pi p^3_{max}$.

We have already seen that the volume of occupied states is equal to $\dfrac{Nh^3}{2V}$, and consequently

$$\frac{4}{3}\pi p^3_{max} = \frac{Nh^3}{2V}$$

$$p_{max} = h\left(\frac{3N}{8\pi V}\right)^{\frac{1}{3}}.$$

Now the kinetic energy $\dfrac{1}{2}\,mu^2$ is equal to $\dfrac{1}{2m}.\,m^2u^2 = \dfrac{1}{2m}\,p^2$, and so the kinetic energy of the electron in the highest occupied state, which we may denote by E_{max}, will be given by

$$E_{max} = \frac{h^2}{2m}\left(\frac{3N}{8\pi V}\right)^{\frac{2}{3}}.$$

You will see, therefore, that at the absolute zero an assembly of N electrons in a box of volume V will have kinetic energies extending over a range from the almost zero value of the lowest state to the value E_{max} given by the above relation. You will also note that E_{max} depends not on N, but on $\frac{N}{V}$ and consequently it is independent of the size of the piece of metal. If we double the volume V of a piece of metal, we also double the number of electrons which it contains, and so $\frac{N}{V}$ remains constant. You can see, therefore, that in spite of the simplicity of our box model, it has satisfied the first requirement of the soft X-ray spectroscopy, because it requires the energies of the electrons to be spread over a range which increases as the volume decreases. Not merely is this requirement satisfied, but the magnitudes are reasonable—if you calculate $\frac{N}{V}$ for sodium using the known value of the density, and assuming one free electron per atom, you obtain $E_{max} = 3.16$ ev, and this is a reasonable value. Apart from this, a very simple extension of the above argument shows that at the

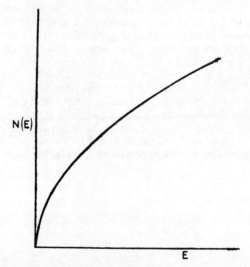

Fig. 44—The N(E) curve of the free electron theory

This $N(E)$ curve is a parabola in which $N(E)$ varies as $E^{\frac{1}{2}}$

absolute zero, the total kinetic energy of an assembly of N electrons in a box of volume V is equal to

$$\frac{3}{5} N E_{max}$$

and so the mean kinetic energy per electron is

$$\frac{3}{5} E_{max}.$$

It is quite easy to show that the $N(E)$ curve is given by the relation

$$N(E) = \frac{V}{4\pi^2} \left(\frac{2m}{\hbar^2} \right)^{\frac{3}{2}} \sqrt{E}$$

where the symbol $\hbar$ is used as an abbreviation for $\frac{h}{2\pi}$.

This means that $N(E) \propto E^{\frac{1}{2}}$, and the relation between $N(E)$ and E is of the form shown in Fig. 44. You will see that this is of the general type indicated by the methods of soft X-ray spectroscopy for the alkali metals, and the calculated values are in reasonable agreement with the facts for sodium, potassium, rubidium and caesium. For lithium the $N(E)$ curve is of the same general parabolic form, but the constant of proportionality is not in such good agreement with the simple theory.

You will see, therefore, that in spite of the great over-simplification of the free electron theory, it has already led us much farther than might have been expected. We have obtained a model in which the electronic energies extend over a range which is of the right magnitude, and which increases as the volume decreases. We have obtained an $N(E)$ curve which is of the form observed experimentally for the alkali metals, and a clear indication that an assembly of electrons at the densities found in metals behaves quite differently from an assembly obeying the classical gas laws. The first developments of the free electron theory were due to Pauli and were concerned with the paramagnetism of the alkali metals to which we shall refer later (page 239). In 1928 the theory was extended in many directions by Sommerfeld, whose work is one of the great landmarks in the history of the theory of metals. The Sommerfeld theory was admittedly much too simple, but it indicated very clearly the distinction between the behaviour of an assembly of electrons at the densities found in metals, and of a classical gas. This distinction is so important that we shall have to examine it further.

21—The Free Electron Theory and the Electronic Specific Heat of Metals

OLDER METALLURGIST: I've been thinking over what you said last time, and it seems to me that this theory of electrons in empty boxes is altogether too simple. Perhaps you will explain how far I ought to take it seriously.

YOUNG SCIENTIST: As I have emphasised, the free electron theory is a valid approximation only for the alkali metals, and even for these a more detailed theory is often desirable. On the other hand the line of argument which leads to the conclusion that at the absolute zero of temperature the electrons will have energies extending over a range is quite general and applies to the more complete theories. In the free electron theory the possible electron states may be visualised as giving rise to the little cells of volume $\frac{h^3}{V}$ in the momentum diagram, and at the absolute zero the assembly of N electrons occupies the $\frac{N}{2}$ lowest energy states which form a sphere round the origin of the momentum diagram. In the more complete theories, wave mechanics indicates more complicated energy relations which we shall consider later, but in these theories it is again Pauli's Principle which prevents all the electrons from entering the lowest state at the absolute zero, and requires them to be spread over the $\frac{N}{2}$ lowest states.

OM: Now you have mentioned wave mechanics, and that brings me to another point on which I have been in doubt. Your description of the free electron theory did not refer to wave mechanics at all, but is the theory really somehow connected with wave mechanics?

YS: Oh, most certainly yes! Wave mechanics can be applied to the motion of an electron in a box, just as it can be applied to other types of electronic motion. If we imagine one electron to be in a cubical box, then the potential is constant within the box, and rises sharply at the boundaries. Since the electron is confined to the box, the most natural assumption to make is that ψ vanishes outside the box. The solution of the Schrödinger equation which satisfies the above conditions is then of the form

$$\psi = \sin \frac{\pi l_1 x}{L} \sin \frac{\pi l_2 y}{L} \sin \frac{\pi l_3 z}{L}$$

where l_1, l_2, l_3 are positive whole numbers, and the sides of the cube are of length L, and are parallel to the x, y, and z axes. Each combination of l_1, l_2, and l_3 corresponds with a stationary state, and the corresponding energy values are

$$E = -W + \frac{h^2}{8mL^2} (l_1{}^2 + l_2{}^2 + l_3{}^2).$$

The zero of potential energy is that of an electron at rest outside the metal, and $-W$ is the potential inside the metal. These energy states are the same as those which we discussed in connection with the momentum diagram on page 144.

OM: That suggests that the electrons can only move in certain ways inside the box.

YS: Yes, only certain types of motion are possible if the electron is to exist in a stationary state. The phenomenon is roughly a three-dimensional analogue of the possible vibrations of a stretched string. If a steady tone is to be produced, the wave lengths of the vibrations of a stretched string must be simply related to the length of the string, and we may say that the vibrational waves fit nicely into the string. In the same way in the problem of the electron in a box, the above equations represent ψ patterns which fit nicely into the box, and form acceptable solutions (see page 69). In this way wave mechanics leads to the relations we discussed in the last chapter.

OM: That's all very well if you are describing one electron alone, but with an assembly of electrons surely things must become immensely complicated, because when two electrons approach one another there will be a mutual repulsion.

YS: Your objection is quite reasonable, but more detailed calculations have been made, and these have shown that for the alkali metals, where there is only one valency electron per atom, the simplifying assumptions of the free electron theory do not produce any very great error.

OM: Even so, it seems to me that the theory is not of much value if all this discussion refers to the absolute zero.

YS: The theory for the absolute zero is only the first stage, and it is in fact by indicating what may be expected when the temperature is raised that the free electron theory has achieved one of its most outstanding successes. Suppose that Fig. 45 represents the momentum diagram of a hypothetical two-dimensional metal, and that the circle represents the limit of the occupied states at the absolute zero. We use a two-dimensional model for convenience in drawing—the model for an actual metal would of course be three-dimensional, and the occupied states would form a sphere. Now see if you can say what will happen when the temperature is raised slightly above the absolute zero.

OM: That's simple enough. All the electrons will be excited into faster motion.

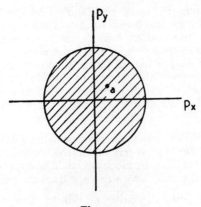

Fig. 45

YS: That is what happens to the molecules of an ordinary gas, but the behaviour of the electron gas is very different. You will understand that if one starts with a gas at the absolute zero, and raises the temperature slightly, the probability of a gas particle of energy E_1 being excited to a state of energy E_2 diminishes rapidly as $(E_2 - E_1)$ increases. In other words large increases in the energy of a gas particle are very improbable. Now suppose we return to Fig. 45 and consider an electron in a state of low energy such as that represented by a in Fig. 45. Then what will happen when the temperature is raised slightly?

OM: The electron will be excited into a state of slightly higher energy, that is, a state which is a little farther from the origin than a.

YS: That's where you have gone wrong, and you must think more carefully. All the energy states near to a are fully occupied, and since Pauli's Principle prevents a state from containing more than two electrons, the electron in state a cannot be excited into a neighbouring state. The only possible excitation is one which would carry the electron to a state outside the shaded circle in Fig. 45, and this would mean such a large increase in energy that the possibility of its occurrence is very small. The conclusion is therefore that an electron in a low energy state such as a cannot be excited by a slight rise in temperature above the absolute zero.

OM: But surely that's absurd? Increase in temperature must mean that the electrons move about faster.

YS: That is what everyone thought until the arguments based on Pauli's Principle were carried to their logical conclusion. In the older theories of electrons based on the classical gas laws there were no restrictions, and as the temperature began to rise above the absolute zero any electron could be thermally excited by a small amount.

But in the new theories based on Pauli's Principle, the first rise in temperature above the absolute zero cannot affect the electrons in low energy states, for the reasons I have just explained. On the other hand, electrons in states near to the Fermi surface can undergo excitation into states of slightly higher energy because there are unoccupied states available, namely the states just outside the shaded circle in Fig. 45. The conclusion is therefore that the first rise in temperature above the absolute zero affects only the electrons with energies near to E_{max}.

OM: Do you mean that if an electron is in a low energy state—say the state a in Fig. 45—it remains in that state indefinitely? That seems impossible because the electron would always be moving in the same direction and would have to escape from the box.

YS: I'm afraid you are getting muddled. The statistical method of description does not preclude an interchange so that a condition of affairs in which an electron—let us call it electron No. 1—in state A and an electron No. 2 in state B interchange so that No. 2 is in state A and No. 1 in state B. This kind of interchange is always going on, but, since electrons are completely indistinguishable, such interchanges have no effect on the properties of the assembly as a whole. Some people would say that it was meaningless to talk of such interchanges because there is no conceivable method by which they could be detected. The thermal excitations to which we have referred result in the exciting of the electron into a new state so that the properties of the assembly are altered.

OM: So it amounts to saying that the first rise in temperature above the absolute zero affects only the electrons with high energies?

YS: That's right. The electrons with energies near to E_{max} can undergo slight excitation into the neighbouring unoccupied states, and this is what happens as the temperature is raised above the absolute zero. You may if you like say that the Fermi surface which bounds the states occupied at the absolute zero becomes diffuse as the temperature is raised—there is no longer a sharp boundary between occupied and unoccupied states in the momentum diagram.

OM: Then as the temperature is raised higher and higher, more and more electrons will be excited.

YS: Yes. That effect may be shown by a diagram such as that of Fig. 46. In this description we denote the probable number of electrons in a given state by $2f$, where f is the so-called Fermi distribution function—the statistics which are based on Pauli's Principle are generally known as the Fermi-Dirac statistics. In this case if $f = 1$, $2f = 2$ and the state is fully occupied, and contains two electrons, one of each spin.

At the absolute zero, all the states up to E_{max} are fully occupied, whilst all those with higher energies are unoccupied. Consequently the condition of affairs may be represented by curve No. 1 of Fig. 46,

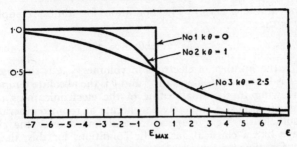

[From " Introduction to Chemical Physics," Slater. Courtesy of McGraw Hill Book Company, Inc.

Fig. 46—To illustrate the Fermi distribution function

where $f = 1$ for all states up to E_{max}, and $f = 0$ for states of higher energy.

At a somewhat higher temperature the corresponding distribution curve has the form of curve No. 2 in Fig. 46, whilst curve No. 3 refers to a very high temperature. These curves show that there is now a probability that states beyond E_{max} are occupied; this probability becoming smaller with increasing energy. Since the total number of electrons is constant, the states just below E_{max} will no longer be fully occupied, and you will see that for these states f is now less than 1. In curve No. 2 the electron states of lower energy are still fully occupied, this being the result of the Pauli Principle which we have just discussed (page 151).

OM: It seems to me that the new theory is only worth worrying about near to the absolute zero, and that I need not bother myself too much about it. I can quite see that at very low temperatures the effects resulting from the Pauli Principle mean that the electron gas has properties quite different from a gas obeying the classical gas laws. But as soon as an appreciable number of electrons have been excited, the two pictures will surely be much the same?

YS: You are quite right in saying that if the temperature were high enough for all the electrons to be excited, there would be little difference between the old and the new theories. But you are wrong in suggesting that this condition of affairs exists at room temperatures.

OM: Surely room temperature is sufficiently far above the absolute zero for all the electrons to have been excited?

YS: No. As we have just seen, the electron gas near the absolute zero has properties quite different from those of a classical gas. At these low temperatures the electron gas is said to be degraded or degenerate—the German word for the phenomenon is *Entartung*. As the temperature is raised the degeneracy is gradually removed, but a more detailed examination shows that owing to the small mass of the electrons, a gas of electrons at the densities found in metals remains almost completely degenerate for many hundred degrees above the absolute zero. The condition for almost complete degeneracy is that

$$\frac{Nh^3}{2V} (2\pi mk\theta)^{-\frac{3}{2}} \gg 1$$

where N is the number of electrons in volume V, m is the mass of an electron, k is Boltzmann's Constant,* and θ is the absolute temperature, and it is owing to the small value of the electronic mass that the electron gas is almost completely degenerate at room temperatures.

At a sufficiently high temperature and low density the electrons will behave like a classical gas. The conditions for this, that is the condition for the almost complete removal of degeneracy, is that

$$\frac{Nh^3}{2V} (2\pi mk\theta)^{-\frac{3}{2}} \ll 1.$$

At the electron densities found in metals the electrons would only behave like a classical gas at temperatures of several thousand degrees Centigrade. You will see from the above expression that the degeneracy will be removed more quickly if the electron density (the number of electrons per unit volume) is small, and in some problems of electronic emission we do in fact have a condition of affairs in which the electrons inside the metal behave like an almost completely degenerate electron gas in equilibrium with a gas of electrons outside the metal, this gas being so dilute that it may be treated as a classical gas.

OM: All this is very strange, and it would seem that if the electron gas in a metal—using your simplified model with which I don't agree—is almost completely degraded at room temperatures, then all the energy relations must be different from those of a classical gas.

YS: That's perfectly correct. In Fig. 47 the full curve shows the energy of the electron gas as a function of the temperature, whilst the dotted line shows the corresponding energy according to the classical laws where the energy was directly proportional to the temperature. You will see that at room temperature where the electron gas is degraded, the curve is almost horizontal.

OM: Surely that must be wrong—it would mean that the electron gas had no specific heat, because the specific heat is proportional to $\frac{dE}{d\theta}$ and is thus zero for a horizontal curve.

YS: That's just the point. To a first approximation the specific heat of an electron gas in a metal according to the new theories is almost zero. This is one of the great triumphs of the new electron theories. All the older theories based on a classical gas of electrons required the electrons to have the specific heat of a normal gas, and this was in contradiction to the facts which indicated that the specific

* The equation of a perfect gas is usually written $pv = R\theta$, where the gas constant R refers to one gram-molecule. The corresponding equation for a single molecule is $pv = k\theta$, where k is Boltzmann's Constant.

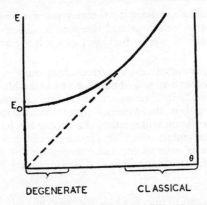

[*From " The Metallic State," Hume-Rothery. Clarendon Press*

Fig. 47—To illustrate the relation between the energy and temperature of an assembly of electrons according to the free electron theory based on the Fermi-Dirac statistics. The dotted line shows the relation according to the classical theory

heats of metals could be accounted for by considering the atomic vibrations alone. The new theories have overcome this difficulty completely, and we are now able to understand how the existence of a gas of electrons can be reconciled with an almost zero specific heat.

OM: If the curve in Fig. 47 is smooth and continuous there must surely be a very small specific heat, as the curve will be exactly horizontal only at the absolute zero.

YS: That's quite right. It can be shown that to a higher degree of accuracy the specific heat of an electron gas at low temperatures, where it is almost completely degenerate is given by

$$C_v = \frac{\pi^2 k^2}{2E_{max}} \, N \, \theta.$$

This term is proportional to the absolute temperature, θ, and at room temperatures it is negligible compared with the specific heat resulting from the thermal oscillation of the atoms. You will know however that the specific heat becomes smaller at low temperatures, and finally vanishes at the absolute zero. At very low temperatures the electronic specific heat becomes relatively larger compared with the specific heat of the lattice, and in some metals it has been found possible to express the specific heat near to the absolute zero as the sum of two terms, the first of which is the normal specific heat of the atomic vibrations of the lattice, and the second is identified as the electronic specific heat.

OM: Does this apply to the supra-conducting region?

YS: No. Supra-conductivity lies outside these theories. You should also note that many of the transition metals have abnormally high specific heats for reasons which we will discuss later.

OM: That brings me back to the old point. You have talked a lot about the energy relations and the specific heats of electrons in a box, but how much of it is to be taken as applying seriously to a real metal?

YS: The general conclusion is correct, and the electrons in normal metals have very small specific heats for reasons which are essentially those I have described. The exact details are modified in the more complete theories, but the general conclusion of the free electron theory is sound, and you will see that the theory has led us a long way. It has led us to a model in which the electronic energies are spread over a range which is of reasonable magnitude, and it has shown how the smallness of the electronic heat can be accounted for.

Suggestions for further reading.

The reader who wishes to study the Free Electron Theory in greater detail may consult the following books:

The Theory of the Properties of Metals and Alloys, N. F. Mott and H. Jones. 1936, Oxford. This book is advanced, but the reader should succeed in following the ideas as distinct from the mathematics.

Introduction to Chemical Physics, J. C. Slater. 1939, McGraw Hill. This book is a text-book, and is not intended for easy reading. It covers a wide range and is strongly to be recommended. The free electron theory is dealt with in Chapter 29.

22—Electrons in a Periodic Field: Brillouin Zones

OLDER METALLURGIST: I hope we can now get on to the problem of how electrons actually behave in the crystal of a metal.

YOUNG SCIENTIST: That is the next stage in the theory, and it will make it clearer if, for a minute, we return to the simple free electron theory. You will remember that we there described the condition of the electrons by means of a momentum diagram (see page 144). Now in the case of free electrons we know that the momentum p, the velocity u, the mass m, and the wave length λ associated with the electron are connected by the relations

$$p = mu = \frac{h}{\lambda}$$

where h is Planck's Constant. You will see therefore that since the momentum is proportional to $\frac{1}{\lambda}$, that is proportional to the *wave number*, we could equally well have described things in terms of a wave-number diagram instead of a momentum diagram. Actually the mathematician finds it more convenient to describe things in terms, not of the wave number $\frac{1}{\lambda}$, but in terms of $\frac{2\pi}{\lambda}$, and this quantity $\frac{2\pi}{\lambda}$ is called the *wave number k*. We can therefore draw a diagram such as that in Fig. 48 in which the three axes k_x, k_y, k_z, represent the components of the wave number k in the directions of the x, y, and z axes. The state of the electron will be represented by a small cell

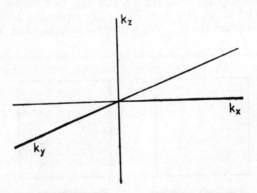

Fig. 48—To illustrate three-dimensional *k*-space

The three axes k_x, k_y and k_z represent the components of the wave number k in the x, y, and z directions

in this k-space diagram, just as an electron state was described by a small cell in the momentum diagram of Fig. 42.

OM: But won't it be easier if we stick to a simple momentum diagram? If the wave number k is simply proportional to the momentum mu, it seems an unnecessary complication to make the change.

YS: What you say is quite right for the *free electron* theory. In this theory the wave number k is directly proportional to the momentum mu, where u is the velocity of the electron. When we deal with electrons in the periodic field of a crystal, the wave number k is still defined by $k = \dfrac{2\pi}{\lambda}$, where λ is the wave length associated with the electron, but k is no longer necessarily proportional to mu. This is where the theory becomes more complicated, and you will find it most easy to understand things if you regard an electron state as being defined by the wave number k.

OM: I'm afraid I find this is all rather puzzling, and I think it would be more easy for me if you could compare what goes on in the theory of the crystal with what occurs in the free electron theory.

YS: We can do it in that way if you like, and perhaps you won't mind if, for simplicity in drawing, we describe some of the developments for a hypothetical two-dimensional metal. This will avoid difficulties in perspective, and it will usually be quite easy to see how the same principles apply to an actual three-dimensional crystal.

OM: You mean that just as in your description of the free electron theory you considered electrons as being fitted into a cube of side L, we are now to regard electrons as being fitted into a square of side L?

YS: That's right. Let us suppose that Fig. 49(a) shows a simple empty square into which we are going to introduce electrons together with sufficient positive electricity to keep the whole electrically neutral. This will correspond with the cubical box of Chapter 20. At the same time let us suppose that Fig. 49(b) represents a *two-dimensional crystal* of a square shape. We will then imagine that we introduce

Fig. 49(a)—Shows the two-dimensional empty box model of the free electron theory

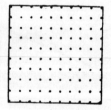

Fig. 49(b)—Shows the corresponding model for a two-dimensional square lattice of atoms

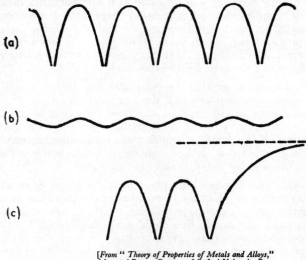

[From " Theory of Properties of Metals and Alloys,"
Mott and Jones. Courtesy of Oxford University Press

Fig. 50
(a)—Shows the variation of potential along a line passing
through the centres of the atoms in a crystal
(b)—Shows the variation of potential for a line parallel to
the first, but not passing through the atoms
(c)—Shows the variation of potential at the surface of the
metal

increasing numbers of electrons into this two-dimensional crystal, and
see how their behaviour differs from that of the two-dimensional box
of free electrons.

OM: It seems to me that you will have to make some assumption
about the electropositive charge present in the crystal. Otherwise
the introduction of increasing numbers of electrons will build up a
negative charge.

YS: That's perfectly right. In the free electron theory we imagined
that as the electrons were introduced into the empty box, a corresponding amount of positive electricity was added, so that the whole remained electrically neutral. In the present theory where we imagine
electrons to be added to the crystal, we are to imagine that the atoms,
or more properly the ions, acquire a gradually increasing electropositive charge, so that the whole is electrically neutral.

For the moment we will merely assume that the crystal has some
definite structure, and not consider its details. The electrons will
then find themselves in a *periodic field*, which is characteristic of the
structure concerned. If for example we considered a line passing
through the centres of the atoms, the potential would vary as shown
in Fig. 50(*a*) with a singularity at each atomic nucleus. The potential

energy of an electron would diminish as it approached a nucleus, just as was the case in the hydrogen atom (page 23). If we considered a line parallel to this but not passing through the nuclei, the potential might vary as shown in Fig. 50(b), whilst Fig. 50(c) shows the variation of potential at the surface. We have now to consider how electrons will behave in a periodic field of this kind.

OM: It seems to me that if we consider Fig. 50(a) we shall at once have a distinction between two kinds of electron. If an electron has sufficient energy to enable it to surmount the peaks in the potential curve, it will be free to move through the crystal. On the other hand, if its energy is too small to enable it to surmount the peaks, it will be stuck in a potential hollow—so there will be a clear distinction between free and bound electrons. Is that right?

YS: No. That is one of the phenomena in which wave mechanics leads to conclusions different from those of the older theories. From the point of view of classical mechanics, what you have said above was perfectly right, and an electron could move through the crystal only if its energy were sufficiently great to carry it over the peaks in the potential curve. But in wave mechanics, if the width of the peak is only of the order of a few wave lengths, an electron of low energy has a certain probability of penetrating the potential hill. This probability falls off rapidly as the width of the potential hill increases, so that for large-scale problems there is little difference between the conclusions of the old and of the new theories. But in the periodic field of a crystal the width of the potential hill is of the order 3A, and this is of the same order as wave lengths of the electrons. Under these conditions wave mechanics indicates that an electron of low energy has a certain probability of penetrating the potential hill, even though its energy would not be sufficient to enable it to surmount the hill on the basis of classical mechanics. The effect is sometimes called the "tunnel effect," because if the potential hill is very narrow, the electron has a chance of, as it were, burrowing or tunnelling through. You will see, therefore, that in the wave mechanics for a periodic field there is no sharp distinction between two classes of electrons as you had imagined. All the electrons have a probability of moving freely through the lattice.

OM: It seems to me that simplifies things enormously. If all the electrons are free to move, we can simply draw a momentum diagram, or a wave-number diagram, analogous to that of Fig. 42, and at the absolute zero, if we gradually introduce electrons, we shall simply fill up the lowest states of the system.

YS: I am afraid it isn't as simple as that. Suppose you try to develop the argument and see what happens.

OM: All right, then. Let Fig. 49(a) be a two-dimensional empty box, and let Fig. 49(b) be the corresponding two-dimensional crystal. Then let Fig. 51(a) be a two-dimensional wave-number diagram for the empty box model; this will be divided up into little cells representing

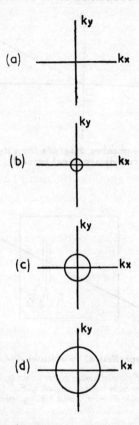

Fig. 51—To illustrate the filling up of electron states in the two-dimensional free electron model at the absolute zero

With increasing numbers of electrons the occupied electron states lie within circles of increasing diameter; in a three-dimensional model the circles would be replaced by spheres

the energy states as in the free electron theory (page 143). Let Fig. 52 be the corresponding wave-number diagram for the two-dimensional crystal.

YS: That will be quite all right. In practice one chooses the axes of the wave-number diagram so that they represent wave motion parallel to the two axes of the two-dimensional crystal. Now suppose you introduce continually increasing numbers of electrons into the empty box model, and consider what will happen at the absolute zero.

OM: At the absolute zero the assembly of N electrons will occupy the $\frac{N}{2}$ lowest energy states, and so the occupied states will form circles round the origin of the two-dimensional momentum diagram—for a

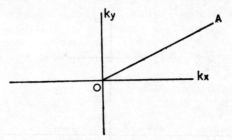

**Fig. 52—Wave-number diagram for a hypothetical
two-dimensional crystal**

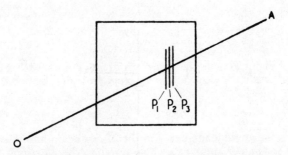

Fig. 53—Hypothetical two-dimensional crystal

*p_1, p_2, p_3, represent a series of parallel atomic planes in the crystal. The line OA in Fig. 53
is parallel to the line OA in the wave number diagram of Fig. 52. It is to be emphasised that
Fig. 52 is a wave-number diagram, whilst Fig. 53 represents the actual crystal*

three-dimensional box there would be a three-dimensional momentum
diagram, and the occupied states would form a sphere as you described
before (page 146). So if one introduces continually increasing numbers
of electrons the occupied states will lie within circles of continually
increasing diameter as I have drawn in Fig. 51(b), (c), (d).

YS: For the free electron or empty box model that is quite right.
Now what do you propose for the model of the two-dimensional crystal
(Fig. 52)?

OM: You have said that all the electrons are free to move in the
lattice, and so the procedure will surely be exactly the same? On
introducing increasing numbers of electrons into the two-dimensional
crystal they will enter the lowest energy states, two electrons per state,
and the occupied states will lie within circles of continually increasing
diameter as in Fig. 51 (b), (c), (d).

YS: That would be correct if it were not for the wave-like properties
of the electron. Suppose Fig. 52 represents your wave-number diagram,

and that we draw a straight line OA from the origin O. Then all points on OA will represent wave numbers in this one direction which corresponds to a definite direction in the crystal—we may represent this direction *in the crystal* by the line OA in Fig. 53, which represents the actual crystal.

OM: That's all right. Then as we introduce electrons into the crystal they will fill up the lowest states round the origin of Fig. 52, and the circle which bounds the occupied states will cut OA at gradually increasing distances from the origin. As we introduce more and more electrons, the region of occupied states will become larger and larger, and the wave numbers k of the highest occupied states will become greater and greater, and the corresponding wave-lengths will become smaller and smaller.

YS: That's right. Now let us return to the direction OA in the actual crystal (Fig. 53), and let us suppose that $p_1p_2p_3$ . . . are a set of atomic planes in the crystal. Then in the general case an electron whose state is described by a wave number on OA in the wave-number diagram (Fig. 52) will pass through these planes with only slight scattering. But if the electronic wave length satisfies the Bragg equation

$$n\lambda = 2d \sin \theta$$

where θ is the angle made between the X-ray beam and the reflecting planes of spacing d, and n is a whole number, then a strong reflection takes place, and the electron cannot travel through the lattice. You can readily see this by considering a beam of electrons shot at a crystal from outside as in Fig. 54. In the general case electrons will penetrate or pass through the crystal, but if the wave length λ and

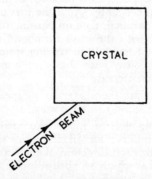

Fig. 54—A beam of electrons of uniform velocity is imagined as striking the crystal. In the general case it will be transmitted with only slight scattering, but if the angle of incidence and the electronic wave length satisfy the Bragg equation strong reflection occurs and the beam does not penetrate the crystal

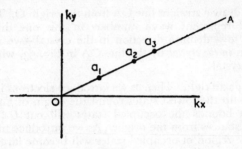

Fig. 55

the angle θ between the incident beam and the plane of atoms are adjusted so as to satisfy the Bragg equation

$$n\lambda = 2d \sin \theta$$

strong reflection takes place, and the electron does not penetrate far into the crystal—it is this fact which is used when one studies crystal structure by electron diffraction methods.

OM: This is all very confusing. Does it amount to saying that for certain wave lengths the crystal structure complicates the behaviour of electrons in a solid?

YS: That's right. If we consider the direction OA in the wave-number diagram (Fig. 52), then in the free-electron model we can add electrons with continually increasing wave numbers and continually increasing energies. On the other hand, with a crystal, for each direction OA there will be a series of critical points in the wave-number diagram at which the wave length satisfies the condition for a Bragg reflection of the electrons by one of the sets of planes in the lattice, and it can be shown that at each of these critical points there is an abrupt increase in the energy on passing to the next highest wave number. If for example a_1 (Fig. 55) is the first point on OA at which the Bragg condition is satisfied, then on passing from O to a_1 the energy increases continuously with the wave number,* but at a_1 there is an abrupt increase in the energy. On passing from a_1 to a_2 the energy again increases continuously with the wave number, and then at a_2 there is a second sudden increase.

OM: That means that there are, so to speak, forbidden ranges of energy which the electron cannot possess.

YS: Yes. In the free electron model the energy increases continuously with the wave number for all directions of the latter. In the periodic field model for each direction of the wave number, there are critical wave numbers at which an abrupt increase in the energy takes place.

OM: I see. Then if in Fig. 55 a_1 represents a wave number which

* As explained previously (page 144) the successive energy states are so close together that we may regard them as forming a continuum.

satisfies the Bragg relation for a reflection from a particular set of planes, it would seem that for different directions of OA the points a_1 must lie at different distances from the origin because if you vary θ in the Bragg equation you will have to vary λ, and hence k.

YS: That's right. Let us suppose that in Fig. 56 OA_1, OA_2, OA_3 ... represent different directions in the wave number diagram, and that on OA_1 a_{11} is the first critical point at which the wave number satisfies the condition for a Bragg reflection of the electron. In this case with a particular crystal structure a_{12}, a_{13}, a_{14} ... might be the corresponding points along OA_2, OA_3, OA_4 ... at which the wave numbers again satisfied the conditions for a Bragg reflection from the same set of atomic planes.

OM: Yes. That's what I meant—the distances Oa_{11}, Oa_{12}, Oa_{13} will be different in different directions because if you vary θ in the Bragg equation you will have to vary λ, and hence the wave number $\frac{2\pi}{\lambda}$, in order to satisfy the condition for a Bragg reflection. But must the points a_{11}, a_{12}, a_{13} ... lie on straight lines?

YS: Yes. That turns out to be one of the direct consequences of the theory. In the two-dimensional wave-number diagram the critical wave numbers at which the conditions for a Bragg reflection are satisfied lie on straight lines which form the boundaries of a polygon. For

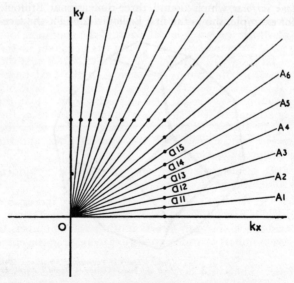

Fig. 56—To illustrate the building up of a two-dimensional Brillouin zone

electron states inside this polygon the energy varies continuously with the wave number, but on passing through the boundary of the polygon there is an abrupt increase in the energy. A polygon of this kind is called a two-dimensional *Brillouin zone.*

OM: If the wave numbers on the edges of the polygon are those which satisfy the conditions for a Bragg reflection in the lattice, it would seem that the shape of the polygon must depend on the crystal structure.

YS: That's right. Each type of crystal structure gives Brillouin zones of characteristic shape.

OM: Do you mean that the zone of Fig. 56 will be surrounded by other zones?

YS: Yes. In Fig. 55 the points a_1, a_2 . . . mark the critical wave lengths for reflection from different sets of planes in the crystal, and these will lie on the edges of different polygons in k-space.

When we deal with a proper three-dimensional crystal, the general principle is exactly the same. For a three-dimensional crystal we construct a three-dimensional wave-number diagram such as that of Fig. 48, where k_x, k_y, k_z represent the components of the wave numbers in the directions x, y, z in the crystal—in general the axes will be chosen so as to be parallel to the crystal axes. Then, for each direction in the three-dimensional k-space, on starting from the origin the energy will increase continuously with the wave number until the critical point is reached at which the wave length satisfies the condition for a Bragg reflection. These critical points for the different directions then lie on *plane surfaces* which bound three-dimensional Brillouin zones. Fig. 57, for example, shows the first Brillouin zone for the face-centred

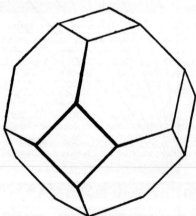

[From " *Theory of Properties of Metals and Alloys* "
Mott and Jones. Courtesy of Oxford University Press

Fig. 57—The first Brillouin zone of the face-centred cubic structure

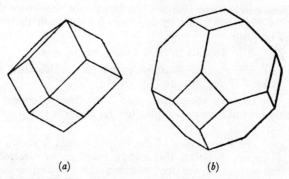

(a)   (b)

[From " Modern Theory of Solids," Seitz. Courtesy of McGraw-Hill Company Inc.

Fig. 58—To illustrate the first and second zones of the body-centred cubic structure

cubic structure. The meaning of this diagram is that for electron states with wave numbers lying within this zone the energy increases continuously with the wave number, but at the surface of the zone there is an abrupt increase in the energy. It must be emphasised that this diagram is a diagram in k-space. It is not a picture of the crystal in real space, but is a diagram in k-space showing the region within which the energy varies continuously with the wave number.

OM: The zone appears to have two kinds of surface planes, and I suppose they correspond with the satisfying of the Bragg equation for reflection of electrons from different types of atomic plane in the lattice.

YS: That's right. The octahedral faces of the zone indicate the wave numbers which satisfy the condition for reflection for the (111) octahedral planes of the crystal, and the second set of faces refer to the (200) reflections. You may remember that in the X-ray or electron diffraction patterns of the face-centred cubic lattice the first two reflections are the (111) and (200) reflections. It is in this way that the X-ray diffraction patterns may be used to deduce the forms of the Brillouin zones.

OM: On X-ray diffraction films the lines for the face-centred cubic structure go in the order (111), (200), (220), (311) . . . —the indices are either all odd or all even. Does this mean that there are other zones outside the one shown in Fig. 57?

YS: That's right. In Fig. 57 we have seen how the first Brillouin zone for the face-centred cubic structure is bounded by octahedral and cube faces, in agreement with the fact that the first two strong diffraction lines are the (111) and (200) reflections. For the body-centred cube, the first Brillouin zone is as shown in Fig. 58(a); this is a rhombic dodecahedron, in agreement with the fact that the first diffraction line from a body-centred cube is the (110) reflection. The second Brillouin zone for the body-centred cubic structure then takes the form of Fig. 58(b), and its faces are farther from the origin than those of Fig. 58(a).

OM: Fig. 58(b) appears to be the same as Fig. 57.

YS: The two shapes are the same, although not the sizes. Fig. 58(b) is a second zone fitting outside Fig. 58(a).

OM: This is very interesting, and I suppose it means that the energy relations are more complicated for electrons in a lattice than for the electrons of the free electron theory.

YS: Yes. The importance of the subject is that it shows there is a distinct difference between the energy relations of electrons in the hypothetical model of the free electron theory, and in the actual periodic field of a crystal. In the free electron theory the whole process was continuous. You could introduce more and more electrons into the empty box with continually increasing energies, and the whole process was smooth and regular. In the actual crystal where there is a periodic field, as you add increasing numbers of electrons they fill up the energy states in wave number space—two electrons per state—but the sudden increase in energy which occurs on crossing the zone boundaries means that the process is no longer smooth and regular as regards the energy.

OM: Am I right in thinking that the zone theories still mean that the energies of the electrons are spread over a range at the absolute zero?

YS: Oh, certainly yes! Pauli's Principle still applies and only two electrons can enter a given state. In the zone theories an assembly of N electrons at the absolute zero still occupies the $\dfrac{N}{2}$ lowest energy states, and so the energies extend over a range. But the energy discontinuities at the zone boundaries mean that the process is more complicated than in the free electron theory; for example, the $N(E)$ curve no longer has the simple form of Fig. 44. As we shall see later, it is these very points which are responsible for the differences between insulators and metals.

Suggestions for further reading.

For further information on Brillouin Zone Theories, the reader may consult the following books:

Elementary.

  An Introduction to the Electron Theory of Metals, G. V. Raynor, Institute of Metals.

  Atomic Theory for Students of Metallurgy, W. Hume-Rothery, Institute of Metals.

  Useful information is also given in *An Introduction to Chemical Physics,* J. C. Slater. 1939, McGraw Hill.

More Advanced.

  The Theory of the Properties of Metals and Alloys, N. F. Mott and H. Jones. 1936, Oxford.

23—Brillouin Zones and Electron Distribution Curves

OLDER METALLURGIST: From what you have said it would seem that for electrons in a periodic field the $\mathcal{N}(E)$ curve will no longer be a simple parabola as it was in the free electron theory.

YOUNG SCIENTIST: That's quite right, and we must now see what types of $\mathcal{N}(E)$ curve are actually formed. For simplicity we will again deal with a hypothetical two-dimensional crystal, and we will suppose that the crystal structure gives rise to a first Brillouin zone which is a square, as in Fig. 59(a). We may now imagine that we introduce increasing numbers of electrons into the crystal, and so gradually fill up the lowest energy states—as I explained before we imagine the positive charge on the ions to increase gradually so that the crystal as a whole is electrically neutral.

OM: I suppose all this will be at the absolute zero, where an assembly of $\mathcal{N}$ electrons occupies the $\dfrac{N}{2}$ lowest energy levels.

YS: That's right. All this theory is developed first for the absolute zero. We then find that for the first few electrons which are introduced, the behaviour is very like that of the free electron theory, and the occupied states lie inside a circle, as shown in Fig. 59(b). The corresponding portion of the $\mathcal{N}(E)$ curve is then a parabola of the form $\mathcal{N}(E) \propto E^{1/2}$, and resembles that of the free electron theory. The shaded region in Fig. 60(a) extends over this part of the $\mathcal{N}(E)$ curve.

OM: Then as more and more electrons are introduced, are the boundaries of the occupied states still circular?

YS: No. As the limit of the occupied states approaches the boundaries of the Brillouin zone, the line bounding the occupied states—one may call it an *energy contour* because it joins states of equal energy—becomes distorted from a circle. The corresponding portion of the $\mathcal{N}(E)$ curve then rises above that of the free electron theory, as shown in Fig. 60(b). In a proper three-dimensional crystal the general process is the same. The two-dimensional circle is replaced by a sphere, and this becomes gradually distorted as the occupied states approach the zone boundary, and again the $\mathcal{N}(E)$ curve rises above that of the free electron theory.

OM: Now, what happens when the surface of occupied states touches the zone boundary?

YS: See if you can't think that out for yourself.

OM: Well, it would seem that if there is an abrupt increase in energy on crossing the zone boundary, then when the occupied states reach the surface of the zone, the next electrons added will go on

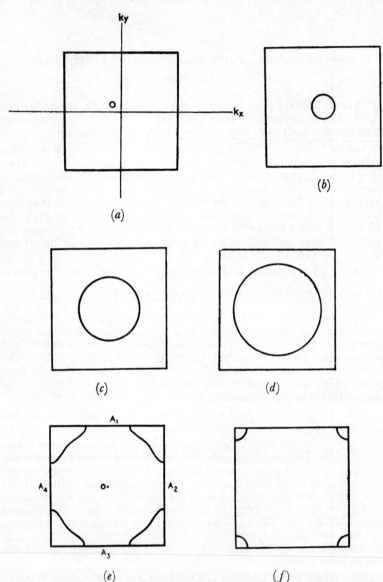

Fig. 59—To illustrate the filling up of electron states for a hypothetical two-dimensional crystal of which the first Brillouin zone is a square

For the first few electrons the Fermi surface is a circle whose radius increases with the number of electrons. When the occupied electron states approach the boundaries of the zone the circles are distorted and curve round so that they are eventually perpendicular to the zone boundary.

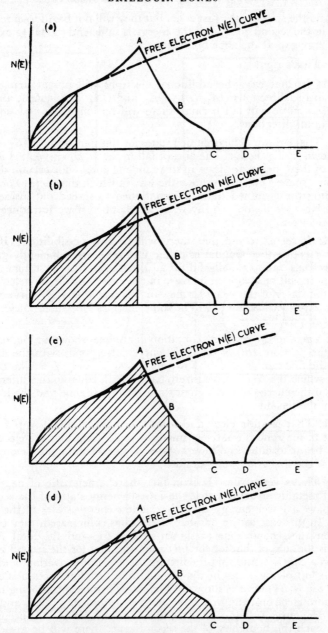

Fig. 60—To illustrate the N(E) curve for the Brillouin zone of Fig. 59. The case shown is one where the first and second zones do not overlap

filling up the states in the first zone, but they will not begin to enter the states in the second zone until the energy is sufficiently great to exceed the energy gap at the zone boundary.

YS: That's right.

OM: In that case the additional electrons will not at first enter states in the directions OA_1, OA_2, OA_3, and OA_4 (Fig. 59(e)), and so the $\mathcal{N}(E)$ curve will fall because there will no longer be new energy states in all directions.

YS: That's right. The occupied states for this part of the $\mathcal{N}(E)$ curve are shown in Fig. 60(c). The abrupt fall in the $\mathcal{N}(E)$ curve at A is the result of there being no states in this range of energy for certain directions in k space. Fig. 59(e) shows the way in which the energy contour bounding the occupied states has continued to spread out inside the zone. Now see if you can say what will happen if we introduce still more electrons.

OM: It seems to me that there will be two possibilities. If the energy steps at the boundaries of the first zone are sufficiently great, the electrons will gradually fill up all the states of the first zone, and then there will be a sudden increase in the energy before any electrons enter the states of the second zone—in this case the $\mathcal{N}(E)$ curve must sink to zero, because there will be some energies for which no electron states are possible.

YS: Yes, and the resulting condition of affairs is shown in Fig. 60(d). Here the portion ABC of the $\mathcal{N}(E)$ curve corresponds with the filling up of the first zone states as shown in Fig. 59(e) and (f). The break CD on which the $\mathcal{N}(E)$ curve is zero has a length equal to the difference between the energy of the highest state of the first zone and the lowest state of the second zone.

OM: That is quite clear and simple, but if the energy gap at the surface of the zone is relatively small, it would seem that the electrons might begin to enter the lowest states of the second zone before the states of the first zone were all filled.

YS: That's very true. It is in fact the characteristic of nearly if not all metallic structures that the lowest energy states of the second zone have a lower energy than the highest energy states of the first zone. In this case as the number of electrons is increased, they begin to enter the second zone as shown in Fig. 61, and the total $\mathcal{N}(E)$ curve is the sum of that for the first zone and that for the second zone. In such a case it is said that the first and second zones overlap, and the opening up of the states in the second zone then produces a sudden rise in the $\mathcal{N}(E)$ curve as shown in Fig. 62. Then on introducing more and more electrons, the first zone becomes completely filled, and the total $\mathcal{N}(E)$ curve is that of the second zone alone. When the occupied states reach the boundary of the second zone, there will be a sudden fall in the $\mathcal{N}(E)$ curve for the same reason as that for the fall at A in Fig. 60. If the second and third zones overlap there will be a sudden

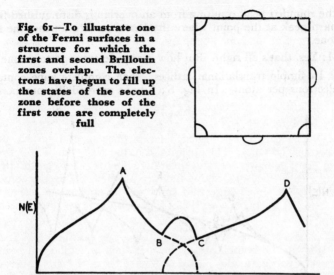

Fig. 61—To illustrate one of the Fermi surfaces in a structure for which the first and second Brillouin zones overlap. The electrons have begun to fill up the states of the second zone before those of the first zone are completely full

Fig. 62—To illustrate the N(E) curve for overlapping zones. The point B represents the stage at which the electrons begin to enter the second zone. At this stage the first zone is not completely full, and the total N(E) is obtained by the summation of the curves for the separate zones. The point C represents the stage at which the first zone is completely filled, and additional electrons then fill up the states of the second zone which may overlap the third zone and so on

rise in the $\mathcal{N}(E)$ curve when the electrons begin to enter the states of the third zone. In this way the theory predicts $\mathcal{N}(E)$ curves with a whole series of peaks and valleys, and each type of crystal structure gives rise to a characteristic $\mathcal{N}(E)$ curve for a given energy gap at the surface of the zone. Fig. 63, for example, shows some early $\mathcal{N}(E)$ curves calculated by Mott and Jones for the face-centred cubic and body-centred cubic structures, on the assumption of an energy gap deduced from a study of the optical properties of copper. Later work has shown that the finer details of these curves are quite incorrect, but the peaks and valleys on the curves are a clear confirmation of the results of X-ray spectroscopy. When the number of electrons is small . . .

OM: Wait a minute. In your description you have continually spoken of introducing increasing numbers of electrons into the crystal, but you have not given me any indication of the magnitudes involved.

YS: You understand how in Fig. 63 the kinks in the $\mathcal{N}(E)$ curve occur at the stages at which the electron states in a new zone are being opened up (for example, point B in Fig. 62), or at which a zone is completely filled (for example, point C in Fig. 62). You will notice how the rounded peak resulting from an overlap is distinguished from the sharp peak at the point where the Fermi surface touches the face of a zone.

OM: Yes, that's all right. But how many electrons go to a zone?

YS: In simple translational lattices, each complete zone contains two electrons per atom. In Fig. 63 I have marked the numbers of

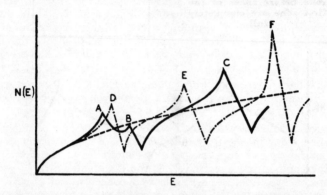

Fig. 63—N(E) curves for the face-centred cubic structure (full line) and the body-centred cubic structure (dotted line) after Mott and Jones. The points A, B, and C correspond with 1.36, 2.10, and 5.9 electrons per atom respectively, and the points D, E, and F correspond with 1.48, 4.21 and 7.7 electrons per atom respectively. These curves are of historical interest as representing one of the earlier theories of copper and silver alloys. They depend on simplifying assumptions, and later work has shown that some of these are incorrect, with the result that the details of the curves are of little value. The curves do, however, show clearly that different crystal structures give rise to N(E) curves whose peaks and valleys are at quite different electron concentrations

electrons per atom corresponding to different points on the curves, assuming the electron states to be fully occupied up to the points concerned. The number of valency electrons per atom is often called the *electron concentration*. In an alkali metal as in copper for example, the electron concentration is 1.0, and in zinc it is 2.0. In an equiatomic alloy of copper and zinc the electron concentration is 1.5.

OM: The various peaks and valleys in Fig. 63 seem to occur at quite different electron concentrations.

YS: Yes. That's the whole point. With a given energy gap at the surface of the Brillouin zone, each crystal structure gives rise to a characteristic $N(E)$ curve, and in this way we can begin to see how for a given number of electrons per atom, the electronic energy may be less for one structure than for another, and we can begin to see which structures should be the most stable so far as the electrons are concerned.

OM: Do you mean that the same principle (page 137) of high $N(E)$ curve, lower energy still applies?

YS: Yes. If you compare the curves for the body-centred and face-centred cubic structures in Fig. 63, you will see that for the face-centred cube, the first peak occurs at 1.36 electrons per atom, whilst for the body-centred cube the first peak is at 1.48 electrons per atom. So as the electron concentration is increased from 1.36 to 1.48 the $N(E)$ curve for the face-centred cube is falling rapidly, whilst that for the body-centred cube is continuing to rise. In this way we can predict that so far as the electron concentration is concerned, the body-centred cubic phase will become more stable as the electron concentration is increased from 1.36 to 1.48.

OM: That's interesting, but it doesn't seem to be of much use because the electron concentration of a metal must be a whole number, 1, 2, 3, 4 . . . according to the valency.

YS: What you say is quite right so far as the pure elements are concerned. But in alloys, the electron concentration need not be a whole number. In a copper-zinc alloy containing 50 atomic per cent zinc, the composition will be CuZn, and there will be three valency electrons to two atoms, and an electron concentration of 1.5. The above $N(E)$ curves then indicate that so far as electron concentration is concerned, the body-centred cubic structure will be more stable than the face-centred cubic structure for the equiatomic copper-zinc alloy.

OM: Oh, I see! I suppose that might be the reason why β brass has a body-centred cubic structure.

YS: I had meant to keep the present discussion to the pure elements. But we may anticipate a little of Part III, and say that the above $N(E)$ curves were the first beginnings of a theory of β brass. As we shall see later (p. 302a), many difficulties have been encountered, and the theory is still uncertain, but it is reasonable to claim that the above $N(E)$ curves did seem to explain why β brass has a body-centred and not a face-centred cubic structure.

You will see therefore that the simple theory of the periodic field has taken us a long way. It has given us an $N(E)$ curve which for small electron concentrations has the same general form as that of the free electron theory, and this is in agreement with the soft X-ray spectroscopic work on the alkali metals. It has shown that for higher electron concentrations the $N(E)$ curves will have a number of peaks and valleys in agreement with Skinner's work on elements of higher valency. Finally, the particular curves of Fig. 63 did seem to lead to an understanding of the theory of β brass. But I must emphasise that later work shows the details of Fig. 63 to be incorrect, and the diagram should now be regarded only as showing the kind of curve indicated by the theory.

24—The Crystal Structures of the Elements: Van Der Waals' Forces and Co-valent Bonds

OLDER METALLURGIST: What you said last time about the zone theories was very interesting, but I find great difficulty in visualising what is going on, and in understanding how the electrons behave when they bind the atoms of a solid together. I can see how the $N(E)$ curves and energy relations are important in determining the relative stabilities of different crystal structures, but I don't follow why there are such great differences between different elements. For example, why does helium liquefy only a few degrees above the absolute zero, whilst tungsten and carbon (diamond) persist as solids for several thousand degrees? Your picture of electron clouds, and your description of $N(E)$ curves would not lead me to expect such great differences.

YOUNG SCIENTIST: In order to meet that difficulty we may consider the crystal structures of some of the more electro-negative elements, and we may begin by considering first what is to be expected when two atoms approach one another. We may suppose that we have two neutral atoms and that these are at a distance from one another which is large compared with the extent of their electron clouds. The atoms will then be independent free atoms, and the electronic energies, electron cloud patterns, etc., will be those of the free atoms which we discussed in Part I. Now let us suppose that two atoms approach one another to a distance which is of the same order as that of their electron clouds. Then the inner electrons of each atom will be over-whelmingly under the influence of one nucleus, and they will be little affected by the presence of the adjacent atom. In contrast to this the outer electrons of each atom will be affected by the presence of the adjacent atom, and this perturbation may alter the state of motion of the outer electrons.

OM: I can quite understand that, but why are there such differences between, say, helium on the one hand, and tungsten or the diamond on the other?

YS: The answer to that question is that with some atoms the perturbation may enable the electrons to take up a new kind of motion, the energy of which is lower than that which they would possess if the two atoms were isolated. If this can happen there is an attraction, and the two atoms hold together to form a molecule whose stability depends on the extent to which the energy has been lowered by the readjustment of the electronic motion. In the same way the assembly of atoms in a metallic vapour unite together to form a liquid or solid because their outer electrons can change their motion in such a way that the energy is lower than that of an assembly of independent free atoms.

OM: Then do you mean that the interatomic forces which produce compound molecules are of the same nature as those which hold the atoms together in the crystal of a metal?

YS: The forces between the atoms in molecules and in metal crystals are all part of the general problem of interatomic bonding or interatomic cohesion.

OM: But if that is so, why are there such enormous differences between the stabilities of the different structures?

YS: The differences in stability result from the fact that in the atoms of some elements the electrons already form very stable groupings, whose electronic motions are only slightly affected by the presence of neighbouring atoms.

OM: You mean that the inert gases all possess very low melting points and boiling points because their outer electrons form a completed octet—or a pair in the case of helium.

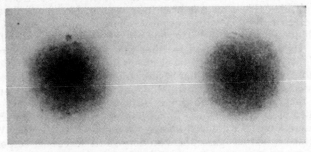

Atom No. 2   *Atom No. 1*

(a) *Atoms far apart*

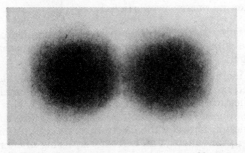

No. 2   *No. 1*

(b) *Atoms close together*

Fig. 64 (a) and (b)—Diagrammatic representation of electron clouds of two atoms of an inert gas

YS: That's right. The two electrons in the case of helium, and the octets in neon, argon, krypton, xenon, and emanation form very stable groupings, and the motion of their electrons can be only slightly perturbed. Consequently no great lowering of energy can result, and a comparatively slight degree of thermal agitation is sufficient to melt the solid, or to vaporise the liquid.

OM: Even though it is weak, there must be some kind of force to hold the atoms of the inert gases together in the solid or liquid state.

YS: Suppose that Fig. 64(a) shows the electron clouds of two atoms of an inert gas when they are relatively far apart from one another. Then, as I have explained in Part I, we cannot draw a definite trajectory of an electron inside these electron clouds, but the electrons are to be regarded as moving about inside the cloud. When the atoms are far apart they will be independent systems and have no effect on one another. Now suppose that two atoms approach as shown in Fig. 64(b), and let us suppose that at a particular instant the electronic motion in atom No. 1 results in its having an excess of electrons on the left-hand side. Then for this brief instant atom No. 1 will be a temporary electrical dipole with a negative charge on its left side. Clearly this will tend to repel the electrons on the right-hand side of atom No. 2. In this way you can see that the motion of the electrons in atom No. 1 will affect that of the electrons in atom No. 2, and it can be shown that a lower energy (that is, an attraction) results if the electrons in the two atoms move in sympathy or harmony with one another than if they move as independent systems. These attractive forces are known as Van der Waals' forces because they are responsible for the attractive term in the well-known gas equation of Van der Waals. In the case of the inert gases the Van der Waals' forces are responsible for the interatomic cohesion which holds the atoms together to form a liquid or a solid. These forces produce an attractive force proportional to $\frac{1}{r^7}$ where r is the distance between the two atoms, and hence an attractive potential energy proportional to $-\frac{1}{r^6}$.

OM: The fact that the melting points and boiling points of the inert gases rise with increasing atomic number suggests that the forces become stronger.

YS: With increasing atomic number the electron clouds of the inert gases become larger, and so, although the outer electrons still form octets, they are increasingly less firmly bound. This means that the electronic motion is more easily disturbed, and so the mutual sympathetic motion between the electrons of adjacent atoms becomes more and more pronounced, and a greater lowering of energy can take place. It is a general principle that Van der Waals' forces increase as the size of the electron cloud increases.

OM: Then have the Van der Waals' forces anything to do with cohesion in elements other than the inert gases?

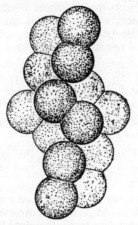

Fig. 65—The crystal structure of iodine

Showing the presence of pairs of atoms formed by diatomic I_2 molecules

YS: Oh, very much so. As a next step we may consider what happens in the crystals of the relatively electro-negative elements. We have already seen how the inert gases are characterised by the possession of outer groupings of eight electrons (or two in the case of helium). Now suppose we consider an element such as iodine which contains seven electrons in its outer shell. Then each atom of iodine requires one more electron to form an octet, and the result is that stable diatomic I_2 molecules are formed in which each atom shares one valency electron with its neighbour so that each atom acquires a share in a complete octet. This concept of shared electrons was first introduced by G. N. Lewis in 1916, and molecules in which the atoms are held together in this way are said to involve *co-valent* or *homopolar* bonds.

OM: But if iodine forms diatomic molecules like that, there would seem to be nothing left to bind the molecules to form a crystal—one would surely expect iodine to be a gas of very stable diatomic molecules, and of very low boiling point?

YS: What happens is that in crystalline iodine, the diatomic molecules persist as such, and they are held together by Van der Waals' forces. That is to say, the outermost electrons of the I_2 molecules affect each other and move in harmony with one another, and in this way a lowering of energy, and hence an attraction results. Fig. 65 shows the crystal structure of iodine, and you will see how the diatomic molecules are clearly present. In this structure you are to regard the two atoms in a molecule as held together by simple co-valent linkages, whilst the molecules are held together by Van der Waals' forces.

OM: At room temperatures iodine is a solid, bromine is a liquid, whilst chlorine and fluorine are gases. Is this because as the atomic number increases the electron clouds become larger and so are more easily deformed, with a resulting greater Van der Waals' force?

YS: Yes. You see exactly the same principle on a lesser scale in the inert gases, where the melting points and boiling points (and hence the stabilities of the solid and liquid) increase with increasing atomic number.

OM: Do all the halogens form diatomic molecules with crystal structures like that of iodine?

YS: Their crystal structures are not the same, but they all form stable diatomic molecules in which the two atoms are held together by simple co-valent bonds.

OM: From what you say above it would seem that an atom of an element of Group VIB would have to share electrons with two atoms if it is to build up an octet by simple co-valent bonds.

YS: That's right. What happens is extremely interesting, and you can understand it from Fig. 66, which shows the crystal structure of tellurium. Here you will see that the atoms of tellurium form long spiral chains in which each atom has two close neighbours. You will see, therefore, that your idea of each atom sharing with two others was correct, and there are long chains of atoms which extend right through the crystal. In this case you must look on each long chain as an immense molecule in which every atom has acquired an octet of electrons by sharing one of its electrons with each close neighbour in normal co-valent bonds. The chains themselves were first thought to be held together by Van der Waals' forces, but the interatomic distances were difficult to explain on this basis, and it is probable that Van der Waals' forces are supplemented by forces more like those which bind the atoms together in a metal. The important thing to recognise is that there are two distinct kinds of force present in the crystal. The crystal structure of selenium is similar, but in the case of sulphur the crystal structure contains rings of eight atoms as shown in Fig. 67. Here again, each atom shares with two neighbours, but the long chains are replaced by closed rings which correspond to S_8 molecules, and these molecules are held together by Van der Waals' forces. It is interesting to note that although metallic selenium has the chain structure of Fig. 66, there are other modifications of the element which contain atoms in eight-membered rings.

OM: It seems to me that the whole principle goes wrong when you get to oxygen. Oxygen forms diatomic molecules, and so there is no chance of an atom sharing with two neighbours.

YS: In the case of the diatomic oxygen molecule each atom shares *two* electrons with its neighbour, and in this way four electrons are held in common, and each atom acquires a share in an octet. The two atoms are said to be held together by *double bonds*.

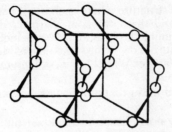

[*Courtesy The Institute of Metals*

Fig. 66—The crystal structure of tellurium

*Showing the spiral chains of atoms in which
each atom has two close neighbours*

[*From " Valency," Palmer. Courtesy of Cambridge University Press*

Fig. 67—The structure of S₈

OM: In the case of the diatomic nitrogen molecule N_2 the same principle would require each atom to share three of its electrons with the other.

YS: That's right. Each nitrogen atom contains five electrons, and so needs three more to complete an octet, and this is done by each atom contributing three electrons to form the so-called triple bond. In the N_2 molecule each atom has two unshared electrons, and gains a share in six others which form the triple bond, and in this way each atom acquires a share in an octet.

OM: Then are the N_2 molecules in liquid or solid nitrogen held together by Van der Waals' forces as was the case for the F_2 molecules of fluorine?

YS: Yes. In solid and liquid nitrogen, oxygen, and fluorine the diatomic N_2, O_2, and F_2 molecules exist as such and they are held together by Van der Waals' forces. The very low melting points of oxygen and nitrogen result from the electron clouds of the O_2 and N_2 molecules being relatively firmly bound, so that the electronic motion cannot be altered sufficiently to produce a marked lowering of energy.

OM: You have explained about the crystal structures of oxygen, sulphur, selenium, and tellurium. What happens with the elements of Group V? From what you have said above, they should either form crystal structures involving diatomic (triple bond) molecules, held together by Van der Waals' forces, or by metallic forces, or else structures in which each atom has three close neighbours and so builds up an octet by means of three single bonds.

YS: That's quite right. Fig. 68 shows the structure of antimony, and you will see that this satisfies the second of your suggestions.

It is a double layer structure where each atom has three close neighbours in its layer, and three others at a greater distance. Here you are to regard each double layer as an immense molecule held together by simple co-valent bonds, whilst the layers themselves are held together either by Van der Waals' forces, or by something like metallic bonds.

OM: Then do you mean that antimony is not to be looked on as an ordinary metal?

YS: Oh, certainly not! There are undoubtedly two different kinds of bonding process present in crystalline antimony, and one of these is almost pure co-valent bonding. Arsenic and bismuth form the same type of crystal structure, but in black phosphorous the structure is different, although each atom has again three close neighbours. You will see that the crystal structures of these elements in Groups V, VI, and VII are such that each atom has $(8-N)$ close neighbours, where N is the number of the group. This is sometimes called the $(8-N)$ rule.

OM: Oh, I see! They all fit into a general scheme with the tetrahedral structure of the diamond of which everyone knows.

YS: That's right. Fig. 69 shows the crystal structure of the diamond, and here each atom has four electrons, and shares one with each of four close neighbours, and the whole crystal is to be looked on as an immense molecule in which the atoms are held together by co-valent bonds. This structure is also formed by silicon, germanium and grey tin, and you will see that the stability of the structure diminishes with increasing atomic number. The melting points fall regularly from diamond, whose melting point is very high and is complicated by the transformation to graphite,* to silicon (1,420° C), and then to germanium (960° C) whilst grey tin is stable only at low temperatures. This is a general principle, and in any one group the stability of the

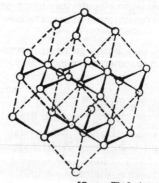

[*Courtesy The Institute of Metals*

Fig. 68—The crystal structure of antimony

Showing the double layers of atoms in which each atom has three close neighbours and three at a greater distance in the next layer

[1]The melting point is sometimes given as ca. 5,000°C, but it is possible that transformation to graphite prevents any real melting.

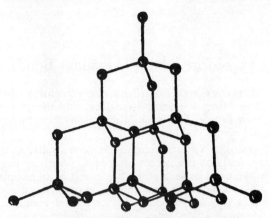

[*From "The Crystalline State," Vol. 1, by Sir Lawrence Bragg, by Courtesy George Bell & Sons Ltd.*]

Fig. 69—The crystal structure of the diamond

Showing how each atom has four equidistant neighbours

co-valent bonds tends to diminish with increasing atomic number, that is in the opposite direction to the change in the strength of the Van der Waals' forces. If, for example, we compare iodine with chlorine, the co-valent bonds which hold the atoms together in the Cl_2 molecule are stronger than those in the I_2 molecule, whilst the Van der Waals' forces between the molecules are stronger in solid iodine than in solid chlorine.

You will see, therefore, that the crystal structures of the above non-metallic and weakly metallic or metalloid elements fall into quite definite and simple classes. At the one extreme there are the inert gases in which only forces of the Van der Waals' type are available for the cohesion which gives rise to the solid or liquid. There are then the elements of very low melting point, namely hydrogen, oxygen, and nitrogen in which stable diatomic H_2, O_2, and N_2 molecules are formed involving single, double, and triple bonds respectively. In the solid and liquid state these molecules are held together by Van der Waals' forces. Finally there are the elements fluorine, chlorine, bromine, iodine, sulphur, selenium, tellurium, phosphorus, arsenic, antimony, bismuth, carbon (diamond), silicon, germanium, and grey tin. These all crystallise in structures obeying the $(8-N)$ rule, and in Group IV the co-valent bonds bind the whole structure together (diamond structure, Fig. 69). In the remaining groups the crystal structures involve co-valent bonds on the one hand, and bonding which may be partly of a Van der Waals, and partly of a metallic nature.

25—More About Co-valent Bonds

OLDER METALLURGIST: The (8-N) rule structures which you described last time are very fascinating, and the general principle seems extremely simple. But has all this got anything to do with wave-mechanics and electron clouds?

YOUNG SCIENTIST: Wave-mechanics has been applied to the problem of co-valency, and has been most successful. We may begin by considering the hydrogen molecule H_2, because it is the simplest possible case of inter-atomic bonding, and unless you understand what happens in this molecule you will have no chance of understanding the more complicated state of affairs which exists in solid metals and alloys.

Suppose now we consider two hydrogen atoms in the normal state, that is, the state with the electrons in the ($1s$) level. Then if these are widely separated, they behave as free atoms, and the energies of their electrons will be the same, namely that of the ($1s$) level. Now let us suppose that the two atoms approach one another. Then several processes take place:

(1) The electron of each atom begins to be attracted by the nucleus of the other atom.

(2) The two nuclei repel one another.

(3) The two electrons repel one another.

All these processes go on together, and the two atoms form a common system whose electronic motion, energy levels, etc., may be calculated by wave-mechanical methods. Just as in a free atom there is a number of energy states defined by quantum numbers, so in the system of two atoms there are stationary states defined by quantum numbers. These quantum numbers are more complicated than those of free atoms, and we need not bother about the details. You should, however, note that as the two atoms approach one another it can be shown that the single ($1s$) energy level of the free atoms splits into *two* levels denoted $\sigma_g 1s$ and $\sigma_u 1s$ whose energies become increasingly different as the atoms approach more and more closely.

OM: It seems to me that the general effect is very like that of the broadening of the levels in a solid metal which you described in Chapter 18.

YS: That's right. The process is essentially of the same type. In the case of two atoms the single level splits up into two levels. In a metal crystal the number of atoms is of the order 10^{23} per gramme, and the single level splits up into a correspondingly large number of levels which produce the energy band of Fig. 28, but the essential process is the same.

OM: Does the splitting up process necessarily produce an attraction?

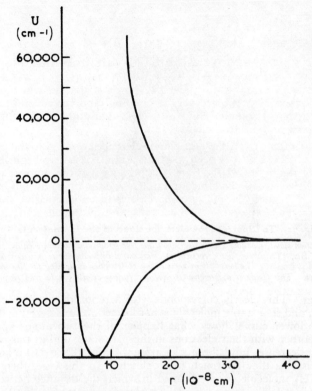

[From " *Molecular Spectra and Molecular Structure*," Vol 1. " *Diatomic Molecules*."
Herzberg. Courtesy of Prentice-Hall Inc.

**Fig. 70—Shows how the internuclear distance affects the total
energy of the H₂ molecule when the electrons are in the repulsive orbital (upper curve) and the attractive orbital (lower
curve) respectively**

*In the upper curve the energy increases steadily as the internuclear distance diminishes, and for
this reason no stable molecule is formed. In the lower curve, where the electrons are in the attractive orbital, the total energy of the molecule decreases as the atoms approach, and then passes
through a minimum, and consequently a stable molecule can be formed*

YS: That doesn't follow. It may result in either attraction or repulsion. We have already seen how when two hydrogen atoms approach
one another the different processes (1), (2), (3) above take place. The
energy resulting from each of these processes can be calculated and is
clearly a function of the distance between the two nuclei. Consequently we can draw a graph showing how the energy of *the assembly
of the two atoms as a whole* depends on the distance between them. In
this way the curves shown in Fig. 70 are obtained. The upper curve
shows what happens if the two electrons are in $\sigma_u 1s$ state. Here you
will see that the energy increases as the two atoms approach one

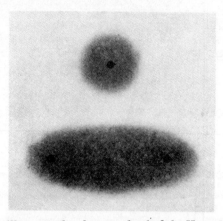

Fig. 71—To illustrate the electron cloud of the H_2 molecule

The electron cloud is axially symmetrical about the line joining the nuclei which are represented by dark dots. The upper figure represents a cross section perpendicular to this axis, and shows the axial symmetry. The lower figure represents a cross section containing the line which joins the nuclei. This figure is diagrammatic only, and further details can be read from Fig. 72.

another. This clearly corresponds with a repulsion between the two atoms, and so a stable molecule is not formed.

The lower curve shows what happens if the two atoms approach one another with their electrons in the $\sigma_g 1s$ state, and in this case the energy decreases until the nuclei are approximately $0.74A$ apart, and then rises as they approach more closely. In this case, therefore, a stable H_2 molecule can be formed in which the distance between the atoms is $0.74A$. In this kind of molecular system Pauli's Principle still applies, and the $\sigma_g 1s$ state can contain not more than two electrons which must have opposite spins. In the H_2 molecule there are only two electrons, and so they can both enter the $\sigma_g 1s$ level—this level is sometimes called a *bonding orbital* because if the electrons are in this state the energy of the system decreases as the atoms approach one another. The $\sigma_u 1s$ level is called an *anti-bonding orbital* because it corresponds with an increase in energy and hence a repulsion as the atoms approach.

OM: Oh, I see! So that's why helium doesn't form a stable He_2 molecule. An He_2 molecule would have four electrons to accommodate, and the attractive $\sigma_g 1s$ orbital could hold only two of them, and the other two would have to enter the anti-bonding orbital, and would give rise to repulsion.

YS: That's right. In the same way you will see that if the electrons in two hydrogen atoms had the same spin, they could not both enter the attractive orbital. In electron bonds of this kind the electrons must have opposite spins, and this is one of the great characteristics of covalent bonding—the two electrons which form the bond have opposite spins.

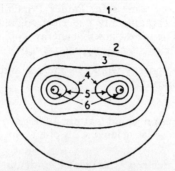

[From " Molecular Spectra and Molecular Structure," Vol 1. " Diatomic Molecules."
Herzberg. Courtesy of Prentice-Hall Inc.

**Fig. 72—Shows the electron cloud density of the H_2 molecule on
a section passing through the two nuclei**

*The curves, Nos. 1, 2, 3 . . . are curves of equal probability density, and the numbers give
the relative values. The diagram shows that the high electron density, that is contours 4, 5, 6,
is concentrated in the region between the nuclei. The internuclear distance is 0.74A. This figure
shows the detail of Fig. 71*

OM: Then when the electrons are shared between the two atoms
like this, are they to be looked on as revolving in a circular orbit mid-
way between the two atoms?

YS: Oh, no! Just as in the case of a free atom we can no longer
think of the electrons as moving in a definite orbit, so in the case
of a molecule we have to give up attempts to follow the electron in its
path, and we can only think of an electron cloud pattern or probability
pattern. In the H_2 molecule, the electron cloud is symmetrical about
the line joining the centres of the two nuclei, and Fig. 71 shows the
general form of the electron cloud in this case. Fig. 72 shows the
same effect in greater detail—the lines are contours of constant electron
density, and you will see that the contours of high density tend to
crowd together in the spaces between the two atoms. This illustrates a
very general principle, namely, that in nearly all cases—ferromagnetism is an exception—an assembly of electrons with a given energy
will occupy a smaller volume, or in a given volume will have a smaller
energy if they are in pairs with opposite spins than if they all have the
same spin.

OM: Do you mean that spinning electrons produce fields which
attract one another if the spins are anti-parallel, and repel one another
if they are parallel?

YS: No. That's not the way to look at it. The position is that if the
electrons have the same spin, they will by Pauli's Principle have to
enter higher energy states. Suppose for example we consider an atom
of carbon for which the normal electronic structure is
$$(1s)^2 \ (2s)^2 \ (2p)^2.$$
Here the $1s$ and $2s$ levels each contain two electrons, one of each spin,
whereas the two electrons in the $2p$ levels have parallel spins. If all

the electrons had the same spin, Pauli's Principle would mean that each s-level could contain only one electron, and each p-level only three electrons. The lowest possible energy would thus correspond to the configuration
$$(1s)^1 (2s)^1 (2p)^3 (3s)^1$$
and in this case the energy would be greater and the electron cloud larger than in the normal
$$(1s)^2 (2s)^2 (2p)^2$$
configuration.

OM: In the electron cloud pattern of Figs. 71 and 72, am I to regard one electron as associated with one atom, and the other with the other?

YS: No. Each electron is associated with the cloud pattern as a whole; the process is sometimes called the exchange process, and the resulting forces the exchange forces. Let us suppose that we have the molecule in the condition in which one electron—let us call it electron No. 1—is associated with atom No. 1, whilst electron No. 2 is associated with atom No. 2. Then since electrons are indistinguishable we should have an exactly identical system if electron No. 2 were associated with atom No. 1, and electron No. 1 with atom No. 2. It is now a general principle of wave mechanics that if a system can exist in two or more configurations, the lowest energy is obtained not by one configuration alone, but by a condition which may be described by the superposition of the wave functions characteristic of the two configurations. Mathematically this is equivalent to a rapid exchange or resonance between the two configurations, so that on the average the system exists in a condition which is neither one configuration nor the other, but is characteristic of the exchange or resonance process. This exchange or resonance produces a lowering of energy which is greater the more nearly equal are the stabilities of the two configurations between which resonance occurs. In the case of the H_2 molecule, the two configurations referred to above are absolutely indistinguishable, and so the conditions for strong resonance or interchange are present. You may perhaps regard the electron as continually passing from one atom to the other, but the frequency of the exchange is so high (about 10^{18} times per second) that we have to imagine the electron as associated with the electron cloud pattern of the molecule as a whole, and, just as in the free atom, we must not ask how the electron moves about within the electron cloud.

OM: In the case of the H_2 molecule you have described, the shared electrons are in s-states. Do the same considerations apply to p-states?

YS: In the case of p-bond orbitals, the general principles are much the same. The co-valent bond is again formed by two electrons of opposite spin, and in general the co-valent bond results from the unpaired electrons of the free atoms. In the case of fluorine, for example, each atom has seven electrons in the outermost or 2-quantum shell. Of these electrons, two are in the $(2s)^2$ sub-group and the remaining five are in the $(2p)$ sub-group. As we have already explained, there are three $(2p)$ orbitals, each of which can contain two

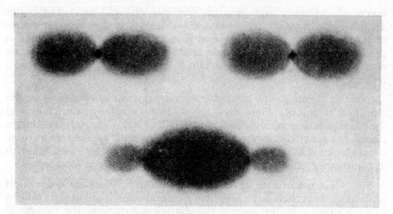

Fig. 73—To illustrate the co-valent bonds formed by _p_-orbitals

(a) *Half-filled p-orbitals of two free atoms approaching one another. Each p-orbital contains one electron, and these must have opposite spins if bonding is to occur*

(b) *The same two atoms after bonding has taken place and the electron cloud is drawn between the two atoms. This type of bond always results from two electrons of opposite spin*

electrons which must be of opposite spin. In the fluorine atom two of the $(2p)$ orbitals will be fully occupied, and will each contain two electrons, and the third orbital will contain one electron only. It is this lone electron which is shared with the adjacent atom in the F_2 molecule, and in the molecule the two shared electrons have opposite spins. When the p-bond is formed the electron cloud is drawn out into the space between the two atoms, so that if Fig. 73(a) shows the electron clouds of the two p electrons in the isolated atoms, the condition of affairs after bonding might be as shown in Fig. 73(b).

OM: It seems that these, as well as the bond in the H_2 molecule, give electron clouds which are symmetrical about the line joining the centres of the two atoms. Is this always the case when electron sharing occurs?

YS: Not necessarily. The above types of bond form electron clouds which are symmetrical about the line joining the two nuclei. These are called σ-bonds—some people call them "sausage bonds" because of their shape. It is, however, possible to have bonds whose electron clouds have a maximum density in other regions—p-states can unite in this way to form what are called π-bonds.

OM: If it is the unpaired electrons which give rise to the bonds, it would seem that in the antimony structure of Fig. 68, and the tellurium structure of Fig. 66, the bonds should be at right-angles to one another because the electron clouds of the three p-states (Chapter 12) are mutually perpendicular.

YS: That's quite right, and is in fact borne out by experiment. In selenium and tellurium, the angles between adjacent bonds in the long spiral chains are 105° and 102° respectively, whilst in the double layers of antimony and bismuth they are 96° and 94°. The bonds are thus slightly distorted from the 90° angles of the electron clouds of the free atoms, but the general principle is quite clear. Bonds of this kind are almost pure p-bonds, and Fig. 74 is a highly diagrammatic representation of the electron cloud distribution in selenium and tellurium.

OM: It seems to me that the whole principle goes wrong in the diamond structure. Here each atom has four valency electrons, and the configuration in the free atom is $(1s)^2 (2s)^2 (2p)^2$. We should therefore expect two p-bonds at right angles, with two others at some other angle. Or perhaps three p-bonds at right-angles, with a fourth in some other direction, whereas the actual structure is tetrahedral.

YS: That point often gives rise to difficulty. You are quite right in thinking that there are only three p orbitals which are at right-angles to each other. In the case of the diamond structure, the process of hybridisation sets in, and the electrons which give rise to the bonds are no longer in p-states or s-states, but in a condition resulting from the superposition of the two. You may if you like regard the crystal structure as derived from carbon atoms in the configuration $(1s)^2 (2s)^1 (2p)^3$ where there are four unpaired electrons, which can give rise to four bonds. These electrons exist in the hybridised condition, and it can be shown that in this state the bonds are directed tetrahedrally, and the electron clouds of the valency electrons are concentrated in the directions of the bonds. So the diamond structure can be looked on as a structure in which the electrons are shared between adjacent atoms, and the probability of finding a valency electron in the crystal is greatest in the directions of the bonds of Fig. 69, although the bonds are neither s- nor p-bonds, but a superposition of the two. It is important to note that when this kind of hybridisation occurs, the total number of orbitals available for bonding is unchanged. In the elements of the Short Periods there is the one s orbital, and the three p orbitals, making a total of four. The process of hybridisation affects the angles between the bonds, and hence the electron cloud distribution, but the maximum number of bonds remains at four per atom.

OM: If that is so, it would seem that there should be a possibility of more than four bonds per atom for the atoms of the transition elements. In the case of the iron group, for example, the transition process (Chapter 15) means that the energies of the $(3d)$ electrons are not very different from those of the $(4s)$ and $(4p)$ electrons, and so the $(3d)$ orbitals should be available for bond formation.

YS: That's perfectly right. In the transition elements of the first Long Period there are five $(3d)$ orbitals, three $(4p)$ orbitals, and one $(4s)$ orbital available for bond formation. This makes a total of nine orbitals per atom, and although all of these are not used in bond formation, there is no doubt that the possible number of bonds per atom is greater than in the elements of the Short Periods. In the ferricyanide ion $Fe (CN)_6^{---}$ for example the iron atom gives rise to

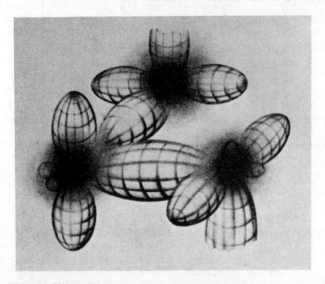

Fig. 74—Shows how the spiral chains of atoms in the crystal of selenium and tellurium (Fig. 66) are the result of the mutually perpendicular nature of the three *p*-orbitals of each atom

The inner electrons of each atom are joined by a shaded region. The two unpaired p-orbitals of the valency electrons of each atom coalesce with those adjacent atoms to form completely filled orbitals, each containing two electrons of opposite spins. The electron clouds which show electrons in each co-valent bond are, of course, not really bounded by sharp surfaces but are diffuse. The surfaces in Fig. 74 are drawn to show the axial symmetry of the bonds, and about four-fifths of the charge would be contained within the volumes shown

six bonds, and the six (CN) radicals are situated at the corners of a regular octahedron, and are bound to the iron atom by electrons in hybridised (*s*, *p*, *d*) orbitals.

OM: In this kind of electron bonding of any importance from the point of view of the metallurgist?

YS: The general idea of co-valent bonding is important in several ways. In the first place it gives a direct understanding of the cohesive forces in structures of the (8-$\mathcal{N}$) rule type. When one considers alloys, there is a number of inter-metallic compounds in which the forces between the atoms are essentially of the co-valent type. It is not, however, possible to draw any sharp dividing line between structures of this kind, and those of a purely metallic nature. An understanding of the simple co-valent bond is therefore essential if the structures of alloys are to be appreciated, and it is satisfactory to know that the theory of the co-valent bond is convincingly established. Apart from this some of the theories advanced by Pauling suggest that the cohesive forces in the crystals of the transition elements are closely related to the processes of hybridisation referred to above, and we shall consider these later in connection with the transition elements.

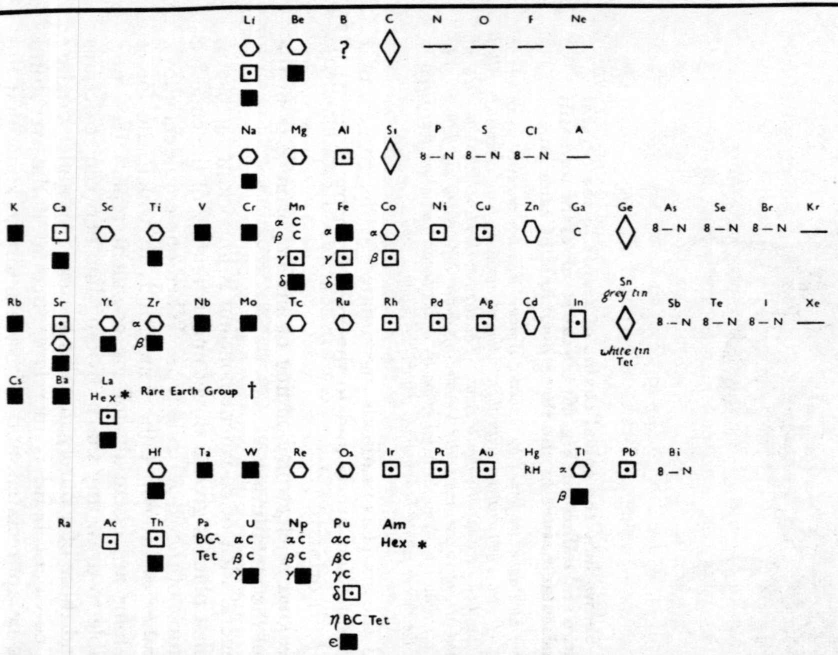

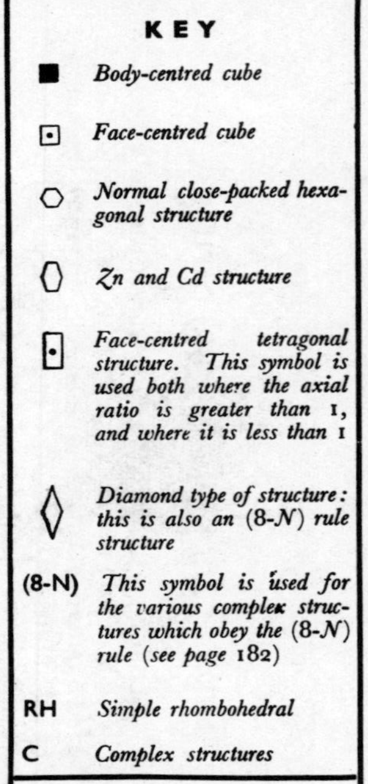

KEY

■ Body-centred cube

☑ Face-centred cube

⬡ Normal close-packed hexagonal structure

⬡ Zn and Cd structure

⬒ Face-centred tetragonal structure. This symbol is used both where the axial ratio is greater than 1, and where it is less than 1

◇ Diamond type of structure: this is also an (8-N) rule structure

(8-N) This symbol is used for the various complex structures which obey the (8-N) rule (see page 182)

RH Simple rhombohedral

C Complex structures

* ABACABAC... stacking. See p. 206b.

† See p. 206b.

Where more than one symbol appears against an element, it implies that different allotropic forms exist: in such cases the allotropic forms are shown in the order of the temperature ranges in which they are stable, the highest temperature being at the bottom. It should be noted that the close-packed hexagonal modifications of chromium and nickel have only been obtained electrolytically

The Rare Earth Elements αCe, αPr, Nd, Gd, Tb, Dy, Ho, Er, Tm, and Lu crystallise in the close-packed hexagonal structure, whilst βCe, βPr, and Yb are face-centred cubic, and Eu is body-centred cubic. There is some evidence that the structures of αPr and Nd are really more complex

Fig. 75—Crystal structures of the metallic elements

26—Typical Metallic Crystal Structures

OLDER METALLURGIST: The $(8-N)$ rule structures to which you referred in Chapter 24 are very fascinating, and I can see how the apparently varied structures of these elements fit into one general scheme. These elements are all of a more or less electro-negative nature, and are not true metals. As far as I remember, the crystal structures of the metallic elements are in general of a much simpler nature.

YOUNG SCIENTIST: That's quite right. In Fig. 75 I have reproduced the Periodic Table, omitting the non-metallic elements, and those whose structures follow the $(8-N)$ rule. We may first omit the Rare Earths and the Actinides, and consider the elements of the A subgroups, including the metals at the beginning of the two Short Periods. These metals all crystallise in one or more of three structures, the face-centred cubic, the close-packed hexagonal, and the body-centred cubic structure. In manganese, there are four allotropic forms, of which two have complicated structures, but the high temperature modifications have the typical body-centred cubic (δ-Mn) and face-centred cubic (γ-Mn) structures.

OM: Am I right in thinking that the unit cell of the face-centred cube has one atom at each corner of a cube, and one atom at the centre of each face?

YS: That's right. The unit cell is shown in Fig. 76, and contains four atoms.

OM: Surely that is wrong? There are fourteen atoms shown in Fig. 76.

YS: You must remember that the crystal structure results from the repetition of the unit cell of Fig. 76 throughout the structure.

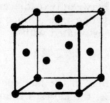

Fig. 76—The face-centred cubic structure

There is one atom at each corner of the unit cell, and one atom at the centre of each face. If a is the side of the cube, the closest distance between two atoms is $\dfrac{a\sqrt{2}}{2}$, and each atom has twelve neighbours at this distance

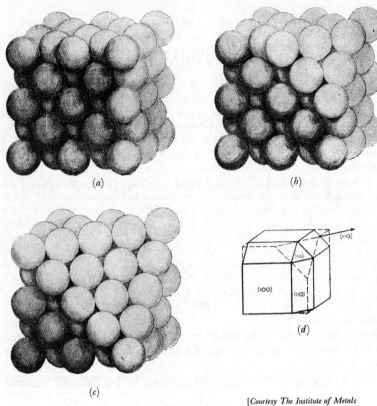

(a)

(b)

(c)

(d)

Fig. 77 (a), (b), (c) and (d)

It follows, therefore, that each atom at the corner of the unit cell is shared between eight adjacent units, and consequently counts as only one-eighth for any one cell. The atoms in the centres of the faces of the unit cell are shared between two adjacent cells, and consequently count as one-half for any one cell. Since the unit cube has eight corners and six faces, it is associated with

$$\left(8 \times \frac{1}{8}\right) + \left(6 \times \frac{1}{2}\right) = 4 \text{ atoms.}$$

OM: I see. It seems that in the face-centred cubic structure, if a is the side of the unit cube, the closest distance between two atoms is $\frac{a\sqrt{2}}{2} = 0.707a$, and that each atom has twelve neighbours at this distance.

YS: That's right—it is often expressed by saying that the *co-ordination number* of the structure is 12. From some points of view you can get a more vivid impression of the structure by means of Fig. 77. Here I have shown eight unit cells, and I have represented each atom by a sphere of such a size that adjacent atoms touch one another. In Fig. 77(*b*) one atom has been removed from the corner of the cube, and you will see that this exposes six atoms, which form an equilateral triangle. In Fig. 77(*c*) these six atoms have been removed, and you will see how the structure consists of layers of atoms in hexagonal array. The spheres all fit together so that each has twelve close neighbours, and the structure is sometimes referred to as cubic close packing. The process shown in Fig. 77(*a*), (*b*), (*c*) could have been started from any one of the eight corners of the cube, and the close-packed planes of atoms are therefore called the octahedral planes—in crystallographic notation they are the (111) planes.

OM: But I thought you said that I was not to look on atoms as hard spheres.

YS: That's quite right. Fig. 77 is purely diagrammatic, and you must not look on an atom as having a sharp boundary surface. For some metals such as copper, silver, or gold, the picture is not really so very misleading. In these metals, as we shall see later (Chapter 29), the electron clouds of the underlying *ions* (for example the $(1s)^2$ $(2s)^2$ $(2p)^6$ $(3s)^2$ $(3p)^6$ $(3d)^{10}$Cu$^+$ions) overlap when the atoms are in the solid crystal. This overlapping of the ions produces intensive repulsive forces, and so the crystals of these metals can be regarded as composed of hard ions held in contact by the valency electrons. Fig. 77 is thus a reasonable picture of copper, silver, or gold, if you regard the surfaces of the spheres (ions) as being slightly diffuse, and the valency electrons as swimming about, and holding the ions together. But Fig. 77 would be a very misleading picture of calcium (face-centred cubic), since in this metal the ions are relatively much smaller compared with the distance between two atoms.

Fig. 78 shows the unit cell of the body-centred cubic structure. There is one atom at the centre of the cell and one at each corner, and you can easily see that the co-ordination number is 8.

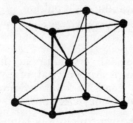

[*Courtesy the Institute of Metals*

Fig. 78—The body-centred cubic structure

There is one atom at each corner of the unit cell and one at the centre. If a is the side of the unit cell, the closest distance between two atoms is $\frac{a\sqrt{3}}{2}$, and each atom has eight neighbours at this distance

OM: Yes. I can see that each atom has eight close neighbours at a distance equal to $\frac{a\sqrt{3}}{2} = 0.866a$ where a is the side of the cube. But it seems that each atom has also six neighbours at a distance equal to a; this is not very much greater than $\frac{a\sqrt{3}}{2}$, so should not the co-ordination number be called 14?

YS: At distances of the order 3×10^{-8} cm, the forces between atoms vary so rapidly with the distance that the difference between a and $0.866a$ is very marked, and the co-ordination number is properly called 8. But you are correct in saying that the difference between the sets of closest and next closest neighbours is not very great, and some writers do describe the co-ordination number of the body-centred cubic structure as 14. If this is done it is better to distinguish between the two sets of neighbours by writing the co-ordination number as $(8 + 6)$.

OM: Am I right in thinking that the body-centred cubic structure is not so close-packed as the face-centred cube?

YS: Yes. In Fig. 79(a) and (b) I have drawn the body-centred cubic structure with the atoms represented by spheres which touch along the lines of closest approach of two atoms. If you compare this with Fig. 77 you will see that there is much more empty space than in the face-centred cube.

OM: It would seem that Fig. 79 is a bad picture of an alkali metal, because you said before (page 97, Part I) that the electron clouds of the ions of the alkali metals were very much smaller than those of the atoms as a whole.

YS: That's right. Fig. 79 is completely misleading as a picture of an alkali metal, but it is not altogether misleading as a picture of α-iron (ferrite), since here the electron clouds of the ions are relatively very much larger, and at the distances of closest approach in the solid metal they overlap and produce a repulsion.

OM: In that case, I don't understand how I am to look at a crystal of an alkali metal.

YS: The alkali metals all crystallise in the body-centred cubic structure, and you are to regard a crystal, of say, sodium, as consisting of an array of relatively small Na⁺ ions swimming in regular array in the electron cloud of the valency electrons.

OM: I can understand your picture of copper with the ions pulled into contact, but your picture of sodium seems more difficult because there is nothing to hold the ions apart.

YS: Let us suppose that we imagine the body-centred cubic structure of sodium to be gradually expanded or contracted, so that the structure remains the same, but the distance between the atoms is a

[*Courtesy The Institute of Metals*

Fig. 79 (a) and (b)—The body-centred cubic structure

variable. It is then possible to calculate the energy of the valency electrons, and of the crystal as a function of the distance between the atoms. The calculations then show that the energy of the crystal as a whole has a minimum value at a certain interatomic distance which is determined mainly by the characteristics of the valency electrons. It is this value of the interatomic distance which corresponds with stable equilibrium, since when the atoms are at this distance apart the electronic energy increases both when the solid is expanded or compressed. In a sense, therefore, we may say that in the alkali metals the valency electrons are responsible both for the attractive forces and for the repulsive forces. It is this fact which makes the alkali metals of such great theoretical interest. They are too reactive to be of much practical value, but the fact that many of their properties depend almost entirely on the valency electrons means that these properties can be used to test relatively simple theories of metals which can later be elaborated to deal with metals in which the electronic processes are more complicated.

OM: I have heard the close-packed hexagonal structure described as one of close-packed spheres. Does this mean that it resembles the face-centred cubic structure?

YS: Figs. 80 and 81 show the unit cell of the close-packed hexagonal structure, and you will see that in this structure the atoms are arranged in hexagonal close-packed layers, stacked above one another so that the third layer is vertically over the first. If c is the height of the unit cell in Fig. 80, and a the length of one of the sides of the hexagon, the ratio c/a is called the *axial ratio*. Each atom has six neighbours in its own layer at a distance equal to a, and six other neighbours, three in the layer above and three in the layer below at a distance equal to $\sqrt{\dfrac{a^2}{3} + \dfrac{c^2}{4}}$. If the axial ratio $\dfrac{c}{a}$ is equal to $\sqrt{\dfrac{8}{3}} = 1.633$, all twelve neighbours are at the same distance a, and the co-ordination number is 12. In actual metals the axial ratio is usually slightly different from

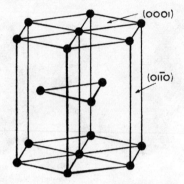

(0001)

(01Ī0)

[*Courtesy The Institute of Metals*

Fig. 80—The close-packed hexagonal structure

The atoms are arranged in layers in hexagonal array, situated above one another as shown. If c is the height of the unit, and a the length of the side of the hexagon, each atom has six close neighbours in its own layer at a distance a. It has also three neighbours in the layer above, and

three in the layer below at a distance $\sqrt{\dfrac{a^2}{3} + \dfrac{c^2}{4}}.$

If the axial ratio $\dfrac{c}{a}$ *is* 1.633 *all twelve neighbours are at the same distance*

$\sqrt{\dfrac{8}{3}}$, and the twelve close neighbours fall into two sets of (6 + 6). For normal metals—zinc and cadmium are abnormal (see page 203)—the axial ratios vary between about 1.57 and 1.64, so the departure from the value corresponding with the close packing of perfect spheres is not very great.

OM: From Figs. 77 and 81 it seems that both the face-centred cubic, and the close-packed hexagonal structures correspond with hexagonal layers laid on top of one another.

YS: That's right. They differ from one another in that the close-packed hexagonal structure has the layers arranged so that the third layer is vertically over the first, whereas in the face-centred cubic structure the fourth layer is vertically over the first. You can understand this by means of Fig. 82(a), which shows one layer of spheres packed closely in hexagonal array. Now suppose you are going to place a second layer on top of the first layer. Then, as you can see from Fig. 82(b), the centres of the spheres in the second layer may be either over the points marked XXX . . ., or over those marked YYY . . . Let us suppose we put them in the X positions as in Fig. 82(c). Then there are two alternatives for the third layer: either this may go vertically over the spheres in the first layer, giving rise to the close-packed hexagonal arrangement, or the spheres in the third layer may be vertically over the position YYY . . ., and then the fourth layer can be put vertically over the first—it is this second alternative which gives the face-centred cubic structure. If we call the three sets of

Fig. 81—The close-packed hexagonal structure

positions *A*, *B*, and *C*, the close-packed hexagonal structure has successive layers in the order *ABABAB* . . . whilst in the face-centred cube the arrangement is *ABCABC* . . .

OM: I'm afraid I find it very difficult to see that from Fig. 77.

YS: It isn't easy to see the repetition from Fig. 77, but in Fig. 83 I have drawn the face-centred cubic-structure so as to show the characteristic *ABCABC* . . . arrangement.

OM: This seems to suggest that the face-centred cubic and close-packed hexagonal structures are very like one another.

YS: That's quite true, and Fig. 84 shows the relation in an alternative way. You will also see from Fig. 75 that there are many cases in which transition metals crystallise in both structures, one being stable above and the other below the so-called *transition temperature*.

This general resemblance between the two structures has been further emphasised by the work of Lipson on the structure of cobalt. This element in the low temperature modification has the close-packed hexagonal structure with the layers arranged *ABABAB* . . . By suitable heat treatment it is possible to obtain cobalt in a structure in which occasional faults exist so that an arrangement such as *ABABCBCBCBABAB* . . . is found. In such structures the spacing between the close-packed layers remains constant and gives rise to sharp X-ray reflections, but the faulting produces diffuse lines for X-ray reflections from other planes.

OM: From Fig. 77 it is clear that the face-centred cubic structure has four sets of close packed planes because the opposite sides of a regular octahedron are parallel. From Fig. 81 it looks as though the

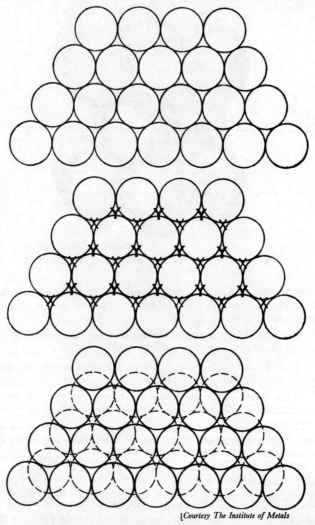

[*Courtesy The Institute of Metals*

Fig. 82

close-packed hexagonal structure had only one set of close-packed planes—or are there others which are not shown in Fig. 81?

YS: No.   In the close-packed hexagonal structure there is only one set of close-packed planes. This is of great importance in connection with the mechanical properties, because when single crystals of these metals are deformed plastically, the process is equivalent to a slipping on the close-packed planes in the direction of the close-packed rows.

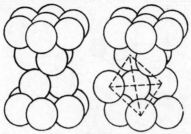

[Courtesy The Institute of Metals

Fig. 83

In this figure the face-centred cubic structure is drawn so as to show how the structure results from close-packed layers standing on one another so that the atoms in the fourth layer are vertically over those in the first. This is shown in the left-hand figure, while in the right-hand figure one additional atom has been added so as to show one side of the face-centred cube. Fig. 84 (below) shows the relation between the close-packed layers and the unit face-centred cube in another way

[Courtesy The Institute of Metals

Fig. 84

In the face-centred cubic structure there are four sets of these close-packed slip planes, whereas in the close-packed hexagonal structure there is only one set.

OM: In the body-centred cubic structure of Fig. 79 there do not seem to be any close-packed layers, and so I suppose the deformation process may be different.

YS: That's a very interesting point. In the body-centred cubic structure the deformation occurs by slip parallel to one of the closely packed rows of atoms in Fig. 79[1], but the tendency to slip on one definite plane is less marked. In general, deformation does occur by slipping on one or more planes in the [111] direction, but the exact

[1] These are called the [111] directions.

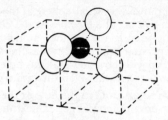

[Courtesy The Institute of Metals

Fig. 85

plane chosen varies from one metal to another, and for a given metal it may vary with the temperature. This is in contrast to the behaviour of the face-centred cubic and close-packed hexagonal structures where the slipping is nearly always parallel to the close packed atomic planes.

OM: It is clear that the face-centred cubic, and close-packed hexagonal structures are close-packed assemblies of spheres, and that the body-centred cubic structure is a more open arrangement. This suggests that there will be larger holes between the atoms in the body-centred cubic structure, and that relatively small atoms will fit more easily into this structure than into either of the close-packed arrangements.

YS: That's a rather confusing point. In so far as the atoms may be regarded as spheres, there is more empty space in the body-centred cubic structure. But if you consider fitting a small spherical atom into the holes between larger spherical atoms of a given radius R, you find that the face-centred cubic or close-packed hexagonal structures can accommodate a larger atom than the body-centred cube. If you looked at Fig. 79(a), you might think there was a relatively large hole at the centre of each cube face. Most careful examination will show, however, that owing to the curvature of the atom at the centre of the cube, and the similar curvature of the atom at the centre of the adjacent

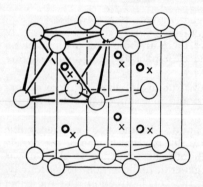
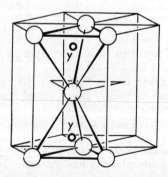

[Courtesy The Institute of Metals

Fig. 86

cube, there is room for only a very small sphere at the centres of the faces. Each hole at the centre of a cube face lies at the centre of a distorted octahedron formed by joining up the four atoms at the corners of a cube face separating two unit cells to the two atoms at the centres of the cells. Simple calculation will show you that this hole will accommodate a sphere not more than $0.154\ R$ where R is the radius of the large spheres.

OM: It seems that a small atom in the hole at the centre of the cubic face will have a very unsymmetrical set of neighbours, and I should imagine there are larger holes slightly to one side.

YS: That's right. The largest holes in the body-centred cubic structure are in positions such as those shown in Fig. 85, and these have four neighbouring atoms arranged tetrahedrally. These holes will accommodate spheres of radius $0.291\ R$.

OM: In the face-centred cubic structure, the largest holes are clearly at the centre of the unit cube, and at the centre of the edges, and each of these is surrounded by six neighbours.

YS: The six neighbours lie at the corners of a regular octahedron, and so the largest holes are often called the octahedral holes, or octahedral interstices. Calculation shows that these will contain spheres of radius $0.41\ R$, where R is the radius of the large spheres of the face-centred cube, and so you will see that, for a given size of spherical atom, the face-centred cube has a larger hole that the body-centred cube.

OM: From their general similarity, I should imagine that applies also to the close-packed hexagonal structure.

YS: Yes. The close-packed hexagonal structure has octahedral

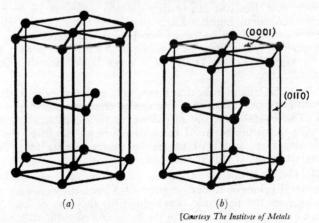

[Courtesy The Institute of Metals

Fig. 87

To show the relation between the close-packed hexagonal structures of zinc and cadmium (a) and the normal close-packed hexagonal structure (b). When compared with the normal structure, the unit cell of zinc and cadmium is stretched out in the direction of the c-axis

holes at positions such as those marked X in Fig. 86. It has also got tetrahedral holes at positions such as Y, and if you look carefully at Fig. 77 you will be able to see the corresponding tetrahedral holes in the face-centred cubic structure; they accommodate spheres of radius 0.225 R.

OM: The structures of the metals of the A sub-groups are certainly very simple except for manganese, tungsten, and uranium. From Fig. 75 it seems that copper, silver, and gold all crystallise in the face-centred cubic structure, but the crystal structures of the remaining true metals of the B sub-groups seem a rather confused jumble.

YS: The position is not really quite as bad as that. Zinc and cadmium crystallise in a curious modification of the close-packed hexagonal structure in which the axial ratio is approximately 1.9. This is shown in Fig. 87(a), and, by comparison with Fig. 87(b), you will see that it is equivalent to a normal close-packed hexagonal structure stretched out in the direction of the c axis. Each atom has six close neighbours in its own layer, but the neighbours in the next layers above and below are very much farther away; and so the co-ordination number is 6.

Curiously enough the crystal structure of mercury, although quite different from that of zinc, is also one in which the co-ordination number is 6. This structure is shown in Fig. 88, and is simple rhombohedral. There is one atom at each corner of a rhombohedron, so that each atom has six close neighbours.

OM: That means that the structures of the Group II B elements obey the $(8-N)$ rule. Is that so?

YS: Considered empirically, the structures in Group II B do satisfy the $(8-N)$ rule, but you can readily see that there can be no question of simple co-valent bonds. Each zinc atom has only two electrons, and so it cannot form co-valent bonds with six neighbouring atoms. It is certainly very suggestive that the $(8-N)$ rule seems as it were to turn up again in Group II B, but it is not known whether this is of real significance.

OM: Of the true metals, that leaves only gallium, indium, thallium, white tin and lead. Have they any special characteristics?

YS: The crystal structure of gallium is very complicated, and the reason for this is unknown. I think therefore we can leave the details of this structure, and concentrate on the remaining four elements indium, white tin, thallium and lead.

OM: That reminds me of a point which you have not made clear. The general principle underlying the $(8-N)$ structures is very simple. But why does the principle break down in the case of lead? This is a true metal, and crystallises in the face-centred cubic structure, and not in the diamond structure as I should have expected from your description.

YS: That's a very interesting point, and you are quite right in saying that lead is a true metal and does not crystallise in the diamond

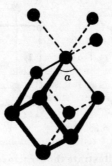

[*Courtesy The Institute of Metals. " Atomic Theory for Students of Metallurgy,"* W. *Hume-Rothery*

Fig. 88—The crystal structure of mercury. The structure is simple rhombohedral and each atom has six close neighbours

type of structure. What happens is the result of two general processes. On the one hand, as I have already explained (page 183) the co-valent linkages become less stable with increasing atomic number, and so the tendency to form (8-N) rule structures decreases on passing from Si→Ge→Sn→Pb. On the other hand, as we saw in Part I (page 114), the stability of the sub-group of two s electrons increases with increasing atomic number. The result is that in lead where the free atom has its outermost electrons in the $(6s)^2$ $(6p)^2$ groupings, the $(6s)^2$ sub-group is so stable that it persists almost unchanged in the solid metal—it is the same process as that which makes the Pb^{++} salts more stable than many of the tetravalent lead compounds. In the crystal of lead it is probable that only two of the four valency electrons are available for cohesion, and hence the diamond structure is not formed. This has not been determined by direct experiment, but has been inferred from a study of the interatomic distances in the crystals of the elements, and we shall consider these later.

OM: It would seem that if your explanation is correct, thallium should be something like a univalent metal, because the univalent Tl^+ thallous salts are more stable than the trivalent thallic salts.

YS: That's right. Thallium crystallises in typical metallic structures —close-packed hexagonal at low temperatures, and body-centred cubic above 230°C. Here again the interatomic distances suggest that the $(6s)^2$ sub-group of electrons persists unchanged, and that only one electron per atom is concerned in the cohesive process. Similarly in indium the interatomic distances suggest that the $(5s)^2$ sub-group is fairly stable, and that the solid element is more like a univalent than a trivalent metal. In this case the crystal structure is face-centred tetragonal, but as you will see from Fig. 89 the axial ratio is so nearly unity that the structure is really only a very slightly distorted form of the typical face-centred cubic structure. In white tin the structure

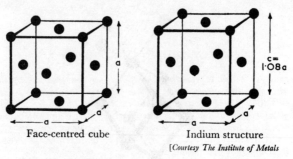

Face-centred cube   Indium structure

[*Courtesy The Institute of Metals*

Fig. 89—To illustrate the structure of indium

The structure is face-centred tetragonal with axial ratio $\frac{c}{a} = 1.08$. The right-hand figure shows that this structure is equivalent to a face-centred cubic structure slightly stretched along one axis

is more complicated, although it is truly metallic, and here again the interatomic distances suggest that the $(5s)^2$ sub-group is persisting to some extent in the solid element. There is a good deal of evidence that the four metals

$$In - Sn \text{ (white)}$$
$$Tl - Pb$$

form a little group of elements which are true metals, but in which the $(5s)^2$ or $(6s)^2$ sub-groups of electrons are so stable that they are either unavailable or only partly available for bonding purposes.

OM: Then does this mean that thallium enters alloys as a univalent element?

YS: Oh, no! That doesn't necessarily follow, and the whole story is not yet known. For example, thallium dissolves in magnesium as a typical trivalent element.

In general, however, you will see that the crystal structures of the metallic elements are surprisingly simple. There are a few exceptions such as Mn, Ga, and white tin. Apart from these, the three typical structures cover nearly all the elements except those of Group II B, and except for indium which is but a slightly distorted form of the typical face-centred cube.

NOTE.—With the exception of Figs. 75 and 88 the illustrations in this chapter are reproduced by courtesy of The Institute of Metals from " The Structure of Metals and Alloys," by W. Hume-Rothery and G. V. Raynor.

Epilogue to Chapter 26

The reader is asked to imagine the following conversation as taking place sixteen years after the conversation in the foregoing chapter, that is, sometime in 1961 or 1962. The participants are our friends the Older Metallurgist and the Young Scientist, but the former has recently retired and the latter must now be designated a Middle-Aged Scientist. They have met by chance while attending a conference and take the opportunity to consider the bearing of later work on their original discussion.

RETIRED METALLURGIST: After sixteen years I imagine there must be some new work on the crystal structure of the metallic elements. Has anything really new arisen?

MIDDLE-AGED SCIENTIST: There has been progress in several directions. The advances in atomic energy have led to the determination of the crystal structures of several of the actinide elements, and some of these have been found to be extremely complex.

Plutonium, for example, exists in at least six modifications which are stable in approximately the following temperature ranges:

Below 122°C.	α Pu; monoclinic.
122°–203°C.	β Pu; monoclinic.
203°–317°C.	γ Pu; f.c. orthorhombic.
317°–453°C.	δ Pu; f.c. cubic.
453°–473°C.	η or δ′ Pu; b.c. tetrag.
473°–640°C.(m.pt.)	ε Pu; b.c. cubic.

The η-modification has the interesting characteristic of a negative coefficient of expansion in one direction of the crystal.

Neptunium exists in an orthorhombic structure up to 278°C, a tetragonal structure between 278° and 540°C, and again a body-centred cubic structure from 540°C to the melting point (640°C).

RM: If you consider these in conjunction with the complex structures of uranium, it seems that the body-centred cubic structure tends to be the stable form at high temperatures.

MAS: That is true—and you see the same thing in titanium, zirconium and hafnium. Moreover, very brilliant work by C. S. Barrett has shown that the typically body-centred cubic alkali metals lithium and sodium can, under the influence of cold work, be made to transform at low temperatures into close-packed hexagonal[1] modifications. So here again the body-centred cubic structure is favoured by high temperatures. As we shall see later (p. 335b) this can be explained from the point of view of the vibrational entropies of the different structures.

---

[1] With lithium there is also a face-centred cubic structure.

RM: Is there any reason for the complicated structures of the actinides? It seems in contrast with the rare earths.

MAS: It was originally thought that all the rare-earth elements crystallised in normal metallic structures. Recent work has shown that this is true for the later rare earths, but that some of the earlier rare-earth metals crystallise in structures which are close-packed, but whose stacking sequences are abnormal, e.g. ABACABAC . . . (Ce, Pr, Nd), or ABABCBCAC . . . (Sm). This suggests that, in the earlier lanthanides, some or all of the $4f$ electrons are able to take part in the metallic bonding (by hybridisation with $6s$ and $5d$ states) whereas in the later lanthanides the $4f$ electrons are concentrated too near the nucleus to play much part in the cohesion.

RM: The ABAC . . . stacking would seem to suggest the presence of atoms in two different states, because some of the atoms have the environment of the face-centred cubic arrangement, and others have that of the close-packed hexagonal.

MAS: Geometrically that is correct, but whether there are two kinds of atom depends on whether you regard metallic bonding as directional, and most people would say that the metallic bond has few or no directional characteristics, except perhaps in the middle of the transition series. But the existence of the long range repetition sequences is very strange.

RM: If you regard the abnormal crystal structures of the earlier lanthanides as indicating that the $4f$ electrons are concerned in the cohesion, then is it possible that the abnormal structures of the actinides result from the effects of the $5f$ electrons?

MAS: That is the obvious suggestion, particularly when it is remembered that the energies of the $5f$, $6d$, and $7s$ electrons are more nearly equal than those of the $4f$, $5d$, and $6s$ electrons in the lanthanides. There have also been suggestions that the curious expansion effects of η-plutonium are due to a transference of electrons from the $5f$ and $6d$ states. These views are not accepted by all metal physicists, and there is at present no satisfactory theory of these complicated structures.

27—Metals, Insulators and Semi-conductors

OLDER METALLURGIST: It seems to me that if one surveys the structures of the metallic elements as a whole, they are characterised by high co-ordination numbers. At the same time, the atoms have comparatively few valency electrons per atom, and so the structures cannot be accounted for by the general type of co-valency theory which was so successful for structures of the $(8-N)$ rule type.

YOUNG SCIENTIST: That's quite correct. Co-valency structures of the $(8-N)$ rule type cannot be formed if the atoms have fewer than four valency electrons. In the case of silicon (diamond structure), for example, each atom has four valency electrons, and shares one with each of its four neighbours, and in this way acquires a share in a complete octet. On passing back to the next element aluminium (face-centred cubic) each atom has only three valency electrons, but the crystal structure is such that every atom has twelve close neighbours. The number of electrons present is clearly insufficient for an atom to form twelve co-valent bonds, and if we look on the matter in a very crude way we can say that on passing from silicon to aluminium a new kind of linkage will have to come into being, the characteristic of which is that on the average only a fraction of an electron is available for any one bond.

OM: That reminds me of one other point. You have spoken of the tetrahedral diamond structure as resulting from co-valent bonds in which an atom shared one of its electrons with each of its four neighbours. But I am not sure whether this means that I am to regard a given electron as being associated with one particular bond, so that an electron spends the whole of its time in the region between two particular atoms.

YS: No. The valency electrons are to be regarded as in continual circulation through the crystal. If you could take an instantaneous picture of the valency electrons in the crystal, the probability of finding an electron in the region of the bonds would be very much greater than the probability of finding it somewhere else, that is, the electron cloud density of the valency electrons is greater in the direction of the bonds. But the whole swarm of valency electrons is to be regarded as being in constant motion throughout the crystal.

OM: But if that is so, surely the diamond should be a conductor, and not an insulator?

YS: That doesn't follow at all. The existence of electrical conductivity requires not merely freedom of motion of the electrons, but also the possibility of obtaining a resultant flow in a particular direction. The difference between a metal and an insulator is not that the electrons are free to move in the one, and bound in the other. It is rather that in the insulator the electrons occupy a group of states, the electronic motion of which does not produce resultant flow in any direction, and which are such that the application of an electric field cannot transfer the electrons to new states outside this group. The result is that although the electrons are free to move, an electric field cannot produce any resultant flow. In contrast to this, the occupied electron states in a metal are accompanied by other states into which the electrons may enter when a field is applied, and in this way a resultant flow in the direction of the field can be produced. It is in fact in this connection that the application of the general theory of Brillouin Zones has been most successful.

OM: Do you mean to say that the Brillouin Zone theories can be applied to crystals like the diamond?

YS: The Brillouin zone theories have been applied directly to the diamond structure—this gives rise to a zone which contains four electrons per atom, and is surrounded everywhere by an energy discontinuity.

OM: I'm afraid I find this all very confusing. You seem to be using two quite different kinds of picture. In your description of the zone theories you dealt with the behaviour of electrons in a periodic field, and you said nothing about electron densities, or co-valent bonds or hybridised orbitals or anything of that kind. On the other hand, in your description of the co-valency $(8-\mathcal{N})$ rule structures you did not say anything about the electronic energies or $\mathcal{N}(E)$ curves. The two theories seem to be quite different and antagonistic.

YS: No. That's not right. The two theories are to be looked upon as complementary rather than antagonistic. The co-valency theory serves to emphasize that the electron density is greatest in the direction of the bond, and that the bond requires two electrons which must have opposite spins. The zone theories emphasize that the electrons belong to, and are free to move through the crystal as a whole. Each emphasizes one part of the truth, and the complete theory will require the two together.

OM: That reminds me of another objection I felt about your description of the zone theories. In Chapters 18 and 19 you explained how the soft X-ray spectroscopy showed that in the crystal of a metal the energy levels of the outer electrons of the free atoms had broadened into a range, and how hybridized orbitals arose when two bands overlapped. But in all this description of the zone theories you have simply spoken of electrons moving in a periodic field, and you have said nothing about s-states or p-states, or hybridized orbitals. Surely your theory is all much too simple, and the valency electrons in a metal must have some of the characteristics, s-states, etc., of their behaviour in free atoms.

YS: What you say is true. The simple theory of the periodic field is an approximation only and it requires further elaboration before it

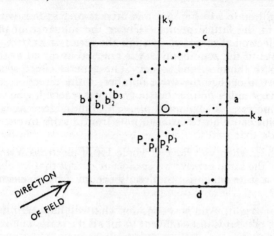

[*From "Atomic Theory for Students of Metallurgy,"*
Hume-Rothery, by courtesy of The Institute of Metals

Fig. 90

is complete. But this does not mean it is valueless. You will remember that the enormously over-simplified free electron theory did show in a remarkable way some of the characteristics of electrons in metals, and the general explanation of some effects still holds in the more complete theories. In the same way the simple theory of electrons in a periodic field explains a further set of properties, and some of the general explanation still holds in the more complete theories. You should never reject a theory because it is too simple—in fact, sometimes it is the over simplification which serves to reveal the essentials free from the complications of secondary effects.

OM: I must say, I think it's all rather doubtful, but let us see how you do account for the difference between insulators and conductors.

YS: Let us suppose that Fig. 90 shows a Brillouin zone for a hypo-thetical two-dimensional metal, and that the energy discontinuity at the boundary is so great that as increasing numbers of electrons are introduced into the crystal, all the states of the first zone are filled before any electrons enter the states of the second zone. Suppose we imagine the crystal to contain one single electron, and that this is in a state P. Let us now imagine an electric field to be applied in the direction shown. Then the effect of the field is to change the wave number k in the direction of the field, and the electron passes through a series of states p_1, p_2, p_3, as shown in Fig. 90. This process continues until the electron reaches a state on the zone boundary—the point a in Fig. 90. The calculations then show that even if the step up in energy at the zone-boundary is comparatively small, there is only a very slight probability of the electron passing into a state in the next zone and, instead of doing this, the electron state jumps from the state a to the state b in Fig. 90; this process corresponds with a Bragg reflection in the lattice planes. Under the influence of the electric field the electron then passes through the series of states b_1, b_2, b_3 . . in Fig. 90 until the zone boundary is reached at c, and at this state it passes into the state d, and so on. The general effect of an electric field is thus to change the wave number in the direction of the field until a wave number on the zone boundary is reached, when an abrupt transition occurs, as explained above. But in general, an electric field will not cause an electron to pass from a state in one zone to a state outside that zone.

OM: Then when you have a whole lot of electrons instead of one alone, does the same general process occur except that an electron can only enter a state which is not already occupied by an electron of the same spin?

YS: That's right. And now consider what will happen if the number of electrons present is just sufficient to fill all the states of a zone?

OM: Oh, I see! You mean that if all the states are occupied, and if an electric field can never transfer an electron to a state in the next zone, then as electrons are indistinguishable, the application of an electric field cannot produce a change in the distribution of the electrons as a whole among the different states, and hence cannot produce a conductivity.

YS: Exactly. This is the way in which the zone theories have thrown light on the properties of insulators. In the old days it was thought that the difference between an insulator and a metal was that in the former the electrons were more firmly bound. But it was soon realised that although differences in the strength of the binding might affect the electrical resistance by a factor of 10 or 100, they could never account for the enormous difference between the resistance of a pure metal on the one hand, and of an insulator such as the diamond on the other. The Brillouin zone theories have supplied an explanation; the picture of an insulator which they present is one in which all the valency electrons are free to move, but in which the number of electrons per atom is such that they exactly fill the electron states of one or more zones, the outermost of which is not overlapped by the next zone. Under these conditions the electric field cannot produce an alteration of the distribution of the electrons among the different energy states, and so cannot produce a resultant flow in any one direction—we are of course, ignoring the effects of very strong electric fields which produce the breakdown of an insulator.

OM: You haven't made it clear how the motion of the electron is to be visualised in Fig. 90. When the electron is in a state P, is it moving in the direction OP?

YS: That's a very important point, and one on which it is easy to go wrong. If we are to imagine the electron as moving about within the crystal, we have to think of it as a wave group or wave packet which is smaller than the crystal. The velocity of the electron is thus

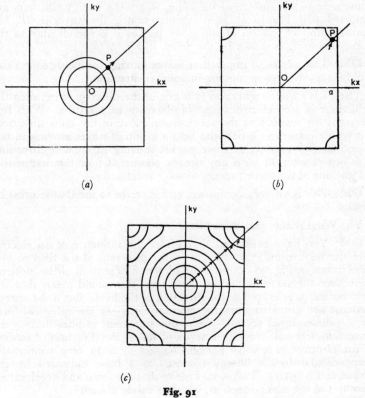

Fig. 91

the velocity of the wave group, and this as we explained in Chapter 9 is equal to

$$\frac{dv}{d\frac{1}{\lambda}}$$

For electron waves this group velocity is proportional to $\frac{dE}{dk}$ as you can readily see from the relations in Chapter 8. In Figs. 59 and 61 we have drawn the limits of the occupied states as the number of electrons per atom is increased. These bounding curves are called energy contours because they connect states of equal energy. You will see therefore that the direction of motion of an electron considered as a wave packet is perpendicular to the k-space energy contour of the electron states concerned. If the energy contours are circles as in Fig. 91(a), then the wave packet is built up of a little group of states in the region of the point P, and the direction of motion of both the waves and the wave group is that of OP. If, however, we consider a point near to the surface of the zone, where the energy contours are distorted as in Fig. 91(b), then the direction of the waves is OP, but the direction of motion of the wave packet is perpendicular to the energy contour, as shown by the arrow in Fig. 91(b).

OM: That seems to imply that waves moving in one direction can build up a wave group moving in another direction.

YS: That's quite right, and it is one of the differences between the behaviour of free electrons and of electrons in a lattice. With free electrons the waves and the wave group move in the same direction, but with electrons in a periodic field a group of waves moving in one direction may produce a wave packet moving in another direction. It is not possible to form any simple picture of how this happens—it's just one of the consequences of wave mechanics.

OM: This is all very confusing, and it seems to me that it must be wrong.

YS: What makes you think that?

OM: You have explained that under the influence of an electric field the wave number k changes in the direction of the field as you have shown in Fig. 90. Now if the direction of motion of the electron itself were the same as that of the waves, this would mean that the electron was accelerated in the direction of the field. But if the energy contours are distorted from the circular form—or the spherical form for a 3-dimensional crystal—then your statement implies that as the wave numbers pass through a series of states, the direction of motion of the electron as a wave packet changes so as to keep continually perpendicular to the energy contours as I have indicated by the arrows in Fig. 91(c). This would mean that the force and acceleration were not in the same direction, which is surely absurd?

YS: No. It is in fact exactly what happens. Your logic is quite right, and although the effects are very difficult to understand, they must be accepted. Where the energy contours are circular in Fig. 91(c) (spherical in a 3-dimensional crystal), the effect of an electric field is to change the wave number in the direction of the field, and the wave group which represents the electron itself is accelerated in the same direction. But for energy states near the surface of the zone, the energy contours are distorted, and the application of an electric field accelerates the electron in a direction which is not that of the field itself. It is essential to realise that near the surface of the zone it is the wave number which changes in the direction of the field, and not the group velocity.

OM: This is all very perplexing, and it would seem that electrons in states near the top of a zone must have properties very different from those of free electrons.

YS: That is so. Speaking generally one may say that electrons in states near the bottom of the first zone behave very like free electrons, and the same applies to electrons in states at the bottom of later zones.

In contrast to this, electrons in states near the top of a zone where the energy contours are distorted may behave quite differently. It is in this way that the Brillouin zone theories have explained the opposite signs of some of the galvano-magnetic and thermo-magnetic effects in different elements. When a metal is submitted to the simultaneous action of a magnetic field and an electric field, or of a magnetic field and a temperature gradient, various different effects (for example the Hall Effect) may be produced, and it was always rather a puzzle why these sometimes had the directions expected for free electrons, and sometimes the opposite direction. The zone theories have explained this by showing how electrons in states near the top and bottom of a zone may behave quite differently.

OM: I see that in Fig. 91(b) the energy contours bend round so that they are perpendicular to the zone boundary at the point where they meet it. This seems to imply that for electron states on the surface of a zone, the velocity of the electron has a zero component perpendicular to the zone face.

YS: That's right. For electron states on the surface of a zone the velocity has a zero component perpendicular to the zone boundary.

OM: If this is so it would seem that electron states at the corner of a zone where two edges intersect—or three faces in a three-dimensional model—have a zero velocity. The same would apply to electrons in states such as a in Fig. 91(b). Does this mean that these electrons are stationary in the lattice?

YS: That's a very difficult point. The electrons are not stationary in the lattice.

OM: But from what you have said above, the velocity must be zero in such cases.

YS: It all depends on exactly what you mean by velocity. The electron can only be thought of as a wave packet, and this wave packet has a zero velocity for the electron states to which you refer. If you imagine the electron located so precisely that you consider its velocity in the region of any one atom, its velocity might be in any direction, the average velocity in any given direction being zero. In such cases it is perhaps justifiable to say that the electron is undergoing rapid changes in motion, but these changes are within the length of the wave packet, and so they cannot be visualised in the form of trajectories. You will remember that we saw before (Chapter 9) that we could never say what went on within the wave packet, and this is one of the cases in which wave-mechanics leads to a condition of affairs which cannot be interpreted in terms of " common sense dynamics." The energy of these particular electrons is thus neither purely potential energy, nor to be thought of as kinetic energy of long range translatory motion of the electron through the metal. It is energy in a form characteristic of the interaction between the wave-like characteristics of the electron, and the periodic field of the lattice.

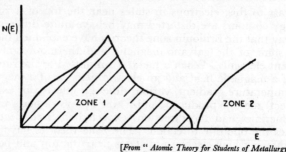

[From " Atomic Theory for Students of Metallurgy,"
Hume-Rothery, by courtesy of The Institute of Metals

Fig. 92

OM: Then when you say that electrons in states on the surface of a zone have a velocity whose component perpendicular to the zone face is zero, does this mean that the electron's velocity perpendicular to the zone face is continually changing backwards and forwards?

YS: Yes. You may if you like say that electrons in states on the surface of a zone are undergoing repeated Bragg reflections backwards and forwards across a set of atomic planes, so that on the average the component of velocity perpendicular to the zone face is zero; but these repeated reflections occur within the length of the wave packet, and so they cannot be visualised in the form of a definite trajectory.

OM: You spoke some time ago of semi-conductors. I understand how substances such as silicon are only weakly metallic, but is there any really characteristic difference between a metal and a semi-conductor?

YS: Speaking generally the electrical resistance of a normal metal is increased by rise of temperature or by the introduction of atoms of another metal to form a solid solution. In contrast to this the resistance of a semi-conductor is decreased by the presence of impurities, and generally decreases with rise of temperature. We may consider first a substance whose zone characteristics are shown in Fig. 92. Here a completely filled zone is separated from the next zone by a very small energy gap. At the absolute zero, this substance would be an insulator, but on raising the temperature electrons might be excited thermally from states at the top of the filled zone into the lower states of the next zone, and after being excited in this way the electrons could behave as free electrons with all the states of the second zone at their disposal. It is important to note that it is the thermal excitation, and not the action of the electric field which excites the electrons into the higher zone. Pure graphite and pure germanium are semi-conductors of this kind, and you can understand why the resistances diminish with rise of temperature—the higher the temperature, the greater the number of the excited electrons, and hence the more electrons available for conductivity.

A substance like pure graphite may be called an intrinsic semi-

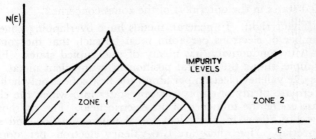

[From " Atomic Theory for Students of Metallurgy,"
Hume-Rothery, by courtesy of The Institute of Metals

Fig. 93

conductor, but many semi-conductors owe their properties to the effect
of impurities. In such cases the condition of affairs may be as shown
in Fig. 93, where a filled zone is separated by a small energy gap from
the next zone, and the impurity atoms introduce new energy states
which lie in the range between the two zones. In this case when the
temperature is raised one or both of two processes may take place. On
the one hand electrons may be excited thermally from the impurity
levels to the second zone where they will be free to act as conduction
electrons. These excited electrons will be in states at the bottom of the
second zone, and so they will have most of the characteristics of ordinary
free electrons (p. 212). Semi-conductors of this type are often called
n type semi-conductors. You can readily see that if the concentration
of impurity atoms is very small, there will be a limit to the number of
electrons which can be excited into the second zone. On raising the
temperature a stage may be reached at which nearly all the electrons
have been excited, and with further rise of temperature the resistance
may increase in the ordinary way owing to the increased amplitude of
the thermal vibrations.

In another class of impurity semi-conductor, electrons may be
excited from states at the top of the first zone into the impurity levels.
This type of substance is called a p type semi-conductor, and since
the excitation leaves a few unoccupied states at the top of the first
zone, the application of an electric field will be able to alter the electronic distribution, and so to produce a conductivity. But in this case
the unoccupied states will be those near to a zone boundary where the
energy contours are distorted, and the behaviour of electrons is very
abnormal (see page 213). Here again saturation effect may be shown
if the number of impurity atoms is small. It is in this way that the
zone theory is able to explain the existence of semi-conductors with
both normal and abnormal properties, and in many cases it is found
that the properties of a semi-conductor are extremely sensitive to the
presence of impurities.

OM: From what you say it would seem that the electrical conductivity of a normal metal must result from the number of electrons
per atom being such that there is a relatively large number of un-

occupied states in the outermost of the zones concerned.

YS: That's right. In general, metals have overlapping zones, and the number of electrons per atom must be such that the zone concerned with conductivity, has plenty of unoccupied states. Fig. 94, for example, shows the general position in a univalent metal. Since there is one valency electron per atom, the first zone is only half filled, and there are plenty of empty electron states into which the electron can pass under the influence of an electric field. Fig. 95 shows the condition of affairs in a divalent metal where the first and second zones overlap. Here there are two valency electrons per atom, and these occupy most of the states of the first zone, and a few of the lower states of the second zone. With a trivalent metal with three valency electrons per atom, all the states of the first zone would be occupied, and would account for two electrons per atom. The exact position of the overlaps would then determine whether the remaining electrons were all in the second zone, or whether some were in the second, and some in the third zone.

OM: That is very interesting, and it seems to explain several points that had puzzled me. When you said that the valency electrons were free to move in the lattice, it seemed to me at first that the electrical conductivity ought to increase with the valency, because the higher the valency the more electrons would be available. But this is not so. It is well known that the univalent metals—the alkali metals, and copper, silver and gold—have the highest conductivities. If I have understood you rightly, in a case such as that of Fig. 96, the electrons in the first zone form, as it were, a complete group which cannot give

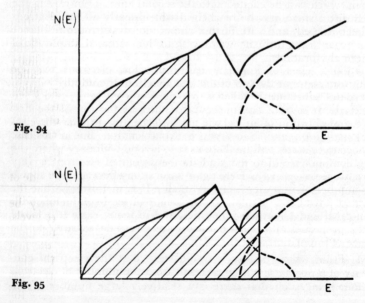

Fig. 94

Fig. 95

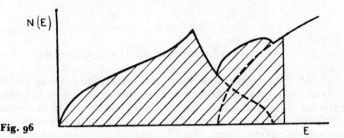

Fig. 96

rise to a conductivity because the electric field cannot transfer them to states in the next zone. So the number of electrons available for conductivity in a trivalent metal is not three times as many as those in a univalent metal.

YS: That is quite right, and it is one of the great triumphs of the zone theories that they give a satisfactory explanation of the fact that the number of electrons effectively available for conductivity does not necessarily increase with the valency of the metal.

OM: As the temperature is raised, the resistance of a normal metal increases, but it always seems rather difficult to understand this, because one would imagine that as the metal expanded, the space available for free electronic motion would increase.

YS: That difficulty is explained by the wave-like properties of the electrons. As the temperature is raised the atomic vibrations increase, and the perfect periodicity of the lattice is diminished. Anything which disturbs the regularity of the lattice diminishes the freedom of motion of the electrons. It is common practice to say that the electrons undergo collisions with the atoms, but this is a rather misleading term, because the process is not to be thought of as a collision between a bullet-like electron and a spherical atom. The process is the interaction between the wave system of the electron and the vibrating field of the lattice, as the result of which an electron is scattered into a new state. It is quite easy to show that the probability of scattering is proportional to the square of the amplitude of the atomic vibrations, and hence is directly proportional to the absolute temperature, and in this way the theory accounts for the fact that the resistance of a normal metal is proportional to the absolute temperature.

You will see, therefore, that the zone theories have led to a very satisfactory explanation of the more general characteristics of the three types of substance, insulators, semi-conductors, and metals. The theory also explains why the conductivity does not increase with increasing valency, whilst the general wave theory of electrons has given a very satisfactory explanation of the main features of electrical conductivity.

Suggestions for further reading:
Semi-Conductors, D. A. Wright. 1950, Methuen & Co. Ltd.
Electrons and Holes in Semi-conductors, W. Shockley. 1950, D. Van Nostrand Co.

28—Atomic Diameters of the Elements

OLDER METALLURGIST: You have explained (Chapters 24 and 26) about the crystal structures of the elements, but you said nothing about the interatomic distances, or the sizes of the atoms in the crystals of the different elements. From what you said in connection with the electron clouds of free atoms (Part I), one would expect the general tendency to be a decrease in the size of the atom in passing along any one Period of the Periodic Table, accompanied by a marked increase on passing from one Period to the next. But I find great difficulty in reconciling the electron cloud picture with the concept of a definite atomic size or atomic diameter.

YOUNG SCIENTIST: You are quite right in saying that the electron cloud picture cannot be reconciled with the representation of the "size" of an atom by one single number. But the study of interatomic distances in crystals has shown that in some cases the results can be systematised if the different atoms, or ions in the case of salts, are assumed to possess definite diameters or radii. This idea was originally introduced by W. L. Bragg in connection with the study of salts such as sodium chloride. In these salts it is quite certain that the structure is built up of ions and not of neutral atoms. Thus Fig. 97 shows the structure of sodium chloride, and this is built up of Na^+ and Cl^- ions arranged in regular array, each ion being surrounded by six others of the opposite sign. Fig. 98 shows the structure of cæsium chloride, where each ion has eight others of the opposite sign. A general study of this kind of salt showed that the interatomic distances could be satisfactorily accounted for by the assignment of a definite "radius" to each kind of ion. These "ionic radii" required slight correction on changing from one structure to another of different co-ordination number—the ionic radius of the Cl^- ion in the NaCl structure, for example, was about 3 per cent smaller than in the CsCl structure; it is a general principle that the ionic radius becomes smaller as the co-ordination number decreases.

OM: It seems to me that ionic radii obtained in this way cannot be a simple measure of the electron cloud density, because they must surely involve the charges on the ions? Suppose, for example, we have two ions A^+ and B^{++}, and that these have electron clouds with exactly the same density distribution. Then if we consider the two salts A Cl and B Cl_2, the attraction between the B^{++} and Cl^- ions at a given distance will be greater than that between the A^+ and Cl^- ions because of the double charge on the B^{++} ions. So the ionic radius of the B^{++} ion will appear to be smaller than that of the A^+ ion in spite of the fact that the two electron clouds are the same.

YS: That is perfectly true, and it was recognised first by Pauling and by Zachariasen that the empirical ionic radii were open to the objection you have raised. This difficulty was partly overcome by the introduction of what are called the " univalent ionic radii " in which the ionic radii are corrected to allow·for the point to which you have referred. The term " univalent ionic radius " is rather unfortunate, because if one deals with calcium, for example, the value given is not that for the radius of a hypothetical Ca^+ ion. It is the "radius" which the actual Ca^{++} ion would possess if it were in a crystal where the forces of attraction were those between univalent ions. It has become increasingly apparent that the " size " of an ion cannot really be represented by a single number, but for many purposes the univalent ionic radii of Pauling and Zachariasen may be used to give a rough indication of the sizes of the electron clouds of the ions concerned.

OM: You have explained (Chapter 26) how crystals of copper, silver, and gold may be regarded as built up of ions pulled together by the valency electrons until the electron clouds of the ions overlap, and so produce a repulsion. In such cases I can understand how the ionic diameters may be of the same order as the distances between the atoms in the crystal of the metal. On the other hand in the alkali metals the distance between the atoms in the metallic element must surely be quite different from the ionic diameters?

YS: That's quite right. It was recognised first by Goldschmidt that interatomic distances in salts and metals often indicated quite different " sizes " of the ions and atoms concerned. This was expressed by saying that the two kinds of structure were *incommensurable*.

When we deal with the metallic elements we find that a certain amount of progress has been made in the same way, and we may first define an *atomic diameter* as the closest distance of approach between two atoms in a crystal of an element. Fig. 99 shows the atomic

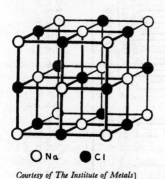

○ Na ● Cl

Courtesy of The Institute of Metals]

Fig. 97—The NaCl structure

Each ion is surrounded by six others of opposite charge

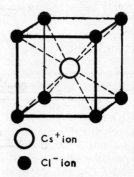

○ Cs⁺ ion

● Cl⁻ ion

[Courtesy of The Institute of Metals

Fig. 98—Cæsium chloride structure

Each ion is surrounded by eight others of opposite charge

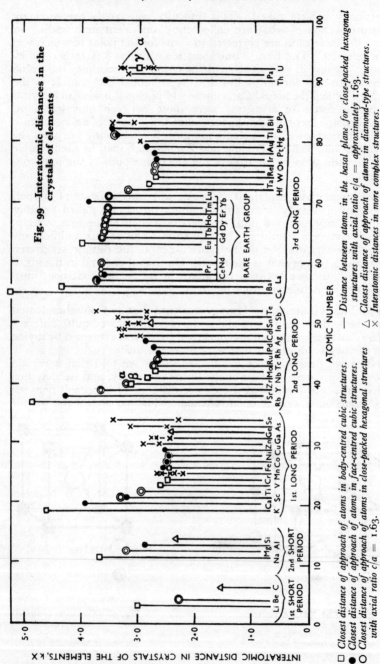

Fig. 99—Interatomic distances in the crystals of elements

— Distance between atoms in the basal plane for close-packed hexagonal structures with axial ratio c/a = approximately 1.63.
○ Closest distance of approach of atoms in diamond-type structures.
△ Interatomic distances in more complex structures.
×

□ Closest distance of approach of atoms in body-centred cubic structures.
● Closest distance of approach of atoms in face-centred cubic structures.
○ Closest distance of approach of atoms in close-packed hexagonal structures with axial ratio c/a = 1.63.

[Courtesy The Institute of Metals. "The Structure of Metals and Alloys," Hume-Rothery and Raynor.

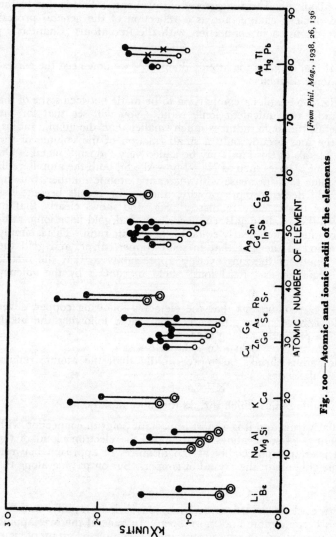

Fig. 100—Atomic and ionic radii of the elements

[From Phil. Mag., 1938, 26, 136]

● ½ (Interatomic distance in the crystal of the element).

○ Pauling univalent ionic radii.

× Goldschmidt empirical ionic radii.

⊙ Zachariasen univalent ionic radii.

diameters of a number of the elements, and you will see how this shows a well marked periodicity. In each Period the alkali metal at the beginning of the Period has by far the largest atomic diameter, and there is a regular decrease in the atomic diameters on passing from an alkali metal to the succeeding elements. This is due to the increased nuclear charge, and is a reflection of the general process which we discussed in connection with the free atoms (Chapters 13 and 14).

OM: If Fig. 99 gives the atomic diameters, we now need the corresponding ionic diameters.

YS: Fig. 100 enables a comparison to be made between some of the atomic radii and univalent ionic radii. You will see that for the alkali metals the ionic radius is much smaller than the atomic radius, so that the ions occupy only a small fraction of the volume of the crystal. Metals of this kind may be called very " open " metals. On passing along a series such as Na→Mg→Al→Si, both the atomic radii and the ionic radii decrease with increasing atomic number, but the atomic radii decrease more rapidly, and so the metals become less " open " as the valency increases. Fig. 100 shows clearly that in contrast to the alkali metals, copper, silver, and gold have ionic radii which are much more nearly equal to the atomic radii. This is simply an expression of the fact that in solid copper, silver, and gold the electron clouds of the ions overlap appreciably, so that the metals may be regarded as " hard ions " held in contact by the valency electrons.

OM: Fig. 100 suggests that the elements following copper, silver and gold behave quite differently from those following the alkali metals. On proceeding along the series

$$Cu \rightarrow Zn \rightarrow Ga \rightarrow Ge \rightarrow As$$

the ionic radius shrinks far more rapidly than the atomic radius, whereas in the series

$$K \rightarrow Ca \rightarrow Sc \rightarrow$$

it is the atomic radius which shrinks the more rapidly.

YS: that's true, and it is a most important point in connection with the structures of some alloys. In copper the electron cloud of the Cu^+ ion overlaps appreciably at the distances of approach between nearest neighbours in the crystal of copper. But on passing along the series

$$Cu \rightarrow Zn \rightarrow Ga \rightarrow Ge \rightarrow As$$

the electron cloud of the underlying ion shrinks rapidly, and the structures become more and more open. In general the overlapping of the electron clouds of an ion containing a completed group of eight to eighteen electrons produces very strong repulsive forces, and there are many cases in which it is quite clear that the " size " of an atom cannot be represented by one single number, and that the behaviour can be understood only by considering whether the " size " is determined mainly by the valency electrons (as in the alkali metals) or also by the electron clouds of the ions. The general ideas expressed in Fig. 100 are most important, and must be thoroughly grasped in order to understand the structures of some alloys.

OM: From Fig. 99 it seems that in the First Long Period, gallium and germanium have slightly smaller atomic diameters than copper. This is in contrast to the behaviour in the second and Third Long Periods where indium and tin (white) and thallium and lead have definitely larger atomic diameters than silver and gold. Is this the result of the process of incomplete ionisation to which you referred before (page 205)?

YS: That's right. The sudden increase in the atomic diameter which occurs at thallium in the Third Long Period suggests clearly that some change in the binding process has occurred, and the suggestion is that in metallic thallium the $(6s)^2$ sub-group is sufficiently stable for its electron cloud to build up round the atoms and so to produce repulsion rather than attraction.

OM: You have not explained whether the atomic diameters summarised in Fig. 99 are to be regarded as real constants of the elements irrespective of their crystal structures.

YS: Fig. 99 must not be looked on as giving more than a rough indication of the " sizes " of atoms in metallic crystals. The main characteristics of the figure are correct, and the general periodicity which the diagram shows is an undoubted fact. But if one wants to go into finer details it is necessary to make allowance for the different co-ordination numbers of the various crystal structures. According to Goldschmidt, a change from a structure with co-ordination number 12 to one with co-ordination number 8 results in a contraction of 3 per cent in the atomic diameter, whilst a change from co-ordination number 12→4 results in a contraction of 12 per cent. This means that the values in Fig. 99 for face-centred cubic and normal close-packed hexagonal structures can be compared directly with one another, but when we change to a body-centred cubic structure we have to remember the above contraction.

OM: Do you mean that if we dissolve gold in copper (both face-centred cubic) the lattice spacing changes linearly with composition, whereas if we dissolve germanium (diamond structure co-ordination No. 4) in copper, the germanium atom behaves as though it were 12 per cent larger than the value given in Fig. 99?

YS: That was the original idea of Goldschmidt, who produced a series of atomic diameters for a standard co-ordination number 12. Later work, however, has shown that the lattice spacing relations of solid solutions are much more complicated than was originally imagined, and the linear relations you suggest are very seldom found. We shall deal with some of these complexities when we consider alloy structures. For the moment you may look on Fig. 99 as giving the general order of the atomic diameters, but you must remember that the values for crystal structures with different co-ordination numbers cannot really be compared directly. The general principle is that the atomic diameter becomes smaller as the co-ordination number decreases. This can readily be understood, because as the co-ordination number increases, the atomic attraction of an atom has, as it were, to be distributed over a larger number of neighbours, and so less is available for cohesion between two particular atoms. In spite of these limitations Fig. 99 is of very great importance, and you will have to memorise the values for the more common metals. You must, for example, aim at a condition in which you almost instinctively think of copper as having an atomic diameter of approximately 2.5 kX, and magnesium one of 3.2 kX. If you can carry these numbers about in your head you can understand and sometimes even predict what happens in alloys.

OM: From Fig. 99 it seems that there is a regular increase in size on passing down the alkali metal group

$$Li \rightarrow Na \rightarrow K \rightarrow Rb \rightarrow Cs$$

where all the crystal structures are body-centred cubic at room temperature. In the alkaline earth group the same thing occurs as far as strontium, but the value for barium is only very slightly greater. This seems to agree with what you have said because the first four alkaline earths are either close-packed hexagonal or face-centred cubic, and so have co-ordination number 12, whereas barium is body-centred cubic with co-ordination number 8, and so the failure of barium to show an increase may be due to the change in co-ordination number. But this kind of explanation does not seem to account for the fact that gold and the few elements which precede it have almost the same atomic diameters as silver and its preceding elements.

YS: That is the result of the lanthanide contraction to which we referred in Chapter 16. The atomic diameter of silver is greater than that of copper, and this is the result of the normal increase on passing from one period to the next. The atomic diameter of gold would be greater than that of silver were it not for the building up of the rare earth group. This as we saw before (Chapter 16) results in the outer electrons of the elements Hafnium→Gold being held more firmly than they would be if the rare earth group had not been built up, and this is why there is no marked increase on passing from silver→gold. It is very useful to remember that the atomic diameters in the series

Hf–Ta–W–Re–Os–Ir–Pt–Au

are very nearly the same as those of the corresponding elements in the previous period.

29—Univalent and Divalent Metals

O LDER METALLURGIST: So far we have discussed the general electron theory of metals, and I think it would help me now if we dealt with some specific examples. From what you have said I imagine the univalent metals will be the most easy to deal with, so let us consider the alkali metals, and copper, silver and gold.

YOUNG SCIENTIST: At room temperatures the alkali metals all crystallise in the body-centred cubic structure, whereas the elements of Group I B crystallise in the face-centred cubic structure. Fig. 101 shows these structures together with the general sizes involved. You will see the regular increase in the size of the unit cell in passing down Group I A, and this is the result of the increasing quantum number of the valency electrons. In Group I B there is a similar increase on passing from copper to silver, but on passing from silver to gold there is no corresponding increase—this, as I explained before, is the result of the lanthanide contraction (p. 116, Chapter 16).

OM: Does the electron theory explain why the body-centred cubic structure is preferred by Group I A and the face-centred cube by Group I B?

YS: If one considers the valency electrons as moving in a simple periodic field, the $N(E)$ curves for the face-centred and body-centred cubic structures are very nearly identical up to 1 electron per atom, and from this point of view there is no very clear reason why the alkali metals all adopt the body-centred cubic structure, since in these metals the ionic radii are very small compared with the atomic radii, and the properties of the structure depend essentially on the valency electrons. In the case of copper, silver and gold where the electron clouds of the ions overlap appreciably, it can be shown that the forces due to the electron clouds of the ions favour the face-centred cubic structure. The mathematics is naturally complicated, but it is perhaps justifiable to say that if you look on these metals as consisting of hard spheres (ions) held in contact by the valency electrons, then the lowest energy not unnaturally results from a structure in which the ions are packed together as closely as possible, and the face-centred cubic arrangement is one way of obtaining this close packing.

OM: If Fig. 101 gives the crystal structures, is one to regard the atoms as being fixed and stationary in their positions at the absolute zero, and as vibrating with increasing amplitude about these positions as the temperature rises?

YS: That is not quite right, although your general idea is perfectly correct. A system of N atoms on a lattice has $3N$ independent modes of vibration, and the actual state of vibration of the lattice is the

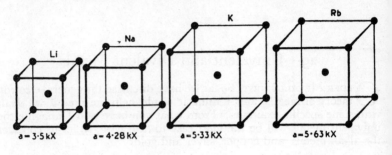

result of the superposition of these modes. According to the quantum theory, the energy associated with a frequency v is

$$\tfrac{1}{2} hv + \frac{hv}{e^{\frac{hv}{k\theta}} - 1}$$

where h is Planck's constant, k is Boltzmann's constant[1] and θ the absolute temperature. In this expression the first term does not involve the temperature, and it represents the so-called " zero point energy," that is the part of the vibrational energy which persists at the absolute zero. The second term is of such a nature that it equals zero at the absolute zero, and then increases with temperature. You will see, therefore, that your general idea that the vibrational energy increases with temperature was correct, but at the absolute zero some vibrational energy persists, and the atoms are not at rest. Further, the nature of the second, or temperature dependent term, is such that on increasing the temperature, the energy associated with the lowest frequencies increases most rapidly. One may say, therefore, that on raising the temperature of the crystal from the absolute zero the atomic vibrations to be first stimulated are those of low frequency and long wave-length, and the crystal may be regarded as swept through by vibrations whose wave-lengths are much longer than the distance between two atoms. On raising the temperature further, the higher frequencies strike up, and finally when the amplitude of the vibrations is of the same order as the distance between two neighbouring atoms, the solid melts.

OM: If that is the general picture, there must be some essential difference between the cohesion in copper, silver and gold, and that in the alkali metals, because the melting points of the latter are very much lower than those of copper, silver and gold.

YS: That is due to a combination of two factors. On the one

---

[1] The equation for a perfect gas is usually written $pv = R\theta$, where the gas-constant R refers to 1 gramme molecule. The corresponding equation referring to a single molecule is $pv = k\theta$, where k is Boltzmann's constant.

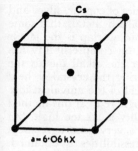

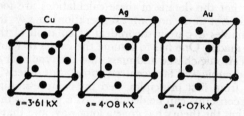

Fig. 101—Crystal structures of the alkali and Group I B metals showing general sizes of the unit cells

hand the atomic diameters of the alkali metals are very considerably greater than those of copper, silver and gold (Fig. 101). In any kind of structure where the atoms are held together by shared electrons, there is a natural tendency for the strength of the binding to diminish as the distance between the atoms increases. Apart from this, the outermost electrons of the Cu^+ ions also give rise to an attraction, by a process which is essentially similar to that involved in the Van der Waals forces (Chapter 24). That is to say a lowering of energy, and hence an attraction is produced if the $(3d)$ electrons of two adjacent Cu^+ ions move in harmony with one another, instead of moving independently.

OM: This seems very curious because you have previously said that the outermost electrons of the Cu^+ ion produce an intense repulsion when they overlap.

YS: That's right—both processes go on together. When the electron clouds of the Cu^+ ions overlap, repulsive forces are produced which oppose a further drawing of the atoms together. At the same time if the electrons of adjacent ions move in harmony, there is a lowering of energy and the atoms are held together more firmly. In a sense you may say that the outermost electrons of the Cu^+ ions serve both to hold the atoms apart, and so to produce an incompressible metal, and also to increase the attraction, and so to raise the melting point.

OM: If that is so, the compressibilities of the copper, silver and gold should be much smaller than those of the alkali metals where there is no appreciable ionic overlap.

YS: That's true. There is a general tendency for the compressibility of a metal of a given valency to increase with the atomic volume, but as you will see from Fig. 102, the compressibilities of copper, silver and gold are so much smaller than those of the alkali metals that some different factor is clearly at work, and the ionic overlap is the factor concerned. Very interesting theoretical work on compressibility has been done by Fuchs, who has shown that for the alkali metals the compressibilities can be calculated by considering the crystal as held together by valency electrons moving in the field of the univalent ions whose overlap can to a first approximation be ignored. If this method is used for copper, the calculated compressibility is far too high, but by considering the effect of the ionic overlap, a very good agreement between the calculated and observed compressibilities is obtained. I am afraid that the details of these calculations are too difficult for us to discuss, but it is not an exaggeration to say that quantum mechanics enables a purely theoretical calculation of the compressibilities to be made. One has to assume the values of Planck's constant and of the electronic charge and mass, and the type of crystal structure (body-centred cubic and face-centred cubic), but otherwise everything is calculated from first principles, and the compressibilities and some of the elastic constants can be deduced. As a practical man, therefore, you will see that the theory has gone a long way, and that the mechanical properties within the elastic range can be calculated for the alkali metals and for copper.

OM: Does the theory go on so that the properties of plastic deformation are accounted for?

YS: I am afraid not. There is a satisfactory theory of the properties within the elastic range, and here the electron theory has been most

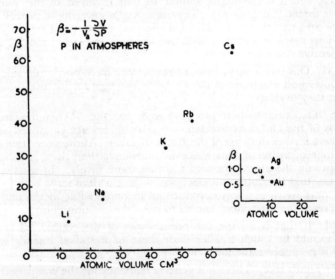

Fig. 102—Showing the compressibilities of the univalent metals

Table VIII

MELTING POINTS OF THE METALS

Element .. Melting point in °C. ..	Li	Be	Na	Mg	K	Ca	Rb	Sr
	179	1278	98	650	64	851	39	771
Element .. Melting point in C. ..	Cs	Ba	Cu	Zn	Ag	Cd	Au	Hg
	26	704	1083	419	961	321	1063—39	

successful. A great deal has been found out experimentally about the mechanism of plastic deformation, but until recently there has been no satisfactory theory. In the last twenty years it has become realised that the plastic properties of metals are intimately connected with internal defects, or departures from a perfectly regular arrangement of the atoms. Certain types of defect, known as dislocations, have been recognised, and a successful theory of dislocations is now (1954) being rapidly developed. This, however, is rather a subject of its own, and we shall consider it later (Chapter 32).

OM: The alkali metals and also copper, silver, and gold are univalent elements, and if I understand you rightly their electronic structures are such that the one valency electron per atom fills the lower half of the first Brillouin zone. There seems, however, to be a complete contrast between the behaviour of the Group II elements in the A and B series. The alkaline earth elements (see Table VIII) have melting points which are much higher than those of the preceding alkali metals. But in Group II B, the metals zinc, cadmium, and mercury have very much lower melting points than the preceding elements copper, silver and gold.

YS: The figures you give are quite correct, and the effects have not yet all been explained in a quantitative manner. The increase in melting point on passing from an alkali metal to the succeeding alkaline earth metal is accompanied by a decrease in the interatomic distances in the crystals of the elements (see Fig. 99), and is simply the result of the increasing charge on the nucleus drawing the whole structure together more firmly. If you regard the metallic structure as resulting from the attraction of the valency electrons swimming among the array of positively charged ions, then in the alkali metals there is one valency electron per atom moving in a field of univalent ions, whilst in the alkaline earths there are two valency electrons per atom in a field of divalent ions. It is thus quite easy to understand the general contraction and firmer binding on passing from an alkali to an alkaline earth.

The fact that copper, silver and gold have higher melting points than the preceding alkali metals potassium, rubidium and caesium is partly the result of the smaller atomic diameters of copper, silver and gold. You can readily understand that in any structure held together

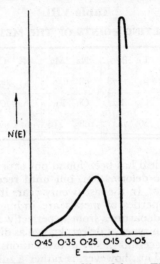

Fig. 103—The N(E) curve for metallic calcium. The first zone is very slightly overlapped by the second
(*After Manning and Krutter*)

by shared electrons, the binding must become increasingly loose as the interatomic distances increase. Apart from this effect, the higher melting points of copper, silver and gold are due to the Van der Waals forces between the Cu^+ ions, to which we referred above, and this factor is very marked. On passing from copper to zinc, the electron cloud of the ion shrinks rapidly (see Fig. 100), and so the interatomic cohesion resulting from the Van der Waals kind of force dies away, and it is perhaps this fact which is the cause of the low melting point of zinc, and similarly for cadmium and mercury in the later Periods.

OM: As regards the general electronic structure of the Group II elements, it seems to me that their Brillouin zones must be of the overlapping type. The first Brillouin zones of all the crystal structures contain exactly two electron states per atom (page 174), and consequently if the zones did not overlap, the two valency electrons per atom would completely fill the zone, and the crystal would be an insulator as described on page 208 of Chapter 27.

YS: That's right. The electrical conductivity indicates that the second zone overlaps the first, but the overlap is small, and this is why the electrical conductivity of the divalent elements is less than that of the univalent elements. The divalent elements have twice as many valency electrons per atom, but the zone restrictions mean that most of these electrons are not effective as regards conductivity (see page 217). Fig. 103 shows the $N(E)$ curve of Manning and Krutter for calcium which crystallises in the face-centred cubic structure, but this $N(E)$ curve is only a very rough approximation.

OM: You have already shown me (Figs. 57 and 58) the first

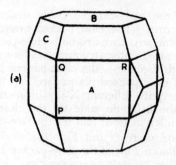

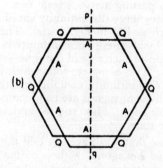

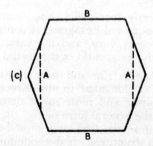

Fig. 104—The first Brillouin zone of the close-packed hexagonal structure

(a) *Shows the zone with one of the small truncated prisms added on an A-face.*

(b) *Shows the shape of the equatorial sections of the zone, with small truncated prisms added on all six faces.*

(c) *Shows a vertical section along the plane p-q.*

Brillouin zones of the body-centred cubic structure, and the face-centred cubic structure. The close-packed hexagonal structure and the face-centred cubic structure are both close-packed structures, but whereas the face-centred cubic structure has four sets of close-packed planes (the octahedral planes), the close-packed hexagonal structure has only one set of close-packed planes (see Fig. 81, page 199). The two structures give quite different X-ray diffraction films, and so it would seem that the Brillouin zone for the close-packed hexagonal structure must be different from that for the face-centred cube.

YS: That is quite correct, and Fig. 104(a) shows what is often called[1] the first Brillouin zone of the close-packed hexagonal structure. This has some rather curious characteristics. Inside the zone, the energy and the wave number vary continuously, and there is an abrupt increase in energy on passing across a zone face. The calculations of H. Jones show that this energy discontinuity vanishes along some of the edges of the zone such as PQ in Fig. 104(a). The first zone which is bounded everywhere by an energy discontinuity is obtained by adding a small truncated prism to each side of the zone—one of these prisms is shown in Fig. 104 (a). This complete zone which is surrounded everywhere by an energy discontinuity contains exactly two electrons per atom, and since the divalent metals are conductors of electricity, there is an overlap from this zone. Figs. 104 (b) and 104 (c) show sections through the complete zone.

OM: It seems to me that you have not told the whole story. Magnesium is close-packed hexagonal with a normal axial ratio, whilst zinc and cadmium are close-packed hexagonal with a large axial ratio. (Fig. 87, page 203.) The shape of the Brillouin zone must surely be different from the two?

YS: That is perfectly true. Fig. 104 shows the general form of the zone for the close-packed hexagonal structure, but the ratio of the height to the width may vary, and the variation is in the opposite direction to that of the axial ratio of the crystal structure.

OM: You mean that for zinc and cadmium where the actual crystal structure (Fig. 87) is elongated in the direction of the c-axis, the Brillouin zone is shorter and more squat than that for magnesium, although both have the general form of Fig. 104. If this is so, it would seem that overlaps from the first zone must begin in quite different directions in the two structures. If the zone for zinc and cadmium is sufficiently short and squat, the occupied electron states will reach the top and bottom of the zone before they reach the sides, and the overlap will occur first at the top and bottom. Is that right?

YS: The overlaps from the first zone of Fig. 104 are of three kinds. There is the overlap from the first zone across the faces A into the small prisms; this may be called the A overlap. There is then the

[1] Many writers now call this the first Jones zone. The difference between the zones of Brillouin and of Jones is difficult to explain simply, and the reader may consult *Atomic Theory for Students of Metallurgy* (1962 revised reprint) by W. Hume-Rothery.

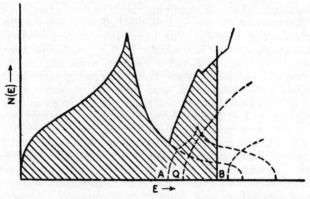

[*Courtesy The Institute of Metals*]

Fig. 105 (a)—Approximate N(E) curve for magnesium

The points A, Q and B correspond with the A, Q and B overlaps referred to in the text. The shaded region is the area of occupied states at two electrons per atom; it will be seen that the A and Q overlaps have occurred, but not the B overlap, although a comparatively few more electrons per atom would make this overlap occur. The diagram is approximate only, and the limit of occupied states is probably nearer to the point B than is shown, although the B overlap has just not taken place

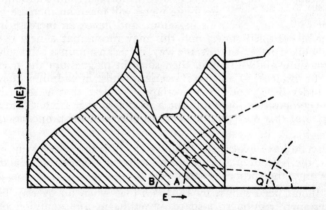

[*Courtesy The Institute of Metals*]

Fig. 105 (b)—Approximate N(E) curve for zinc and cadmium

The overlaps occur in the order B, A, Q. At two electrons per atom the B and A overlaps have occurred, but not the Q overlap. It must be emphasised that these diagrams are qualitative sketches only and are not accurate. [A more detailed curve is now available for magnesium (see The Physical Metallurgy of Magnesium and Its Alloys, G. V. Raynor. 1959, Pergamon Press), but the present diagram 105(a) has been retained in order to facilitate comparison with Fig. 105(b), as no accurate curves exist for zinc and cadmium—1961]

overlap across the top and bottom faces B; this may be called the B overlap. Finally there is a third kind of overlap through the zone edges Q; this may be called the Q overlap.

In the case of zinc and cadmium, the crystal structure is elongated in the direction of the c-axis, and the Brillouin zone of Fig. 104 is relatively short and squat. With increasing numbers of electrons per atom, the overlaps occur in the order B, A, Q, and with two electrons per atom the overlaps at B and A have occurred, but not that at Q. In the case of magnesium where the axial ratio is 1.62, the Brillouin zone is relatively much taller, and the overlaps occur in the order A, Q, B. With two electrons per atom overlapping has occurred at A and Q, but not at B, although a very slight increased number of electrons per atom cause the overlap to occur. The resulting $\mathcal{N}(E)$ curves for the two structures are shown in Fig. 105 (a) and (b), and these indicate clearly how the order of the overlaps is different in the two cases. In this figure the shaded area indicates the limit of the occupied states at two electrons per atom. Magnesium is an extremely interesting metal from this point of view, because overlapping has occurred in two directions, and very nearly in the third.

It should be emphasised that these diagrams are only rough approximations, and do not give the $\mathcal{N}(E)$ curves accurately.

OM: Are these relations of any real value?

YS: They are of great importance in the understanding of some alloys of magnesium, zinc and cadmium. If we alloy these metals with elements of higher valency so as to form a solid solution, then increasing percentage of the solute metal will mean an increase in the number of valency electrons per atom, and hence an increase in the number of occupied states, and this may mean that a new overlap suddenly takes place. In the same way, if we can obtain a solid solution of magnesium and cadmium, then since in magnesium the overlaps are in the order A, Q and no B overlap, whilst in cadmium they are in the order B, Q, and no A overlap, it is clear that at some intermediate composition there must be a sudden change from a B to an A overlap, and this may produce curious effects in the properties of the alloys.

OM: You have explained (Chapter 27) how the opening up of the states at the bottom of a new zone adds to the electrical conductivity, but are any other properties affected?

YS: It has been shown by H. Jones that when an overlap begins in a certain direction in k-space, it results in an expansion of the crystal in the same direction. In this way it has been possible to explain some of the abnormal relations between the lattice spacings and the composition of alloys, and we shall consider some of these later. The important thing to notice is that the theory has now reached the stage where a great deal is known about the general characteristics of the electron distribution in the close-packed hexagonal structure, and the theory now permits the calculation of some of the elastic constants of beryllium. As with the univalent metals the theory does not account satisfactorily for the properties connected with plastic deformation, and at present these lie quite outside the electron theory of metals.

30—Transition Elements

OLDER METALLURGIST: Speaking generally, it seems that most of the strongest metals and those of highest melting point are found among the transition elements, and I should like to know how these look in terms of electron theories.

YOUNG SCIENTIST: The transition elements form a very interesting group, and we may begin by considering some of their main characteristics. In Fig. 106 I have summarised the crystal structure data, and you will see that all the transition elements crystallise in one or more of the three typical metallic structures, the body-centred cubic, face-centred cubic, or close-packed hexagonal structures. Allotropy is very common, and is generally confined to the typical structures, although abnormal and complicated structures are formed by α- and β-manganese, and by α- and β-uranium—the latter is of course an actinide element, and should perhaps not be included among the normal transitional elements. If its inclusion is justified, the facts suggest that Groups VI and VII occupy a critical position in the Long Periods.

OM: The existence of the normal crystal structure suggests that the difference between the transition metals and the remaining metals is not due to the type of crystal structure. But the high melting points of the transition metals suggest that the cohesion is somehow stronger.

YS: That's right, but what exactly do you mean by strong cohesion?

OM: I should say there was strong cohesion when it was difficult to pull the atoms slightly farther apart.

YS: That's a good definition, but if you use it you do not necessarily require the melting points. A melting point is by definition the temperature at which both liquid and solid phases are in equilibrium, and so if some factor makes the liquid phase relatively more stable, the melting point will fall even though the cohesion in the solid remains strong.

OM: You want something like the inverse of the compressibility.

YS: That's right. The compressibility is a measure of the ease with which the atoms in a solid can be squeezed closer together, and since the process is reversible, a low compressibility means that it is difficult to squeeze the atoms together, and also that it is difficult to pull them apart, and so indicates strong bonding. The compressibility is a good property to study, because it involves the solid phase alone, and in Fig. 107 I have shown the compressibilities of the transition elements. In each Long Period the compressibilities diminish rapidly on passing from Group I A→II A→III A→IV A, and this indicates that there is a rapid increase in the strength of cohesion.

Fig. 106

[By courtesy of The Philosophical Magazine]

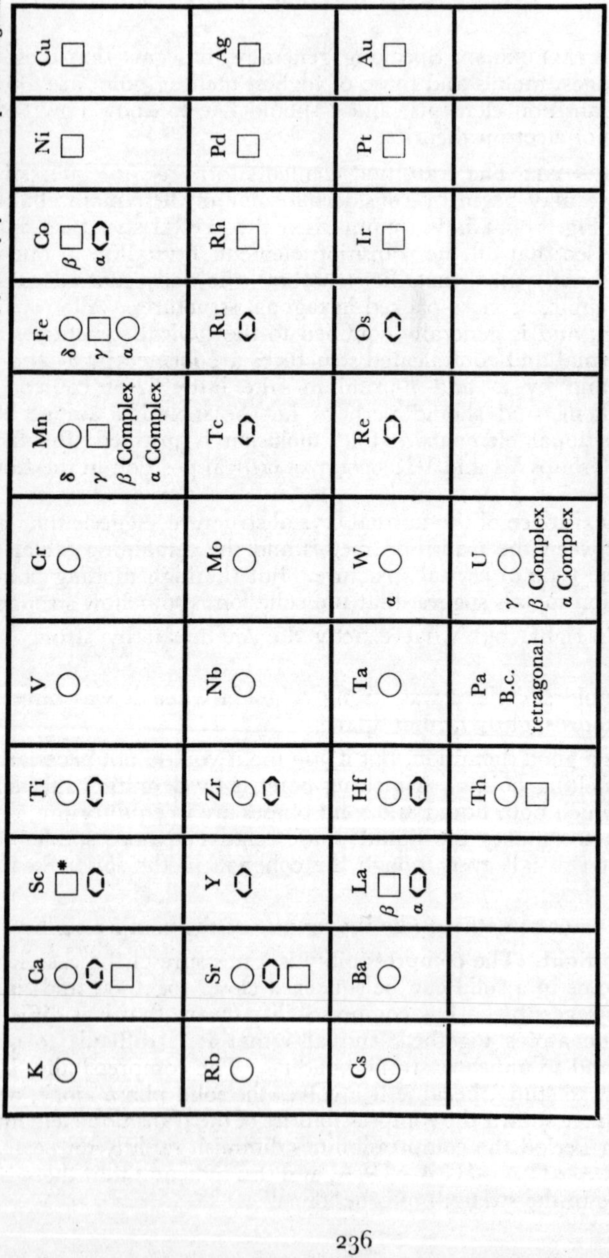

K ○	Ca ○ ⬡ □	Sc *□ ⬡	Ti ○ ⬡	V ○	Cr ○	Mn δ○ γ□ β Complex α Complex	Fe δ○ γ□ α⬡	Co β□ α⬡	Ni □	Cu □
Rb ○	Sr ○ ⬡ □	Y ⬡	Zr ○ ⬡	Nb ○	Mo ○	Tc ⬡	Ru ⬡	Rh □	Pd □	Ag □
Cs ○	Ba ○	La β□ α⬡	Hf ○ ⬡	Ta ○	W ○ (α)	Re ⬡	Os ⬡	Ir □	Pt □	Au □
			Th ○ □	Pa B.c. tetragonal	U γ○ β Complex α Complex					

The crystal structures of the transition metals

○ = B.c. Cube; □ = F.c. Cube; ⬡ = C.p. Hex. *In all cases, the allotropic forms are shown in the order of the temperature ranges in which they are stable, the form stable at the highest temperature being at the top.*

* It is not known which allotrope is stable at the higher temperature.

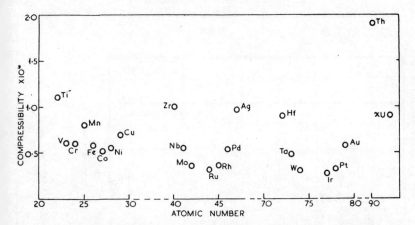

Fig. 107—Compressibilities of the transition elements. The compressibilities of the alkali metals are greater than those of the following alkaline earths, and both are too great to be shown in the diagram

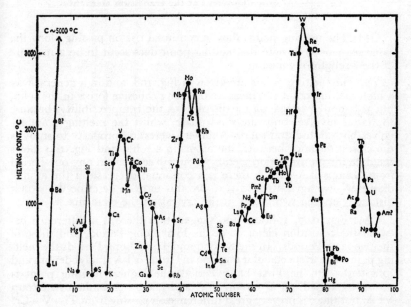

[From "Atomic Theory for Students of Metallurgy,"
Hume-Rothery. Courtesy The Institute of Metals

Fig. 108—Melting points of the transition elements.

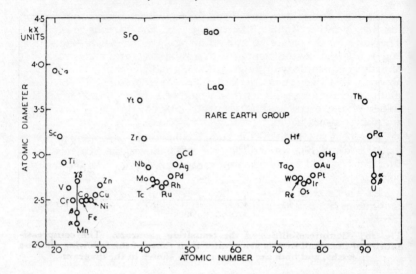

[*Courtesy The Institute of Metals*

Fig. 109—Atomic diameters of the transition elements.

OM: The melting points show a continual rise on passing along the same sequences, so here the melting point does seem to be a measure of the strength of cohesion.

YS: The melting points are given in Fig. 108, and in a general way a high melting point is a measure of strong cohesive forces in the solid, but it is not so satisfactory a quantity as the compressibility, because the latter involves only the solid phase, whilst the melting point involves both liquid and solid. Another interesting property to study is the closest distance between the atoms in a solid, and Fig. 109 shows the data for the transition metals. You will see that in any one Period from Groups I A→IV A there is a continual decrease in the atomic diameter—we agreed (p. 219) to use this term to describe the closest distance between two atoms in the crystals of the elements.

OM: Figs. 107, 108 and 109 suggest that there is a difference between the transition elements of the First Long Period, and those of the two later Periods. In the Second and Third Long Periods the melting points rise to spectacular maxima in Group VI A (molybdenum and tungsten). In the First Long Period, the highest melting point is shown by vanadium in Group V A and not by chromium in Group VI A, but there is no very great difference on passing from Ti→V→Cr. The melting point of manganese appears to be quite out of sequence, and the decrease in melting point on passing from iron→cobalt→nickel is far less than the changes for the elements of the later Periods.

YS: That's quite true, and if you look at Figs. 107 and 109 you will see that a rather similar difference occurs for the other properties. The value for the compressibility of manganese refers to α-manganese, and is affected by the complicated crystal structure, and is thus not directly comparable with those for the normal elements. You will see, however, that when compared with the value for titanium the compressibility of chromium is higher than would be expected from the relative values of the corresponding elements molybdenum and zirconium, and tungsten and hafnium, in the later Periods.

OM: That suggests that the atomic cohesion in chromium is not so strong as would be expected from the behaviour of the elements in the later Periods, and so confirms the deduction drawn from the melting points.

YS: That's right. But, on the other hand, the atomic diameters continue to contract normally on passing from titanium→vanadium→ chromium.

OM: Yes, but in the later elements, the behaviour isn't the same in the three Periods. The atomic diameter for γ-manganese (2.67 kX) is slightly greater than those for chromium, iron, cobalt, and nickel for all of which the values are about 2.5 kX. On the other hand, in the later Periods the atomic diameters continue to diminish as far as Group VIII A (ruthenium and osmium), and there is then a distinct increase on passing from ruthenium→rhodium→palladium, and from osmium→iridium→platinum. Everything suggests that the First Short Period is different from the Second and Third.

YS: That's quite true. The physical properties suggest clearly that in the Second and Third Long Periods, the strength of bonding reaches a maximum in the region of Group VI A—VII A, but that in the First Long Period the maximum is reached rather earlier in the Period, and that the maximum is not followed by such a steep fall. It is also clear that the properties for manganese are out of sequence.

OM: This all seems rather confusing, because you said before that in the transition elements there were nine bonding orbitals—one s, three p, and five d—and so one would expect the strength of the bonding to increase continuously on passing from potassium to copper, because the orbitals could accommodate all the electrons.

YS: That point has given rise to a lot of difficulty, and exactly what happens is not really known. One hypothesis which aroused much interest is that of Pauling, according to whom the cohesive forces in the elements of the First Long Period result from electrons in hybrid ($4s$, $4p$, $3d$) orbitals—in the later Periods the same process is assumed with higher quantum numbers. As you have said, one $4s$, three $4p$, and five $3d$ orbitals are available for hybridisation, and if all of these were used for bonding there would be nine bonding orbitals. From a study of the facts we have been considering, Pauling concluded that only some of the d orbitals were available for bond formation. By considering the magnetic properties it was concluded that only 2.56 of the $3d$ orbitals were available for bond formation; the remaining

2.44d orbitals are regarded as atomic d orbitals, and when an electron is in one of these it is associated mainly with one atom, and does not take much part in the bonding process.

OM: How were the numbers 2.56 and 2.44 obtained?

YS: They were deduced from a study of the magnetic properties. You will remember that in Chapter 14 we saw that as electrons began to fill up the p and d sub-groups in free atoms, they kept their spins parallel as long as this was possible. The same principle applies to the filling up of the atomic d orbitals of the transition metals, and in this way the following scheme has been suggested.

From potassium to vanadium, the number of electrons in bonding orbitals increases steadily from one to five, and no electrons enter the atomic d orbitals. This accounts for the regular increase in the strength of binding which, as we have seen above, occurs in the series

$$K \rightarrow Ca \rightarrow Sc \rightarrow Ti \rightarrow V$$

In this series of elements—and in the corresponding elements of the later Periods—you are to imagine a steady increase in the number of electrons concerned in the binding process. The concentration of bonding electrons per unit volume increases enormously on passing along the above series, and both the atomic diameters and the ionic diameters decrease, but the atomic diameter decreases to a relatively greater extent, and so the crystal structures become less and less " open " (Chapter 28, page 222).

OM: I thought I had read somewhere that only the s electrons were concerned in the cohesion process in these elements.

YS: That was the original idea of Mott and Jones,[1] but I think it has become increasingly clear that the sequence of properties to which we have referred above requires some other explanation, and although Pauling's views may eventually require some modification, they are I think sound as regards the increase in the numbers of bonding electrons on passing from potassium to titanium in the First Long Period, and from rubidium to molybdenum, and from caesium to tungsten (omitting the Rare Earths) in the later Periods.

On reaching chromium, Pauling assumes that only 5.78 electrons per atom enter the bonding orbitals, and that the remaining 0.22 electrons per atom begin to enter atomic d orbitals which are not concerned in the cohesive process. As a rough approximation he then assumes that the number of bonding electrons remains roughly at 5.78 per atom on passing from chromium to nickel, and in this way he deduces the following scheme.

Element	Cr	Mn	Fe	Co	Ni
No. of Bonding Electrons ..	5.78	5.78	5.78	5.78	5.78
No. of Electrons in Atomic d orbitals	0.22	1.22	2.22	3.22	4.22

[1] *The Theory of the Properties of Metals and Alloys*, N. F. Mott and H. Jones.

Now we have seen that Pauling assumes that there are 2.44 atomic *d* orbitals per atom . . .

OM: But surely the number must be a whole number?

YS: No, that does not follow. We are thinking of the crystal structures as a whole, and there is no reason why the numbers of electrons in atomic *d* orbitals should be a whole number per atom.

OM: Do you mean that some atoms are in one condition, and some in another?

YS: If you took an instantaneous snapshot of the crystal structure, you would find some atoms with more electrons in atomic *d* orbitals than others. In the complicated structures of manganese it is very probable that this distinction between different kinds of atom is permanent, and the structure may be said to have atoms in different electronic states. In the more symmetrical structures such as those of chromium and iron, the number of electrons in the atomic *d* orbitals of a given atom will change from time to time, but Pauling's hypothesis is that these electrons do not give rise to much cohesion.

OM: Then do the electrons in atomic *d* orbitals affect any other properties?

YS: According to Pauling, they are responsible for some of the magnetic properties. We have seen that Pauling's assumption is that there are 2.44 atomic *d* orbitals per atom. From the scheme given above, you will see that in chromium, manganese, and iron, there are 0.22, 1.22 and 2.22 electrons per atom in atomic *d* orbitals, and since these numbers are all smaller than 2.44 (the number of atomic orbitals), the electrons can all have the same spin. Now we have seen that a spinning electron is associated with a magnetic moment of one Bohr magneton (Chapter 13, page 94), and consequently Pauling argues that the saturation magnetic moments of the above elements should be 0.22, 1.22, and 2.22 Bohr magnetons per atom. When, however, we pass to cobalt with 3.22 electrons per atom in atomic *d* orbitals, there are more electrons than orbitals, and consequently some of the atomic *d* electrons will have to form electron pairs of opposite spin, which do not contribute to the saturation moment. You can readily see that for the elements cobalt and nickel the number of unpaired atomic *d* electrons given by the above scheme is 4.88 — 3.22 = 1.66, and 4.88 — 4.22 = 0.66 respectively. The actual observed values for iron, cobalt, and nickel are 2.2, 1.7, and 0.6 respectively, and Pauling deliberately assumed the number of atomic orbitals which gave the best agreement with the above figures. You will see that, according to Pauling's hypothesis, the maximum possible value of the saturation moment would be 2.44, and the number of electrons required for this lies between iron and cobalt—experiment does in fact show that iron-cobalt alloys give the highest saturation moment.

OM: It seems to me that the scheme doesn't really agree with the facts. It doesn't account for the difference beween the First and the later Long Periods, and apart from the abnormal behaviour of manganese in the First Long Period, the suggestion of a constant valency of 5.78 does not agree with the obvious weakening of the strength of bonding on passing from ruthenium→rhodium→palladium, and from osmium→iridium→platinum.

YS: A good many people would agree with you there, and alternative schemes have been proposed in which the general Pauling viewpoint is adopted, but the details are different.[1] According to Hume-Rothery, Irving, and Williams[2] the Pauling scheme with a continual increase in the number of bonding electrons on passing from Group I A to Group VI A is essentially correct in the Second and Third Long Periods, and in these Periods the valency remains high as far as the elements in Group VIII A (ruthenium and osmium) and then falls on passing to rhodium and palladium, and to iridium and platinum. This is in accordance with the general trend of the predominant valencies in the chemistry of these elements. A further suggestion made by these authors was that, for the elements of Group VI–VIII in the First Long Period the predominant valencies are lower than in the corresponding elements of the later Periods, whilst the decrease in the predominant valencies on passing from iron→cobalt→nickel is much less than on passing from ruthenium→rhodium→palladium, and from osmium→iridium→platinum. There is in fact a very marked parallelism between the physical properties of Figs. 107 to 109, and the predominant valencies of the elements concerned. Hume-Rothery, Irving, and Williams therefore interpret the physical properties as indicating that, in the Second and Third Long Periods, the numbers of bonding electrons per atom increase from one to six on passing from Group I A to VI A, and then remain high as far as Group VIII A, but fall rapidly on passing from osmium→iridium→platinum, and from ruthenium→rhodium→palladium. In contrast to this, the same authors regard the numbers of bonding electrons per atom as being smaller in the corresponding elements of the First Long Period. Thus, for iron, cobalt, and nickel the numbers of bonding electrons per atom are regarded as being between three and two, with a slight decrease on passing from iron→cobalt→nickel.

OM: In that case the physical properties would indicate a lower valency for manganese.

YS: Yes. And that agrees with the known facts, because the divalent manganous compounds are known to be very stable—this is the result of the fact that divalent manganese contains five electrons outside the argon shell, and the resulting $(3d)^5$ grouping is an exactly half-filled $(3d)$ sub-group, and additional stability arises from this.

OM: That seems a very nice scheme, but it breaks down with chromium, because if there is an exactly half-filled $(3d)^5$ grouping in chromium, there will be only one electron left over for bonding, whereas all

---

[1] As explained later (p. 253) Pauling, in later writings, has slightly modified the above picture, but these slight changes do not affect the point at issue here, and are therefore left until the later discussion.

[2] W. Hume-Rothery, H. M. Irving, and R. J. P. Williams. *Proc. Roy. Soc.* 1951. A. **208.** 431.

the physical properties suggest that the bonding in chromium is stronger than that in manganese.

YS: That's quite right. The free atom of chromium has an outer configuration of $(3d)^5 (4s)^1$, but there are no univalent compounds of chromium. The predominant valencies of chromium are 3 and 6, and the 3-valent state is relatively more stable compared with the 6-valent state than in the corresponding compounds of molybdenum and tungsten. So you can see how well the predominant valencies are reflected in the physical properties—the bonding in chromium is clearly stronger than that in manganese, but is weaker than that in molybdenum or tungsten.

OM: Then do you mean that I am to regard manganese as purely divalent in the metallic state—if I understand it rightly the number of bonding electrons is the same as the valency.

YS: In the Pauling sense, the term valency is used to describe the number of bonding electrons. In the complex structures of α- and β-manganese, it is highly probable that the structure contains atoms in two or more states. In the normal structures of γ- and δ-manganese, the valency is uncertain, but according to the views of Hume-Rothery, Irving, and Williams the divalent state of manganese plays an important part in the structure. Since these views were advanced, the experimental methods of neutron diffraction have shown that γ-manganese does not consist of atoms in the divalent state, although from the point of view of resonance theory the divalent state may still play an important part.

OM: Can these alternative valency schemes be reconciled with the magnetic properties?

YS: Oh, certainly! The observed saturation moments of 0.61, 1.71, and 2.22 Bohr magnetons per atom for nickel, cobalt, and iron could be obtained by many combinations of atoms with permanent moments, and of those with no resultant spin.

OM: Do you mean that one can have regular superlattice structures of magnetic and non-magnetic atoms?

YS: That hypothesis has been advanced by several workers, but recent work by means of neutron diffraction has disproved the existence of long range ordered structures of atoms with two different spins. In neutron diffraction, the scattering factors depend on the spin of an atom, and so permit the detection of a superlattice of magnetic and non-magnetic atoms, which would not be shown by X-ray diffraction methods. The neutron diffraction methods show that if atoms do exist in different states in, say iron, the life of these cannot be greater than about 10^{-13} sec., and any resonance process involving different states must be very rapid.

OM: To summarise—there is no general agreement on the exact valencies of the transition elements after Group IV A in the First Long Period, or after Group VI A in the Second and Third Long Periods. But whatever scheme of valencies is adopted, there is a division into bonding and non-bonding electrons in the later Transition Elements of each Period?

YS: That is correct from the viewpoint of the resonating-valence-bond theories of metals. In technical terms, these theories describe the electrons by what are known as Heitler-London-Heisenberg wave-functions—these are wave-functions similar to those used in the theory of co-valent bonds, and each electron is described by a function which is localised on one atom, or on one pair of atoms, although exchange of electrons can occur, so that the electrons pass from one atom to another. But this approach is not accepted by many mathematical physicists, and an alternative approach is to describe the electrons by means of what are called Bloch functions, in which the function for each electron extends throughout the whole crystal—it is this type of function which underlies the ordinary theory of Brillouin zones, to which we have referred—these theories are sometimes called " collective electron theories." From this viewpoint all the electrons outside the rare gas shell are to be regarded as contributing to the cohesion, so that in nickel, for example, ten electrons are concerned in the atomic bonding in the crystal.

OM: In that case, how do you account for the break in the sequence of physical properties?

YS: That's a difficult point, and the collective electron theories have not succeeded in accounting for the breaks in physical properties. They would interpret these changes by saying that in the region of Group VI the wave-functions became increasingly repulsive in character.

OM: Why then, should there be the parallelism between the physical properties and the chemical valencies?

YS: I don't think one can answer that—except that in a general way the predominant chemical valencies indicate the numbers of electrons which may be perturbed sufficiently to take part in chemical combination, and we can perhaps understand how this is related to the extent to which the electrons can be perturbed to take part in bonding in the solid.

OM: Then what is the valency in solid nickel from the viewpoint of the collective electron theories?

YS: From the viewpoint of the collective electron theories I don't think one can speak of a definite valency in nickel. From this viewpoint, all the ten outer electrons take part in the bonding, but their electron clouds give rise to repulsion as well as attraction. You should note, however, that in the collective electron theories there is a tendency to use the term " valency " in a sense quite different from the numbers of electrons concerned in the cohesion. In some of these theories, the electrical conductivity is regarded as due to a relatively small number of electrons whose wave functions are of a predominantly s type, and the term valency is sometimes used to describe the number of these electrons per atom. In the case of nickel, for example, there are about 0.6 electrons per atom of this kind and the valency in nickel is sometimes said to be 0.6. If used in this sense, the valency is very much less than the number of electrons concerned in some way with the bonding.

OM: Then it amounts to saying that the term valency has no real meaning in the collective electron theories although it has a meaning in theories of the Pauling type.

YS: That's right.

OM: It seems to me that the picture given by the collective electron theories is rather indefinite and that there doesn't appear to be any clear distinction between the valency electrons and the electrons of the ions.

YS: That's perfectly true. You will remember that in the case of copper we regarded the crystal as composed of relatively hard ions held in contact by the attraction of the valency electrons. But at the same time we saw that the outermost electrons of the ions influenced each other, and so gave rise to forces of the Van der Waals type which increased the cohesion (page 227). In the preceding elements nickel, cobalt, iron and manganese, the $(3d)$ group of electrons is still in the process of being built up, and is thus much less stable. This means that its electrons are much more easily perturbed by the forces resulting from adjacent atoms, and so we can understand how this perturbation produces the attractive forces. In the transition elements there is thus a much less sharp division between the valency electrons and the electrons of the ion than there is in the case of copper, and this is after all only what would be expected from the structures of the free atoms (Chapter 15).

OM: It seems to me you really mean that there is no satisfactory theory of the Transition Elements.

YS: Well, yes. There isn't yet a satisfactory theory, but there is much more understanding of them than there was twenty-five years ago.

Suggestions for further reading:

The Nature of the Chemical Bond, L. Pauling (Cornell University Press). This book covers a wide range and is of great interest.

The Transition Metals and their Alloys, W. Hume-Rothery and B. R. Coles. Advances in Physics. Philosophical Magazine Supplement, 1954, Vol. 3, page 149.

Atomic Theory for Students of Metallurgy, W. Hume-Rothery (Institute of Metals).

Epilogue to Chapter 30

The reader is asked to imagine the following conversation as taking place sixteen years after the conversation in the foregoing chapter, that is, sometime in 1961 or 1962. The participants are our friends the Older Metallurgist and the Young Scientist, but the former has recently retired and the latter must now be designated a Middle-Aged Scientist. They have met by chance while attending a conference and take the opportunity to consider the bearing of later work on their original discussion.

RETIRED METALLURGIST: Now that sixteen years have passed since our original discussion, I imagine that there are newer and (I hope) better theories of the transition metals.

MIDDLE-AGED SCIENTIST: There has been endless speculation, and many theories or hypotheses have been advanced, but I am afraid we are not much farther forward than we were.

RM: May I take it that the general ideas of the Pauling hypothesis are still valid?

MAS: The Pauling hypothesis itself has undergone a good deal of modification and extension. You will remember that in the original hypothesis, Pauling considered that there were 2.44 atomic d-orbitals, and 2.56 bonding d-orbitals per atom, and that the latter hybridised with the three p and one s orbital per atom to give 6.56 bonding orbitals, of which 5.78 were actually used for bonding. The unused 0.78 orbitals per atom were regarded as metallic orbitals which were necessary for the substance to be a metal—these unused orbitals probably play the same part as the unoccupied states in the band- or zone-theories of metals.

In a later paper,[1] Pauling extended this scheme so that in copper there were 5.44 electrons/atoms concerned in the metallic cohesion, and this number (i.e., the valency of the metal) was regarded as falling to 4.44 for zinc, 3.44 for gallium, and 2.44 for germanium, and similarly for the corresponding elements of the later Periods.

RM: But that is surely nonsense? Those valencies would be in contradiction to the electron-concentration ideas.

MAS: There you are wrong. You will find that if you consider any series of valencies which increase or decrease by uniform steps in the sequences Cu, Zn, Ga . . ., etc., the electron concentration principles still work. The conventional valencies (Cu1, Zn2, Ga3 . . .) give you the β-phases at an electron concentration of 1.5 (CuZn, Cu_3Ga . . .).

---

[1] L. Pauling, *J. Amer. Chem. Soc.* 1947, vol. 69, 542; *Proc. Roy. Soc.* 1949 A, vol. 196, 343, 350.

The supposed Pauling valencies (Cu 5.44, Zn 4.44, Ga 3.44 . . .) would give you β-phases at electron concentration:

$$CuZn = \tfrac{1}{2}(5.44+4.44) = 4.94$$
$$Cu_3Ga = \tfrac{1}{4}(16.32+3.44) = 4.94.$$

So the electron concentration principle still holds.

RM: I see. But it seems to me that valencies of 4.44 and 3.44 for zinc and gallium are nonsense. The elements are known to be exclusively divalent and trivalent in their chemistry, and nobody has got at the $3d$ electrons of their atomic cores or ions. You yourself emphasised how the $(3d)^{10}$ sub-group rapidly shrinks and becomes more firmly bound on passing from $Cu \rightarrow Zn \rightarrow Ga$ . . . .

MAS: Most people would agree with you there, and this extension of the Pauling ideas has not found much acceptance. Apart from this, however, Pauling in a later paper[1] proposed a new explanation of the magnetic properties of iron. In the earlier view the saturation moment 2.22 μ_B for iron was regarded as arising from the unpaired spins of the 2.22 electrons in the atomic orbitals. In the later view he regarded the atomic orbitals as containing two unpaired electrons which gave rise to a saturation moment of 2.0 μ_B, and the additional 0.22 μ_B was regarded as the result of interaction between the conductivity or bonding electrons and the electrons of the core. This was an idea originally due to Zener, and is accepted by some physicists.

RM: But then, that would mean there were six electrons per atom left over for bonding, instead of 5.78.

MAS: That's right, and the latest editions of Pauling's book[2] makes it clear that he now regards the valencies of the transition elements of Groups VI A–VIII C as 6.0, instead of the 5.78 of the older views.

RM: Then which do you think is right?

MAS: Many people would say that both are wrong! The physical properties of the elements do not really support the view of a constant valency of six. The behaviour of manganese in the First Long Period is undoubtedly abnormal and, on the Pauling view, this suggests a lower valency than for chromium or iron. There is, further, a difference between the elements of the First and Later Long Periods which is not reflected in the Pauling scheme—in particular there is a weakening of the bonding on passing from $Ru \rightarrow Rh \rightarrow Pd$ and from $Os \rightarrow Ir \rightarrow Pt$.

RM: What about the behaviour of copper, zinc, etc.?

MAS: Pauling ascribes a valency of 5.56 to copper, silver, and gold, and then a falling off by unit steps on passing to Zn, Cd, Hg (4.56), Ga, In, Tl (3.56) continuing to 1.56 in As, Sb, Bi.

RM: That seems to give rise to the objection I raised before.

[1] L. Pauling, *Proc. Nat. Acad. Sci.* 1953, vol. 39, 551.
[2] *The Nature of the Chemical Bond*, L. Pauling. 1960, 3rd Edition, p. 403 (Cornell University Press).

MAS: That is quite true, and very few people accept the Pauling view of the valencies of the B-sub elements.

RM: On the whole it would seem that the first Pauling paper was the best of the lot.

MAS: Many people would agree with you there, although the idea of unused metallic orbitals is probably right, and the explanation of the magnetic properties of iron may be correct. But it is a common criticism of the later Pauling papers that any advance which has been made has been accompanied by ideas which are not acceptable.

RM: Has anything new resulted on the experimental side?

MAS: It is, I think, becoming increasingly recognised that it is the the Second and Third Long Periods which show what one may call the normal sequences of the transition metals. Now if you examine the crystal structures of the later transition elements, you will see that these show the sequence

c.p. hexagonal→b.c. cube→c.p. hexagonal→f.c. cube

on passing along the Period. The very stable body-centred cubic phases in Groups V A and VI A are followed by the close-packed hexagonal metals of Groups VII A and VIII A, and then by the face-centred cubic metals of Groups VIII B and VIII C. The interesting fact has now emerged that in some alloys of metals in Group VI A with those of VIII B or VIII C (e.g., Mo–Rh, Mo–Pd) close-packed hexagonal intermediate phases are formed. So a mixture of, say, molybdenum and rhodium atoms crystallises as though it were composed of technetium atoms. Furthermore, the composition limits of these phases vary roughly as though they depended on a characteristic mean group number.

RM: That suggests they are electron compounds like β-brass (p. 318).

MAS: Yes. But when so little is known of the real theory it is perhaps safer to speak of a characteristic mean group number. This will be the same as a characteristic electron:atom ratio if all the electrons outside the preceding rare gas shell are considered, or if a constant number of electrons has become atomic. The importance of the discovery lies in the clear suggestion that the type of crystal structure depends on the electron:atom ratio.

31—Transition Elements and Ferromagnetism

OLDER METALLURGIST: To the metallurgist, the chief characteristic of the transition metals is the appearance of ferromagnetism in iron, cobalt, and nickel. From what you have said, I suppose this is somehow connected with spinning electrons?

YOUNG SCIENTIST: The modern electron theory has thrown a great deal of light on magnetic properties, and one of the first applications of the free electron theory was in connection with the paramagnetism of the alkalis.

OM: Is it right to say that paramagnetism is a kind of weak ferromagnetism?

YS: Well, that's not a statement which would get you high marks in an examination, but it's not altogether wrong. The existence of ferromagnetism has of course been known for a very long time, but it was not until the middle of the nineteenth century that it was shown conclusively by Faraday that, as regards their magnetic properties, substances could be divided into three main classes. We may imagine that we have a substance in the form of a rod, and suspended in a non-uniform magnetic field—let us say the field between the two poles of an electro-magnet. Then if the rod tends to set itself parallel to the magnetic field (see Fig. 110(*a*)) it is said to be *paramagnetic*, whilst if it tends to set itself at right angles to the field it is *diamagnetic* (Fig. 110(*b*)). The third class of substance, the ferromagnetics, has the property of becoming permanently magnetised. This permanent magnetism may be destroyed by heating the substance to a sufficiently high temperature, and above this temperature the ferromagnetic substance becomes paramagnetic. This naturally suggests that ferromagnetism is an extreme form of paramagnetism, or at any rate that it is more closely related to paramagnetism than to diamagnetism.

OM: If I remember rightly, the capability of magnetisation is

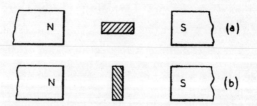

Fig. 110—To illustrate the tendency of paramagnetic substances (a) to set themselves parallel to a non-uniform magnetic field, and of diamagnetic substances (b) to set themselves perpendicular to a magnetic field

measured by the susceptibility κ, which is defined so that if in a field of strength H, the intensity of magnetisation is I, then

$$I = \kappa H$$

YS: That's quite right. For diamagnetic substances the susceptibility is negative, whilst for paramagnetics it is positive. For ferromagnetics the susceptibility is, of course, positive, and is very large until the field H becomes so strong that the specimen approaches the saturation limit.

OM: In the equation above I refers to unit volume, so that if one deals with unit mass, *the mass susceptibility* χ will be equal to κ/ρ where ρ is the density. If one considers the elements as a whole, are the values of χ scattered over wide ranges, or do they fall into groups?

YS: Speaking generally, the non-transition metals are either weakly paramagnetic or weakly diamagnetic, with mass susceptibilities of the order 10^{-6} to 10^{-7}. The data are summarised in Table IX. If one deals with the gram-atomic weight of an element, one obtains the *gram-atomic susceptibility* which is equal to χ multiplied by the atomic weight. As the atomic weights of most metals lie in the range 10–200, this means that the gram-atomic susceptibilities of these elements are of the order $\pm 10^{-4} - 10^{-6}$. The metals of the rare earth group are much more strongly paramagnetic, and some of the transition metals are somewhat more paramagnetic than the normal metals. All of the elements crystallising according to the (8-N) rule are diamagnetic, and this diamagnetism is very pronounced for antimony and bismuth. Ferromagnetism is confined to the elements iron, cobalt and nickel in the First Long Period, and to some of the rare earth metals (e.g., gadolinium and dysprosium), but in the latter the ferromagnetism is destroyed at a low temperature. It is only right to warn you that, for the less common elements, the data are not always too accurate, because very small traces of iron as an impurity may affect the measured values.

OM: It seems curious that there should be different classes, because one would think that spinning electrons would always produce the same effect.

YS: Let us begin by considering the simple free electron theory of electrons in a box (Chapter 20). Then at the absolute zero of temperature, an assembly of N electrons occupies the $\dfrac{N}{2}$ lowest energy levels, every occupied level containing two electrons, one of each spin. We might represent the condition of affairs by Fig. 111(a) in which the levels occupied by each spin are shown separately. Now suppose we place the assembly in a magnetic field of strength H. The energy of each electron whose spin is parallel to the field will then be diminished by an amount $H\mu$, where μ is the Bohr magneton (Chapter 13, page 94). Similarly the energy of each electron with anti-parallel spin will be increased by $H\mu$, and the condition of affairs may be represented

Table IX—MASS SUSCEPTIBILITIES OF THE ELEMENTS

		$\chi \times 10^6$				$\chi \times 10^6$
H	1	− 1.97	Ag	47	− 0.20
He	2	− 0.47	Cd	48	− 0.18
			In	49	− 0.11
Li	3	+ 0.50	Sn	50	− 0.25
Be	4	− 1.00	Sb	51	− 0.87
B	5	− 0.69	Te	52	− 0.31
C	6	− 0.49	I	53	− 0.36
N	7	− 0.8	Xe	54	− 0.34
O	8	+106.2			
F	9	—	Cs	55	− 0.22
Ne	10	− 0.33	Ba	56	+ 0.9
			La	57	+ 1.04
Na	11	+ 0.51	Ce	58	+15.0
Mg	12	+ 0.55	Pr	59	+25.0
Al	13	+ 0.65	Nd	60	+36.0
Si	14	− 0.13	Il	61	—
P	15	− 0.90	Sm	62	—
S	16	− 0.49	Eu	63	+22.0
Cl	17	− 0.57?	Gd	64	Ferro.
A	18	− 0.48	Tb	65	—
			Dy	66	Ferro.
K	19	+ 0.52	Ho	67	—
Ca	20	+ 1.10	Er	68	—
Sc	21	+ 7.0	Tu	69	—
Ti	22	+ 3.3	Yb	70	—
V	23	+ 5.0			
Cr	24	+ 3.5	Lu	71	—
Mn	25	+ 9.7	Hf	72	—
Fe	26	Ferro.	Ta	73	+ 0.83
Co	27	,,	W	74	+ 0.28
Ni	28	,,	Re	75	+ 0.37
			Os	76	+ 0.05
Cu	29	− 0.086	Ir	77	+ 0.14
Zn	30	− 0.157	Pt	78	+ 0.97
Ga	31	− 0.24			
Ge	32	− 0.12			
As	33	− 0.31	Au	79	− 0.15
Se	34	− 0.32	Hg	80	− 0.168
Br	35	− 0.39	Tl	81	− 0.24
Kr	36	− 0.35	Pb	82	− 0.12
			Bi	83	− 1.35
Rb	37	+ 0.21	Po	84	—
Sr	38	− 0.20	At	85	—
Y	39	+ 2.1	Rn	86	—
Zr	40	+ 1.3			
Nb	41	+ 2.2	Fr	87	—
Mo	42	+ 0.93	Ra	88	—
Tc	43	—	Ac	89	—
Ru	44	+ 0.43	Th	90	+ 0.57
Rh	45	+ 0.99	Pa	91	+ 2.6
Pd	46	+ 5.2	U	92	+ 0.17

[*From* Modern Magnetism, *Bates. Cambridge University Press*

The gram-atomic susceptibility is equal to the above mass susceptibility multiplied by the atomic weight

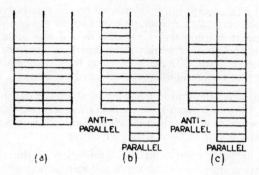

ANTI-
PARALLEL

ANTI-
PARALLEL

PARALLEL

PARALLEL

(a)

(b)

(c)

[*Courtesy The Institute of Metals*

Fig. 111

by Fig. 111(*b*). It is clear that in this case the energies of the highest occupied anti-parallel levels are greater than those of the highest occupied parallel spin levels, and a lower energy can be produced if some of the anti-parallel electrons change their spin. It must be remembered, however, that an occupied level can contain only one electron of a given spin, and so the electrons which change their spin will have to go into states above those which were previously occupied. It is clear, therefore, that a stage will be reached in which the decrease in magnetic energy on changing from anti-parallel to parallel spin is balanced by the increase in kinetic energy, and a situation such as that shown in Fig. 111(*c*) will result. In this case there is clearly a preponderance of electrons with parallel spins, and hence a paramagnetic effect. This, however, is not quite the whole story, because it can be shown that in quantum mechanics the translatory motion of the electrons produces a diamagnetic effect which in the simple theory is one-third that of the paramagnetic effect illustrated in Fig. 111. The net result is thus a paramagnetic effect which is two-thirds of that indicated by the simple scheme of Fig. 111. If the electron gas is assumed to be completely degenerate, the calculated value of the paramagnetic susceptibility is of the order 10^{-6}, and is thus in agreement with the facts.

OM: That doesn't seem to be quite right. The first four alkali metals are weakly paramagnetic, but according to Table IX caesium is diamagnetic and this is surely in contradiction to theory.

YS: You must remember that the above simple theory refers to an assembly of electrons in a box, whereas an actual metal contains both valency electrons and metallic ions. It follows, therefore, that in comparing the conclusions of the simple theory with the observed magnetic constants of the alkali metals, one must take into account the behaviour of the ions. It can be shown that ions with completed groups of two, eight or eighteen electrons are weakly diamagnetic, with a susceptibility of the order 10^{-6}, that is, of the same order as the paramagnetic susceptibility calculated by the free electron theory. It is this which accounts for discrepancies such as the one you referred to above, and it is important to realise that if one metal is weakly paramagnetic and another weakly diamagnetic, it does not necessarily imply any fundamental difference between the two; the whole difference may be due to the diamagnetic effect of the ions.

OM: From what you said in Chapter 21 about the degeneracy of an electron gas, it would seem that the paramagnetic susceptibilities of the alkali metals must be almost independent of temperature if the paramagnetism is due to the valency electrons.

YS: That is quite right, and the application of the Fermi-Dirac statistics to what may be called the weak spin paramagnetism of the alkali metals was in fact one of the first applications of the free electron theory to the problem of metallic structure.

OM: It seems to me that the free electron theory may be all very well for the weak paramagnetism of the alkali metals, but that it must be unsatisfactory for ferromagnetism. If ferromagnetism is in any way due to electron spin, it must imply an overwhelming predominance of spins pointing in one direction. But if an electron state can contain only one electron of a given spin, this would imply an increase in the energies of the electrons because they would have to occupy higher electron states than if they were in pairs of opposite spin. The ferromagnetic state would thus have a higher energy, and would be unstable.

YS: Your general idea is quite sound, and the ferromagnetic state cannot be explained by the above free electron theory. It is clear that any preponderance of electrons with one spin must lead to an increase in the Fermi energy, and if the ferromagnetic state is to be stable there must be some other compensating factor which lowers the energy. In the line of approach developed by Heisenberg the process concerned is supposed to be the exchange energy to which we referred in connection with the H_2 molecule. You will remember that we saw that the condition of affairs in the H_2 molecule was equivalent to a rapid interchange or exchange of the electrons between the two nuclei, and that the lowest energy resulted when the two electrons had opposite spins. Mathematically this is expressed by a certain integral, the so-called exchange integral, and for covalent bonds this is negative, and the most stable state is that in which the electrons have opposite spins. In special circumstances it is, however, considered that the exchange integral may be positive, and then the ferromagnetic state may be stable. For this to occur certain conditions have to be satisfied. In the first place the atoms must have an incomplete shell of electrons, and this incomplete shell must have a relatively low electron cloud density near the nucleus. From the forms of the radial factor which we described in Chapter 12, this means that the quantum number l must be large, and the d and f sub-groups are those concerned. The next condition is that the atoms must not be too far apart, because if the distance between adjacent atoms is large, the interaction is very weak, and the exchange integral is so small that the resulting energy is insufficient to stabilise the ferromagnetic state. On the other hand the atoms must not be too close together, because if their electron clouds overlap too much, normal bonding occurs with electrons in pairs of opposite spin. Ferromagnetism is thus possible only if the distance between adjacent atoms is within a certain range which will depend on the " size " of the overlapping electron shells. If we use the symbol d for the distance between two atoms, and m for twice the distance from the nucleus to the region where the electron shell concerned has its maximum density, we may define a quantity D by the ratio d/m, and in this case the variation of the exchange integral with D has the general form of the curve of Fig. 112. Here you will see that at small values of D (that is, when the atoms are close together) the exchange integral is negative, whilst at large values of D it approaches asymptotically to zero. When the different elements are examined, it is found that for those of the iron group D has the correct intermediate value, where the exchange integral is positive so that ferromagnetism may be shown. The rare earth metals were thought to be such that D was slightly too large for ferromagnetism, although it was considered possible that some of these might be ferromagnetic at very low temperatures, analogously to gadolinium, and this has been confirmed by the discovery that a few other rare earths are ferromagnetic at low temperature, e.g., dysprosium. It is interesting to note that pure manganese, which satisfies the condition of an incomplete d shell, is non-magnetic. This is thought to be because D is too small, and it is thought that manganese nitride, which is ferromagnetic, acquires this property because the nitrogen atoms enter the interstices and push the manganese atoms farther apart. It is possible that new ferromagnetic alloys may be developed from alloys of other transition elements with incomplete d shells if crystal structures can be obtained with the appropriate interatomic distances.

OM: Do you mean that in a ferromagnetic metal such as iron, I am to regard each atom as having so many unoccupied $3d$ states?

YS: The elementary magnets of the ferromagnetic state are the spinning electrons, and the saturation moment at low temperatures,

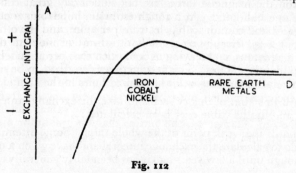

Fig. 112

expressed in Bohr magnetons per atom, is equal to the number of unpaired electron spins in the d shell. In nickel and cobalt the number of unpaired electron spins is equal to the number of vacancies or " holes " in the d shell, and the saturation moment is thus equal to the number of holes in the d shell.

OM: If I understood you rightly, that means that the ferromagnetism is associated with the atomic orbitals of the Pauling theory and it is the number of unpaired spins in these orbitals which are responsible for the saturation moment.

YS: That's right. In the Pauling theory the saturation moment is associated with the atomic d orbitals, but this view is not universally accepted. The alternative view is based on what is generally called the *collective electron theory*. According to this, all of the d electrons in the crystal form a common band, which will hold ten electrons, five of each spin. It is convenient to regard this as consisting of two half-bands, each containing five electron states per atom of the same spin. In paramagnetic cobalt or nickel these half-bands are partly filled to the same extent. In the ferromagnetic state, the exchange forces result in the one half-band being completely filled and the other half-band only partly filled, so that the saturation moment is equal to the number of holes, or unoccupied states, in the one half-band.

OM: That picture makes it easier to understand the fact that the saturation moments on Bohr magnetons are not whole numbers. But am I to regard all the atoms in, say, cobalt as being in the same state?

YS: From the viewpoint of the collective electron theory the atoms for nearly all purposes may be regarded as in the same condition. There have been theories of superlattices of magnetic and non-magnetic atoms, but these have not been confirmed by the new methods of neutron diffraction, and it is fairly certain that if the atoms do exist in different states, interchange is so rapid that for most purposes they can be regarded as all being the same.

OM: Then, in the case of iron, I suppose the picture is more or less the same except that there are more holes in the one half-band?

YS: That is what was originally thought, but it is now recognised that in iron the magnetic forces are not sufficiently great completely to fill the one half-band. At a rough estimate, in ferromagnetic iron, the one half-band contains 4.65 electrons per atom, and the other half-band about 2.45, thus giving a resultant saturation moment of about 2.2 Bohr magnetons, and leaving over 0.9 electrons per atom which are in predominantly s states. This is sometimes described by saying that in iron there are paired as well as unpaired holes in the d band.

OM: All this kind of theory seems to take the exchange integral for granted; and has its value ever been calculated?

YS: That is the weak point of the whole thing. Some attempts have been made to calculate the exchange integral and have given a negative sign, although until a few years ago it has been fairly generally assumed that a positive integral might well be obtained if the calculations were carried through more accurately. Recently several physicists, notably Zener, have doubted this, and have suggested that the exchange integral will always be negative and that some other cause must be found for ferromagnetism. The view has been advanced that the forces responsible for ferromagnetism are due to the interaction between the s electrons, which are responsible for the electrical conductivity, and the electrons of the d band. In a crude way, the picture is that in any one atom the spins of the s and d electrons are mutually aligned, and that when the s electron travels on to the next atom it carries its spin with it and lines up the spin of the d electrons of the new atom to match those of the atom it has left. At present this is very much a matter of speculation and you are right in thinking that the ultimate cause of ferromagnetism is really not known conclusively. You should note, however, that in a later paper Pauling adopted this point of view, and regarded the saturation moment of iron $(2.22 \ \mu_B)$ as resulting from the parallel spins of two electrons (i.e., $2 \ \mu_B$) together with an additional contribution from the interaction of the core and the conductivity electrons. This led to a revised Pauling scheme of valencies[1] in which the valency 5.78 of the earlier theory (p. 240) was replaced by a constant valency of 6.0.

OM: It seems to me that all the theories you have described suffer from one outstanding weakness, namely that the single crystals of ferromagnetic substances are often unmagnetised. When I was at school I was taught that the non-magnetic state of iron was one in which each crystal grain was permanently magnetised in a definite direction, and that the non-magnetic condition simply resulted from the individual crystal magnets pointing in different directions. But as far as I understand it, single crystals of iron have now been prepared in a non-magnetic state, and so the old explanation is no longer valid, and your theory seems to offer no help.

YS: That point has given rise to a lot of discussion and you are correct in saying that single crystals of ferromagnetic substances can be obtained in an apparently unmagnetised state. The explanation is that the single crystals are not magnetically uniform, but consist of a number of small domains which can each be magnetised in certain directions. In the non-magnetic state the various domains are magnetised in different directions, and their effects neutralise one another, and there is no resultant magnetic moment. When an external field is applied, the domains are regarded as being magnetised in the same direction, and then remain in this condition when the field is withdrawn.

OM: That seems to be a purely *ad hoc* assumption and most unconvincing.

YS: No. It is not really as bad as that. Direct experimental evidence for a domain structure in ferromagnetics has been obtained by methods

---

[1] *The Nature of the Chemical Bond*, Linus Pauling. 1960, Cornell University Press.

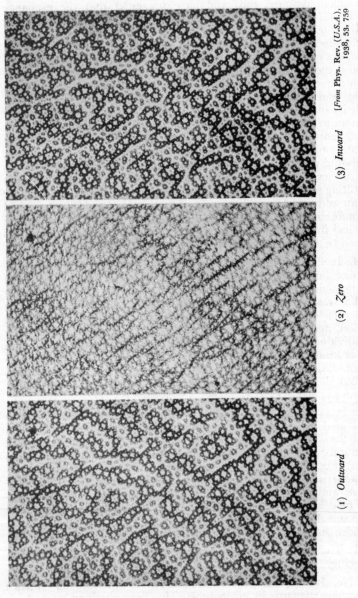

(1) *Outward*   (2) *Zero*   (3) *Inward*   [*From* Phys. Rev. *(U.S.A.),*
                                                                   1938, 53, 759

Fig. 113(a)—Patterns of magnetic colloid on the basal plane of a cobalt crystal with applied normal field

The spaces and deposits are interchanged in (1) *and* (3). *Magnification approx.* 75×

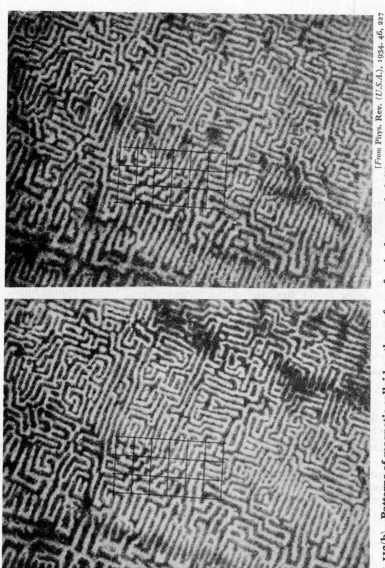

Fig. 113(b)—**Patterns of magnetic colloid on the surface of a single crystal of silicon-iron with the field normal to the surface**

The two photographs show the same region with different directions of the applied field. The black lines on the one pattern occupy the centres of the white spaces in the other. The group of six squares is about 70μ × 35μ

[*From* Phys. Rev. (*U.S.A.*), 1934, 46, 227]

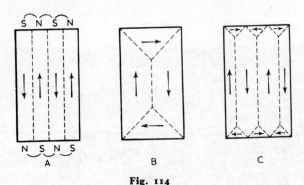

Fig. 114

in which carefully prepared surfaces of ferro-magnetic crystals are covered with a fine suspension of magnetic oxide of iron. Under these conditions it is found that definite patterns are formed within the individual crystals, thus indicating a unit of structure smaller than the single crystal. Some of these patterns are shown in Figs. 113(a) and (b), and the light and dark portions may change when the specimen is magnetised in different directions. It is only right to warn you that many of the older photographs of this kind were in error owing to the straining of the surface during the polishing, but this source of error was soon eliminated, and it is now generally agreed that strain-free surfaces give rise to patterns, and that magnetic domains do in fact exist within the crystal grains.

OM: The splitting up into magnetic domains seems rather improbable.

YS: No. That's not really right. If a single crystal is magnetised in one direction there will be free poles at the surface, but the splitting up into domains may prevent the existence of these free poles and so lower the energy. Some kinds of arrangements found are shown in Fig. 114.

OM: When a magnet is heated the ferromagnetism is destroyed. This, I suppose, is the result of the thermal vibrations knocking the atoms about, but I have never understood why there is not a gradual transition from a ferromagnetic to a paramagnetic state with a whole range of intermediate stages.

YS: The ferromagnetic state in which all the elementary magnets take up the same orientation may be regarded as the result of a " cooperative process " in which the energy required to change the orientation of an elementary magnet increases as the orientation becomes more perfect. If, for example, the specimen is magnetised completely so that all the elementary magnets point in the same direction, then a change in the orientation of any one elementary magnet will be opposed by the order of the whole assembly, and the energy involved will be large. The less perfect the order of the assembly the less will be the restraining force on any one elementary magnet. When this idea is developed mathematically, it is found that on raising the temperature from the absolute zero, the magnetism is destroyed at first slowly, and then with a sudden rush over a comparatively narrow range of temperature at the so-called *Curie Point*. This general effect of temperature is typical of a co-operative phenomenon, and the mathematical treatment explains quite clearly why the destruction of magnetism appears to be concentrated over a comparatively narrow range of temperature.

OM: Apart from their ferromagnetism, the transition metals are characterised by abnormally high electrical resistances. This has often puzzled me, because their high melting points suggest that at room temperatures their atomic vibrations will be relatively small, and this would lead one to expect a relatively low resistance.

YS: That point has been explained satisfactorily by the new theories. You will remember that we saw (page 217) that the electrical resistance resulted from an interaction between the wave systems of the electrons and the thermal vibrations of the crystal lattice. If we use the term " collisions " to describe these interactions, then a collision scatters the electron from one state to another. The factors which determine the probability of a collision are naturally very complicated, but it can be shown that the probability of an electron being scattered into a given state is greater the higher the $N(E)$ curve of the state concerned. In a transition metal the conductivity is due mainly to electrons of the s-like nature—$4s$ in the case of the elements of the First Long Period, and with higher quantum numbers for the later Periods. As the result of collisions these electrons may be scattered into other similar states, just as in the case of the alkali metals. But apart from these $s \rightarrow s$ transitions, there is also the possibility of an electron being scattered into a state derived from the d states of the free atoms. It can be shown that the $N(E)$ curve for the d band is very much higher than that for the s band, and this means that there is a correspondingly high probability of the electron being scattered so that it undergoes a transition from a predominantly s-like state to a d-like state. This kind of $s \rightarrow d$ transition is present in the transition metals but not in the alkalis, and it is the possibility of a transition of this kind which is the cause of the high electrical resistance of the transition elements.

Suggestions for further reading:

Advances in Physics, W. Hume-Rothery and B. R. Coles, *Philosophical Magazine* Supplement, 1954, Vol. 3, page 149.
Atomic Theory for Students of Metallurgy, W. Hume-Rothery.
Magnetism and Matter, E. C. Stoner.
Modern Magnetism, L. F. Bates.
Progress in Metal Physics, Vol. 3, 1952: article by Ursula M. Martius.

32—The Problem of Plastic Deformation

OLDER METALLURGIST: From the practical point of view, the plastic deformation of metals is of the greatest importance. You have said on several occasions that the electron theory has not explained the plastic properties of metals, and I confess that I found your statement rather depressing. Do you mean that there is no satisfactory theory of plastic deformation?

YOUNG SCIENTIST: The position isn't quite so bad as you suggest. The essential fact of plasticity is that cohesion persists during a process in which the distortion is very large and much beyond the elastic range. The general idea of a metallic bond which is not strongly directional does enable us to understand why the plastic cohesion persists during the distortion. In the case of a structure built up by co-valent bonds, the electron clouds are markedly concentrated in certain directions, and we can understand how if a bond is directional it cannot persist during deformation, and cannot easily heal up when once it is broken. The picture of a metallic bond resulting from the motion of electrons between atoms without pronounced directional characteristics is clearly much more easily reconciled with the existence of plasticity.

OM: There are substances like glass which go through a plastic range, but am I right in thinking that this phenomenon is distinct from that of the plasticity of metals?

YS: That's quite right. Glasses in their normal state are really supercooled liquids which have not crystallised. If you heat a glass at not too slow a rate,[1] you find that there is a continuous transition from what is usually called " solid glass," to an obvious liquid, and there is no sharp melting point as there is with a crystalline solid. This does not mean that glass is structureless, because there is increasing evidence that the molecular arrangement in liquids is not completely random, but does involve some kind of a structure, although this is not a long range ordered structure like that of a crystal. A solid glass is thus to be regarded as a very viscous liquid, and examination shows that the details of its plastic flow differ from those of a single crystal of a metal.

OM: It will probably be most simple if we deal first with the characteristics of single crystals of pure metals. I know from experience that if we prepare single crystals of perfectly pure metals, they are usually very soft, and have to be treated with the greatest care if they are not to suffer permanent deformation, but I am not sure whether such crystals have any real elastic range within which they

---

[1] If heated too slowly the glass may devitrify or begin to change from a super-cooled liquid to a crystalline solid.

may suffer deformation, and return to their original length when the load is removed?

YS: When stress—either tensile, compressive, or torsional—is applied to a single crystal under what we may call normal experimental conditions, there is first a very small elastic range within which Hooke's Law is obeyed. The strain is proportional to the stress, and on removal of the load the crystal returns to its original size. The elastic range is very small but is definite, although it diminishes as the temperature rises, and becomes extremely small as the melting point is approached.

OM: What exactly do you mean by " under normal experimental conditions "?

YS: I mean the condition of a normal test in which the load is applied and withdrawn comparatively rapidly. If the load is applied for long periods, the phenomenon of " creep " is encountered, and it is doubtful whether even at low temperatures a single crystal has any real elastic limit. At high temperatures it is quite certain that single crystals show creep under exceedingly small loads.

You should note, however, that the distinction between " creep " and " ordinary " plastic deformation is to some extent arbitrary, and may depend on the accuracy of the experimental apparatus.

If we take a single crystal of a metal, and apply a gradually increasing load, there will first be a small range. of elastic deformation. In the case of the alkali metals and copper, this part of the process can be accounted for satisfactorily by the new electron theories of metals, and the elastic constants can be calculated. You will see, therefore, that the electron theory is approaching the stage at which it may be useful. In so far as the practical man is interested in quantities such as Young's Modulus, the theory has reached the stage at which they can be calculated from first principles. Of course, the alloys actually needed for industrial purposes are not pure metals, but the theory must clearly first deal with pure metals before it is applied to alloys.

OM: Then does the theory enable you to predict the point at which the elastic limit is reached?

YS: No. From what is known about the vibrational displacements of atoms in *molecules* we should expect the elastic range of metal crystals to be much greater than it is. Actually, as you will know, the elastic range of a metal crystal is very small, and if an increasing load is applied to a single crystal, plastic deformation sets in, and if the load is then removed the crystal acquires a permanent set. The process has been examined in great detail by measurements of the change in external shape of a specimen, combined with X-ray diffraction methods which enable the change in orientation of the crystal to be followed, and which also give some information about the deformation process. At present I'm afraid that this lies outside the electron theory, except that the general idea of the metallic linkage does perhaps enable one to understand how the crystal holds together during and after the deformation process.

OM: Am I right in thinking that when plastic deformation begins, the process is one of slipping on definite crystal planes?

YS: If the stress on a single crystal is increased beyond the elastic limit, different processes may set in, but the most general type of deformation process is one in which planes of atoms move over one another, and slip bands appear on the surface of the specimen; examples of these are shown in Fig. 115. With copper, silver, and gold where the crystal structures are face-centred cubic, slipping occurs on the close-packed octahedral planes (that is, the octahedral planes exposed in Fig. 77) in the direction of the close-packed rows, and this is nearly always the case with face-centred cubic or close-packed hexagonal structures. For the alkali metals where the structure is body-centred cubic, slip occurs in the direction of the closest-packed rows of atoms (Fig. 78). In this case there are no close-packed planes, and the plane of slip varies with the temperature. In a sense, therefore, the direction of slip is more fundamental than the plane of slip.

OM: If one considers the close-packed rows and planes of the face-centred cubic structure (Fig. 79) there seems to be a large number of alternatives; there are four sets of close-packed planes each with three sets of close-packed rows. If we call each combination of a direction and a plane a *mode* of deformation, it would seem reasonable for slip to occur in the most favourable mode, that is, the one for which the component of stress is the greatest.

YS: That's quite right. If you know the orientation of the crystal relative to the direction of stress, you can calculate the component of stress in each of the twelve possible modes of slip, and then the direction actually chosen is that for which the component of shear stress is the greatest. If the specimen is submitted to a gradually increasing load, slip is extremely small until this component of shear stress exceeds a certain limiting value—in the case of copper this limiting value or critical shear stress is 0.1 kg/mm², whilst for silver and gold the values are 0.06 and 0.09 kg/mm² respectively.

OM: It seems to me that any process in which one whole close-packed plane of atoms slips bodily over another is impossible on account of the immense numbers of atoms concerned. Even if the energy required to move an atom from one site to another were very small, the fact that there are something of the order 10^{16} atoms per sq. cm. of the slip plane would mean that a large force would be required to produce slip, whereas every metallurgist knows that only a very small force is necessary to deform a single crystal of a pure metal.

YS: What you say is quite right, and it is now generally recognised that the process of slip does not take place by the simultaneous sliding of one whole plane of atoms over another. It is now thought that the slip takes place by the passage of a small, intensely distorted region which gradually moves across the slip plane. In this way the number of

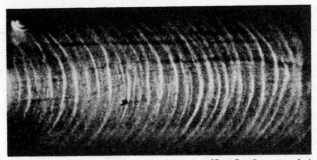

[*Proc. Roy. Soc.*, 1937 163*A*

Fig. 115—Slip bands on single crystals of sodium

(*after Andrade and Tsien*)

atoms in motion at any one instant is relatively small and so your difficulty is overcome. The boundary between the slipped and un-slipped regions is called a *dislocation*, and although the introduction of a dislocation involves a considerable amount of energy, once the dislocation has been introduced it moves freely.

OM: It seems to me that it is improbable because it implies that a perfect single crystal should be strong, whereas single crystals of most pure metals are notoriously weak.

YS: That's a very difficult point. You are correct in saying that from the point of view of the dislocation theory, a perfect crystal should be strong. But you must remember that, as we saw in Chapter 17, single crystals of metals are not perfect and the dislocation hypothesis is therefore not in contradiction to the facts, although the whole position would admittedly be much more satisfactory if really perfect crystals could be produced, and were shown to be strong (see p. 272a).

OM: It would seem that if a dislocation is to permit one half of a crystal to slide over another, the dislocation must extend pretty well across the whole width of the crystal.

YS: In the original theory of G. I. Taylor, that is what is assumed. In Fig. 116 you will see the kind of process which is suggested. This figure represents a cross-section perpendicular to the slip plane which cuts the section along the line *AB*. The actual slip plane is thus perpendicular to the plane of the paper, and passes through *AB*. In Fig. 116(*b*) there is a compressed region above the slip plane, and an extended region below, with the result that at one point there is a serious misfit or dislocation. If this dislocation moves from left to right, the effect will be to carry the upper half of the crystal one step to the right relative to the lower half. In Fig. 116(*e*), the region above the slip plane is expanded, and that below is compressed, and if the dislocation moves to the left, the final result of the process is the same as in Fig. 116(*c*). Taylor called these two types of disloca-tion positive and negative dislocations respectively, and they are now

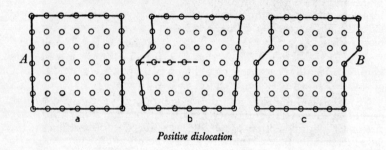

Positive dislocation

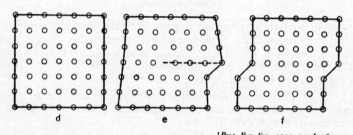

[*Proc. Roy. Soc.*, 1934, 145A, 369

Negative dislocation

Fig. 116

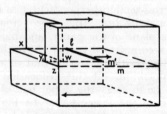

Fig. 117

called Taylor Dislocations, or Edge Dislocations. They lie in the slip plane and move in the direction of slip. It is a property of these dislocations that they cannot end within a crystal. They must either extend right across the crystal from one side to the other or form a closed loop.

OM: It seems to me that if that is so there will have to be another kind of dislocation because a closed loop will not enable the dislocation always to lie in the same direction as that of slip.

YS: That is quite true, and if an edge dislocation does end within a crystal, it gives rise to another kind of dislocation known as a *screw dislocation*. Suppose that as in Fig. 117 an edge dislocation such as *lm'* extends only part of the way across the crystal so that the portion above *wxlm'* has slipped, whereas that above *zym'm* has not slipped. There will then be a new boundary between slipped and unslipped material and this produces a dislocation lying in the same direction as that of slip. The structure of these screw dislocations for a simple cubic lattice may be understood from Fig. 118, where (*a*) shows the undistorted crystal and (*b*) shows the structure after slip has occurred in one part, with the introduction of the screw dislocation whose atomic arrangement is shown in (*c*). In (*d*) is shown the structure after further slip has occurred. Just as there are positive and negative edge dislocations so there may be right-handed and left-handed screw dislocations.

OM: It seems to me that all these examples are very improbable, and that even if they are accepted they do not agree with the facts.

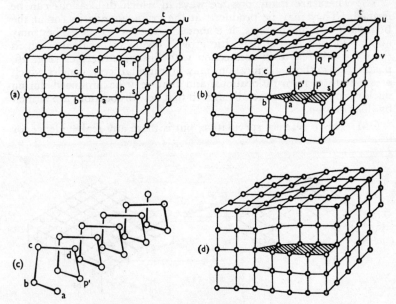

Fig. 118—To illustrate a screw dislocation in a simple cubic lattice

The general evidence is that single crystals become weaker as they become more pure and more perfect, whereas the above picture would require a perfect crystal to be strong.

YS: That is not quite right. The dislocation theory does require a perfect crystal to be strong, and you are correct in suggesting that the lack of experimental evidence on this point is unconvincing. The introduction of a few dislocations should then weaken the crystal, but the interesting thing is that the introduction of a larger number of dislocations may begin to strengthen it again, because the presence of one dislocation may interfere with the movement of another. In Fig. 116(*b*), for example, we have a contracted region above the slip plane, and an expanded region below, and the dislocation moves from left to right. The existence of a dislocation of opposite sign might then stop this movement, and so strengthen the crystal. You will see, therefore, that the objection you raised above is not necessarily valid. If we dealt with a crystal which contained very few dislocations, then increasing perfection should lead to increased strength. But if the crystal contained a larger number of dislocations then increasing perfection might weaken the crystal, because the interference which one dislocation exerts on another would be removed.

OM: I must confess that I still think it all sounds rather doubtful, but if one does accept the theory, is one to regard the dislocation as being formed naturally in the crystal, or only as the result of previous deformation?

YS: There are many possible ways in which dislocations can be formed. They may be produced at the grain boundaries, or at the boundaries of the mosaics, if a mosaic structure exists. They may also be formed during dendritic growth owing to accidents such as those we referred to in connection with lineage structures (Fig. 26, p. 120). Also thermal vibrations may produce lattice vacancies which accumulate to form dislocations, and they may be produced during nucleation. It is also generally agreed that new dislocations are formed by deformation.

OM: This is all very speculative, but is there any real evidence for it?

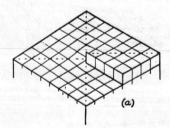 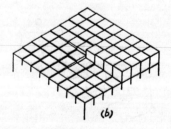

Fig. 119

Cadmium crystal extended at 250°C

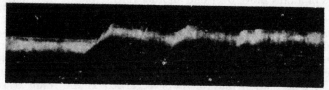

[*From* Kristallplastizitat, *Boas and Schmid*

Zinc crystal extended at 300° C

Fig. 120

YS: Yes. In the last five to ten years there have been great advances in the theory of dislocations which is now much more than speculation. The most striking confirmation is in connection with the process of crystal growth. When crystals of metals are allowed to grow by condensation from the vapour phase, it is found that growth occurs much more rapidly than would be expected if the structure were perfect. The facts required some process by which the growth could continue in such a way that imperfections remained in the surface of the growing crystal and were perpetuated as the growth occurred. It was shown by Frank that if a screw dislocation emerged from the face of a crystal it gave a model such as that of Fig. 119, and then as new atoms were deposited the irregularity was preserved. This has been strikingly confirmed by the observation of spirals on the faces of growing crystals, and in this way a single hypothesis accounts both for the process of slip and of crystal growth. The theory of dislocations has made remarkable progress in the last ten years (1944–54) and you will find very good accounts in books by A. H. Cottrell and by W. T. Read.[1]

OM: In considering deformation, the close-packed hexagonal structure seems remarkable, because there is only one set of close-packed planes. If slip occurs on these, there must surely be very marked directional properties.

YS: That's quite correct, and Fig. 120 shows some of the extraordinary effects when zinc and cadmium crystals are extended above room temperature. Even at room temperature the results are most remarkable, and I have been shown single crystals of cadmium prepared by E. Orowan which could be stretched out by hand. The

[1] *Dislocations and Plastic Flow in Crystals*, A. H. Cottrell. Clarendon Press. *Dislocations in Crystals*, W. T. Read, jun. McGraw-Hill.

sensation was most curious and was like pulling out a rather creaky piece of elastic which did not contract on releasing the tension. These crystals had the close-packed glide planes suitably orientated for easy slip, but if crystals are prepared with the close-packed planes perpendicular to the direction of tension, the resistance to stretching is enormously greater.

OM: Is a simple slip of the same type the only way in which the layers of atoms move over one another during plastic deformation?

YS: In simple slip, relatively large blocks of metal slide over one another, and as far as can be judged from the appearance of slip lines, the sliding is confined to restricted regions—you will understand, of course, that a visible slip line may involve a large number of atomic planes. Another process of deformation is that of *twinning*, and this type of deformation may often be regarded as the result of simple shear in which every plane of atoms slides over its neighbour in a definite direction by an amount which is a fraction of a unit spacing. If the first plane of atoms slides a distance a over its neighbour, and the second plane slides a similar distance relative with the first, you can see that the total movement of the second plane is $2a$. In the same way, the third, fourth and fifth planes move total distances of $3a$, $4a$, and $5a$ respectively. The result of this is that the part of the crystal which twins undergoes a general movement in a particular direction, and after the twinning this part of the crystal is again a single crystal, but with an orientation different from the part which has remained undisturbed. It can readily be shown that in the twinned part of the crystal the position of each atom is a reflection or mirror image of an atom in the part which has not been disturbed;[1] the two halves of the twin crystal are mirror images of one another across the twin plane. Distortion by twinning is very common, and you will see that it results in each layer of atoms moving a short step over the adjacent layer, whereas in distortion by slip the motion is confined to whole blocks of metal which slip on a limited number of planes.

OM: In your description you have spoken of planes of atoms slipping over one another, but when a crystal is distorted, does it remain a single crystal except for the introduction of new dislocations?

YS: During the first stages of slip, a single crystal stretched in tension remains essentially a single crystal. Its orientation changes as the result of the slip.

OM: That's a point which the usual illustrations do not bring out clearly. If Fig. 121 (a) shows the crystal in its initial state, with the slip planes marked, and if Fig. 121 (b) shows the condition of affairs after extension, the slip planes are parallel to those in Fig. 121 (a), and so surely the orientation has not changed?

---

[1] There is a second kind of twinning in which the orientation of the twin can be made to coincide with that of the matrix by rotation about an axis, the twin axis, which is the direction of shear.

YS: You are forgetting that in Fig. 121 (*a*) the axis of the specimen is vertical, whilst in Fig. 121(*b*) it is sloping sideways. In an ordinary tensile test the specimen remains vertical, and you have therefore to imagine Fig. 121(*b*) tipped up vertically as in Fig. 121(*c*), from which you can readily see how the orientation has changed. Fig. 122 shows the same effect for deformation in compression. In the same way the fact that slip is in a definite direction implies a change in orientation during deformation.

OM: If that is what happens, there will be complications near the grips.

YS: That is perfectly correct. If you take a single crystal in the form of an ordinary tensile test piece with a long parallel portion thickening out at each end, most of the parallel portion will deform uniformly as in Fig. 121, but at each end the specimen will have to deform more on one side than on the other because the two ends remain vertically above one another.

OM: These changes in orientation suggest that as deformation proceeds, the mode of slip, which was at first most favourable (that is, for which the component of shear stress was a maximum) may eventually become no more favourable than some other mode. In this case two kinds of slip might take place, but it is difficult to be sure about this, because the first kind of slip might disturb the atomic arrangement in such a way that it was more difficult for the second kind to start up.

YS: What you say is quite right, and the results vary from one metal to another. The effects are well marked in the face-centred cubic structure where there are four sets of octahedral slip planes each with three sets of close-packed rows. Here slip on one plane in one direction

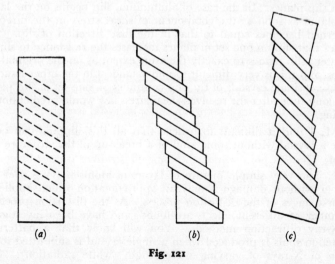

(*a*)　　　　　(*b*)　　　　　(*c*)

Fig. 121

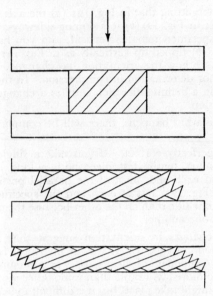

[*After C. S. Barrett*, The Structure of Metals

Fig. 122

may soon change the orientation to such an extent that another mode of slip becomes equally favoured, and then double slip begins, and two sets of slip lines are formed. The new slip planes which are brought into action as the result of the change in orientation may be called latent slip planes. In the case of aluminium, slip begins on the latent slip planes as soon as the component of shear stress in the direction concerned becomes equal to that in the first direction of slip. This implies that slip on one set of planes increases the resistance to slip on the latent slip planes to exactly the same extent as on the original slip planes, and this is very difficult to understand. On the other hand, in the case of single crystals of tin, slip continues on one set of slip planes for a long time after the resolved shear stress law would predict double slipping.

OM: I find it difficult to believe that all this slipping can occur inside a crystal without some kind of a break-up of the structure as a whole.

YS: The very simple picture of layers of atoms moving over one another without damage is only an approximation which applies to the first stages of the distortion process. As the distortion proceeds, a number of different effects are found, and have been investigated by X-ray diffraction methods. You will know that a pattern of diffraction spots is produced when a single crystal is submitted to the action of X-rays of varying wave length (white radiation). If a

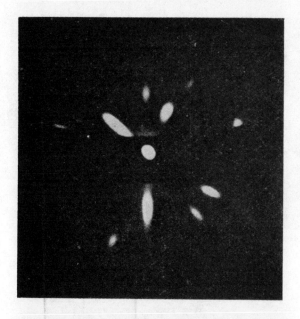

Fig. 123—Laue diffraction photographs of deformed single crystals of aluminium. Some of the sharp spots of the undeformed crystals have elongated into streaks.

[Scient.-Papers. Inst. Phys. Chem. Research, Tokyo

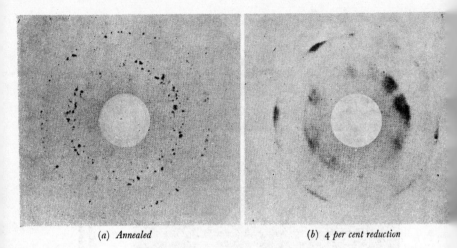

(a) *Annealed*

(b) *4 per cent reduction*

[*Proc. Roy. Soc.*, 1939,

(c) *80 per cent reduction*

(d) *85 per cent reduction*

Fig. 124—Back reflection X-ray diffraction photographs of copper after different degrees of reduction

distorted single crystal is treated similarly, some of the spots become elongated into streaks. The effect is known as asterism and an example example is shown in Fig. 123, and is generally regarded as due to a bending of some of the crystal planes. This is not universally accepted because a similar effect would result from the breaking up of the crystal into small crystallites of suitable orientation, and it is possible that the two effects may sometimes take place together.

Apart from the effect of asterism, it is found that as deformation of a polycrystalline metal continues, the X-ray diffraction spots become diffuse; this is shown in Fig. 124. This diffuse broadening of the diffraction spots or lines may result from variation in lattice spacings in different parts of the crystals or from the breaking up of the crystals into very small crystallites of differing orientation. It is possible to separate these two effects to some extent, and much interesting work has been done by Wood, who has shown that when metal is severely worked, the broadening of the diffraction lines does not proceed to more than a certain limit, and this indicates that there is a limit to the extent to which deformation breaks up a metal into smaller crystallites. This effect is shown in Figs. 124(a), (b), (c), and (d), where Fig. 124(a) shows a back reflection X-ray diffraction photograph of annealed copper; each individual spot is a reflection from one crystal. Fig. 124(b) is from the same specimen after 4 per cent reduction by rolling. The individual dots are now disappearing and are being replaced by a ring; this indicates that the original grains have been broken up into smaller crystallites. If this process continued indefinitely, the diffraction lines should become more and more diffuse, but Figs. 124(c) and 124(d) show that this is not the case, and indicate that there is a lower limit to the size of the crystallites. The innermost ring of Fig. 124(c) is the (400) reflection and is larger than that of the corresponding ring in Fig. 124(b). This indicates that at 80 per cent reduction the lattice is expanded and strained, but at 85 per cent reduction (Fig. 124(d)), part of this strain has been relieved, and the ring is of nearly the same size as in Fig. 124(b). For copper and silver under what may be called ordinary deformation processes, this lower limit to the particle size was estimated by Wood to be about 10^{-5} cm. This value is, however, of no great significance because it is now generally recognized that several processes are taking place together and that much of the line-broadening observed by Wood is due to lattice distortion rather than to particle size effects. This means that the actual particle sizes deduced by Wood are probably incorrect, but it leaves undisturbed Wood's main conclusion that, since the line broadening does not continue indefinitely, there is a limit to the extent to which the crystallites are broken up during what may be called ordinary deformation processes. This must not, however, be looked on as an absolute limit independent of the deformation process, because it has been shown by Bridgman that when copper is sheared whilst under very high hydrostatic pressures the copper crystals are broken up to such an extent that only one or two diffuse diffraction lines are shown, and the crystallites are of the order 10^{-7} cm.

OM: Am I right in thinking that all this lies rather outside the electron theory we have been considering?

YS: Yes, I'm afraid that is so. The electron theories have given a satisfactory explanation of the properties of metals within the elastic range. The dislocation theory has made great advances in explaining some characteristics of plastic deformation but there is at present an unfortunate gap between electron theory and dislocation theory and we can but hope that this will soon be filled.

Suggestion for further reading.

For a general description the reader may consult *The Structure of Metals* by C. S. Barrett. McGraw-Hill.

Epilogue to Chapter 32

The reader is asked to imagine the following conversation as taking place sixteen years after the conversation in the foregoing chapter, that is, sometime in 1961 or 1962. The participants are our friends the Older Metallurgist and the Young Scientist, but the former has recently retired and the latter must now be designated a Middle-Aged Scientist. They have met by chance while attending a conference and take the opportunity to consider the bearing of later work on their original discussion.

RETIRED METALLURGIST: From all that I've heard, there have been great developments in the theory of dislocations since we last discussed these matters, and I am uncertain as to how many of our previous conclusions are still correct.

MIDDLE-AGED SCIENTIST: I am glad to say that practically all of what I said before is still correct. One interesting point has, however, arisen in connection with your previous request for direct evidence that perfect crystals would be much stronger than the ordinary metals with which we deal. In recent years much attention has been paid to the properties of metal "whiskers." These are thin filamentary crystals which are formed under different conditions.

RM: I seem to have heard of trouble at electrical contacts resulting from the growth of whisker crystals.

MAS: That is one example, and filamentary crystals are sometimes slowly exuded from surfaces of metals such as cadmium or tin, whereas somewhat similar crystals have been formed by deposition from the vapour phase, or by the decomposition of a halide vapour. The interesting thing is that some of these whiskers have been shown to be enormously stronger than ordinary metals. Thus, whiskers of iron are nearly a hundred times stronger than ordinary single crystals.

RM: You mean that the whiskers are quite free from dislocations?

MAS: In some cases a whisker crystal is associated with a single screw dislocation whose orientation is unfavourable for deformation by bending or by ordinary axial tensile stress. The important thing is that there is now direct evidence that nearly perfect crystals are much stronger than ordinary metals.

RM: Has there been any direct demonstration of the presence of dislocations?

MAS: That's another branch of science in which great advances have been made. It has been found that an etch pit forms relatively easily at the point where a dislocation line passes through the polished surface of a metal. In this way it has been found possible to study the distribution of dislocations. Fig. 124(e) shows an example of this kind.

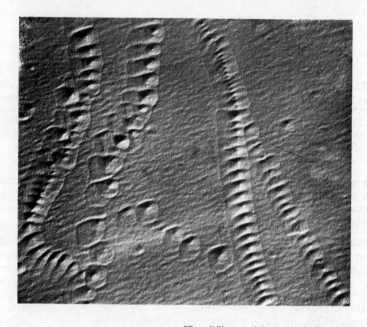

[*From "Elements of Structural Metallurgy," Hume-Rothery. Courtesy The Institute of Metals*]

Fig. 124(e)

RM: That is a good picture, but others I have seen at lower magnifications have looked like some of the supposed microstructures I got in my young days. I was taught to reject them as being due to faulty preparation.

MAS: It's a common comment that some of the dislocation pictures do look very much like badly prepared microsections, and much care has to be taken to ensure proper methods of preparation. But it is a nice question to ask whether you really observed dislocations as a student fifty years ago, and were ticked off for bad work!

RM: I probably was. But are there no more direct methods than this?

MAS: Another great advance is the direct observation of dislocations in transmission electron micrographs of very thin films of metals. The irregular atomic arrangement in a dislocation affects the transmission of electrons, and in this way dislocations have been seen in the electron microscope—Fig. 124(*f*) is an example—and it has even been possible to observe their movement.

[*From "Elements of Structural Metallurgy," Hume-Rothery. Courtesy The Institute of Metals*]

Fig. 124(f)—Thin-film transmission electron micrograph showing a pile-up of dislocations at a twin boundary in 18:8 stainless steel. It should be noted that this behaviour is not typical of most face-centred cubic metals. × 20,000 (After F. W. C. Boswell)

RM: So dislocations are now a definitely established experimental fact, and not merely a theoretical speculation?

MAS: Yes! That's the great advance which has been made in the last fifteen years. During this period an immense science of dislocations has been developed, and the whole subject has made astonishing progress. I'm afraid, however, that most of this is highly mathematical and geometrical, and can hardly be explained in a simple way. You should read the two books referred to on p. 265, and you will find much of interest in a review article by P. B. Hirsch in *Metallurgical Reviews*, 1959, Vol. 4, p. 101.

PART III—THE NATURE OF AN ALLOY

33—Liquid Miscibility and Primary Solid Solution in Alloys

OLDER METALLURGIST: Before we start on the structure of alloys there is one point which I should like made clear. In your description of pure metals, you emphasised that the electron theory was restricted almost entirely to properties within the elastic range. This was rather depressing to me as a practical man, because I am so frequently concerned with metals in the worked state. In the case of alloys the position seems even more confusing, because here I am concerned not merely with cold worked alloys, but also with alloys in a variety of conditions resulting from their different methods of preparation or heat treatment. I may for example have an alloy in the " as cast " state, and this may have one kind of microstructure in which various phases are present. After the alloy has been annealed, its microstructure and properties may be quite different, and by various kinds of heat treatment (quenching, tempering, ageing, etc.) other structures with further properties may be obtained.

YOUNG SCIENTIST: In general if we take an alloy of a given composition, it can, as you say, be obtained in a variety of conditions, depending on the exact methods of preparation, heat treatment, etc. So far as the number of phases and their crystal structures are concerned, if the alloy is held at a given temperature there is an equilibrium state which the alloy tends to approach as time goes on. If the temperature is not too low compared with the melting point of the alloy, the equilibrium state can be reached in a reasonable time, and the properties of the alloy in the equilibrium state can then be studied at the temperature concerned. For example a copper-zinc, 32 atomic per cent zinc alloy will in the cast state contain two phases, but if annealed for a few hours at 700° C it will become a single phase alloy, and this is the stable structure at 700° C. In this particular case, the single phase concerned can be retained by quenching, and so the structure which is stable at 700° C can be studied either at 700° C where it is stable, or at room temperature where it is held in a supercooled or metastable condition. This is not necessarily so, and in some alloys changes take place so rapidly that phases stable at high temperatures can be studied only at the high temperatures concerned.

Speaking generally it may be said that the electron theory of metals and alloys is at present concerned mainly with the properties of single phases, and of the equilibrium between two or more phases under conditions in which the equilibrium has been established. In practice this means that the theory is mainly concerned with alloys which can be annealed to equilibrium at some temperature.

OM: In that case the theory will be of very little use to me as a practical man.

YS: I don't think that follows at all. There are many cases where you are concerned with conditions which are very nearly those of true equilibrium—for example alloys are often " homogenised " by annealing at some temperature for a time which produces equilibrium conditions or something very near to them. But apart from this, an understanding of the equilibrium condition is nearly always necessary if the non-equilibrium condition is to be understood. You will of course know that before the electron theory was developed, a great deal of time was spent in studying the so-called equilibrium diagrams of alloys. These are diagrams in which the structure of the alloy is shown as a function of the composition and temperature. If this diagram is known, it is often possible to predict in a rough qualitative way what will happen under conditions when equilibrium is not attained. For example in the case of the copper 32 atomic per cent zinc alloy to which we referred to above, solidification from the liquid state can produce true equilibrium conditions only if diffusion takes place in both solid and liquid phases; if the rate of solidification is too great for this diffusion to occur, it is quite easy to show that an alloy with two phases will result. The importance of these equilibrium diagrams has long been recognized, and in some cases the electron theories have led to a considerable understanding of why a given diagram has a particular form—it is even possible to calculate the positions of some of the phase boundaries. In fact it may be said that in so far as the equilibrium diagrams are of practical value to metallurgy, the modern theories are of direct application. They also enable us to understand why certain types of crystal structure occur at particular compositions in some alloys, and in this way we are reaching the position at which alloys with a desired *structure* can be built up by the selection of suitable elements. There is of course a great deal of semi-empirical knowledge of the relations between the physical properties of alloys and their structures, and so we are rapidly approaching the stage at which alloys with desired *properties* can be built up.

OM: If we confine our attention to equilibrium conditions, one finds that in the majority of cases, two metals can be melted together to form one homogeneous liquid. But there are some exceptions where two immiscible liquids are formed—the systems copper-lead and lead-zinc are examples. These systems appear to be distributed more or less at random over the Periodic Table, and I have never been able to understand the controlling factors.

YS: That is a very difficult problem, and it is probable that several different controlling factors are at work, some of which are not yet understood. Some of the systems where immiscible liquids are formed are those in which the sizes of the two kinds of atom are very different. You will remember that in Fig. 99 (page 220) the elements thallium and lead have atomic diameters of the order 3.5 kX, and these are distinctly greater than those of most metals except the alkalis and later alkaline earths. It is perhaps significant that thallium and lead form immiscible liquids with several metals, and there is a number of other systems in which the formation of immiscible liquids coincides with a marked difference in the sizes of the atoms of the two elements concerned.

Immiscible liquids are also formed in some alloys of selenium and tellurium where definite intermetallic compounds are formed. In such cases the existence of two liquids is undoubtedly connected with the stability of the compound (see Chapter 36). It is probable that definite compound molecules are formed which persist as such in the liquid, and produce a liquid whose structure is so different from those of one or more of the constituent elements that miscibility does not occur until a relatively high temperature is reached. But apart from these effects there are systems such as aluminium-cadmium where immiscible liquids are formed for no very obvious reason, and it must be admitted that the electron theories have not so far been successful in explaining these phenomena.

OM: If we turn now from the liquid alloys to the solid state we find that in a large number of binary alloy systems, the addition of small quantities of one metal to another results in the formation of an alloy which is homogeneous,[1] and which has many of the characteristics of the pure metal. In the early days of metallography this class of alloy was examined microscopically, and as there was no evidence of a new phase, alloys of this kind were called solid solutions of the one metal in the other. For example, Fig. 125 shows the equilibrium diagram[2] of the system copper-zinc, and from this it will be seen that copper can take up as much as 30–40 atomic per cent of zinc before a two-phase alloy is met with. As far as I remember, it was always guessed that these solid solutions would have the same crystal structure as their parent metals, although there was no direct experimental evidence for this in my University days.

YS: That's quite right, and the development of X-ray crystal analysis in the period 1915–25, showed that the original idea had been correct, and that solid solutions of this kind have the same crystal structure as that of the parent metal—they are sometimes called *terminal solid solutions* or *primary solid solutions* to distinguish them from intermediate phases of variable composition such as β brass in Fig. 125. Fig. 126 for example shows powder X-ray diffraction films of pure silver and of a solid solution of cadmium in silver, and you will see that the X-ray diffraction pattern is the same in the two cases. This indicates that the solid solution of cadmium in silver has a face-centred cubic structure like pure silver.

[1] As explained above the description refers to alloys which have been annealed to equilibrium, unless it is expressly stated to the contrary.

[2] Readers who are not familiar with metallurgical equilibrium diagrams should consult *Metallurgical Equilibrium Diagrams*, by W. Hume-Rothery, J. W. Christian and W. B. Pearson, *Metallography*, by C. H. Desch, or *An Introduction to Physical Metallurgy*, by W. Rosenhain and J. L. Haughton.

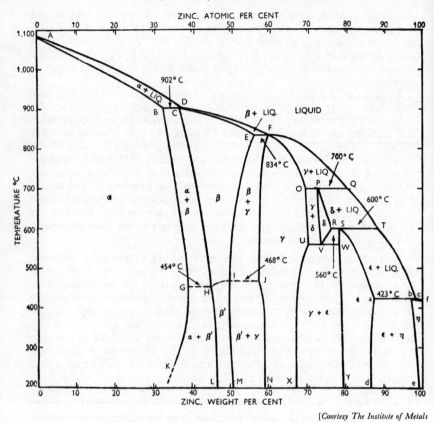

[Courtesy The Institute of Metals

Fig. 125—Equilibrium diagram of the system copper-zinc

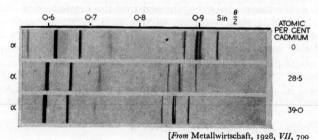

[From Metallwirtschaft, 1928, VII, 700

Fig. 126

OM: On the other hand, the positions of the lines on the two films are not quite the same, so this would seem to indicate that the lattice spacing or size of the unit cell has changed; and I suppose that is after all only what one would expect if one kind of atom goes into solid solution in the lattice of another. It seems to me that there are two main possibilities—the atoms of the solute may enter the holes or interstices between those of the solvent, or alternatively the solute atoms may replace those of the solvent so that the two kinds of atom occupy a common lattice. Are the X-ray methods sufficiently developed to distinguish between these two alternatives?

YS: The distinction can be made quite simply by a combination of lattice spacing and density determination. Let us consider a face-centred cubic metal of atomic weight X, and dissolve in it a atomic per cent of metal of atomic weight Y. Then as we have seen (Chapter 26, page 194) the unit cell of the face-centred cube contains 4 atoms. Let us suppose that we measure the lattice spacing, and hence the volume of the unit cell, V. Now let us suppose that the solid solution is of the interstitial type. Then the unit cell will contain X atoms at each corner and at the centre of each face, and altogether there will be four X atoms associated with each unit cell. The mass of these four atoms will be

$$\frac{4X}{A}$$

where A is Avogadro's Number. For each X atom there will be $\dfrac{a}{100 - a}$ atoms of in Y interstitial solid solution, and consequently the total mass associated with the unit cell will be

$$\frac{4X}{A} + \frac{4a}{(100 - a)} \cdot \frac{Y}{A}.$$

This mass will be contained in the volume V, and the resulting density can be calculated and compared with the experimental value. If the measured density is found to be too small, the results suggest that the solid solution is substitutional. In this case since there are a atoms of atomic weight Y, and $(100 - a)$ atoms of atomic weight X, the mean atomic weight is

$$\frac{aY + (100 - a)X}{100} = X + \frac{a(Y - X)}{100}$$

and the mass associated with the unit cell is

$$\frac{4X}{A} + 4a\frac{(Y - X)}{100\,A}$$

You will see that this expression may be greater or less than $\dfrac{4X}{A}$ according to whether Y is greater or less than X.

The first work of this kind was carried out by Owen and Preston in 1922–23, and their results showed that solid solutions such as those of the system copper-zinc were of the substitutional type.

OM: That's what one would expect from the atomic diameters which were shown in Fig. 99 (Chapter 28, p. 220). It is clear that the interstitial type of solid solution is only to be expected when one atom is very much smaller than another. In fact from Fig. 96, one would expect that only boron and carbon had sufficiently small atomic diameters to give rise to interstitial solid solutions.

YS: That's right. The outstanding example of an interstitial solid solution is the solution of carbon in γ-iron (austenite) which forms the basis of the steels. Apart from this, hydrogen, boron, nitrogen, and probably oxygen form interstitial solid solutions in some metals, but among the metallic elements themselves the differences in atomic diameter are seldom sufficiently great to permit the formation of interstitial solid solution, and most if not all of the primary solid solutions in binary alloys of metals are of the substitutional type. An interesting example is that of silicon (atomic diameter 2.35 kX) which dissolves substitutionally in copper and iron (A.D. *ca* 2.5 kX) but interstitially in niobium (A.D. 2.8 kX).

OM: That doesn't seem to me to be quite right. In Fig. 99 the atomic diameters of caesium and rubidium are so large that one might expect other metals to dissolve in them interstitially.

YS: Actually, one finds that the alkali metals do not[1] take up elements of other groups into solid solution. This serves to emphasize a point which we shall often encounter, namely that arguments about solid solutions based on atomic diameters or the sizes of the atoms are usually of a negative nature. In the case of interstitial solid solutions, for example, one can argue legitimately that atoms of one element are too large to enter into interstitial solid solution in another metal. But as the example of the alkali metals shows one cannot argue that an interstitial solid solution will be formed when the sizes of the atoms are suitable—one can only say that so far as the sizes of the atoms are concerned, the formation of an interstitial solid solution is possible. In actual practice hydrogen, boron, carbon, nitrogen, and oxygen are the only common elements which enter into interstitial solid solution, so that this kind of solid solution is the exception rather than the rule.

OM: If we now consider substitutional solid solutions it seems to me that the relative sizes of the atoms must again be important and that we shall not expect different atoms to fit together easily on a common lattice unless they are more or less of the same size.

YS: That is perfectly correct, and one can even make a first attempt at a quantitative theory. For this purpose we may define the atomic diameters of the elements as the closest distance of approach between two atoms in the crystal of the element. It is then possible to say that if the atomic diameters of two metals differ by more than about 15 per cent, the primary solid solutions are usually restricted—they may be of the order of a few atomic per cent, but not more. We may describe this condition of affairs by saying that the *size factor is unfavourable*. If the atomic diameters differ by less than 15 per cent we may say that the size factor is favourable; in this case wide solid

---

[1] Lithium is an exception to this statement, but its atomic diameter is too small for there to be any possibility of other metals entering into interstitial solid solution.

solutions may be formed, but as emphasized above we cannot say more than this, and it is most important to realise that the mere existence of a favourable size factor does not necessarily result in the formation of a wide solid solution. You will see, therefore, that the concept of size factor is most useful as a kind of negative test—if the size factor is unfavourable we can say that the primary solid solutions will probably be restricted; but if the size factor is favourable we can only say that a wide solid solution *may* (not must) be formed.

OM: Does this kind of size factor argument apply to all metals, or only to specially simple ones?

YS: The idea of a critical limiting difference of about 15 per cent was first advanced by Hume-Rothery, Mabbott, and Channel-Evans in 1934 as the result of a systematic study of solid solutions of different elements in copper and silver. A general study of the solid solutions of different elements in magnesium, aluminium, iron, nickel and some other transition metals has shown that the zones of favourable size factor are again bounded by a critical difference of roughly the same extent (15 per cent), but you must not look on this as a sharp critical value. The modern electronic theory shows quite clearly that we cannot represent the size of an atom by a single number, but empirically we can say that if the atomic diameters are defined as above, then as regards the formation of solid solutions, the size factor becomes unfavourable at a difference of about 15 per cent.

OM: It seems to me that there will be complications when one deals with elements such as thallium which you said (Chapter 26, page 205) were to be regarded as only partly ionised in the crystals of the element, but which might be fully ionised in an alloy. In such a case it would seem that as regards solid solutions, the effective atomic diameter might be smaller than that deduced from the interatomic distance in the crystal of the element.

YS: That is perfectly correct. When indium, white tin, thallium and lead dissolve in some metals they undoubtedly enter into solid solution in the fully ionised state, and the effective atomic diameters seem to be about $0.3kX$ smaller than those based on the closest distance of approach in the crystals of the elements.

Another complication is found with elements such as gallium, or α-manganese where one interatomic distance in the crystal of the element is very much shorter than the remainder. Here there are suggestions that from the point of view of solid solutions in other elements, the effective atomic diameter is somewhat greater than that given by the abnormally short distance of approach. In the case of gallium, for example, each atom has one close neighbour at $2.44\ kX$, whilst the remaining interatomic distances are considerably greater. Here there is some evidence that the atomic diameter of gallium should be regarded as about $2.6\ kX$ from the point of view of solid solution in other elements. Complications of this kind undoubtedly exist, but on the whole it is remarkable how much has been covered by the simple concept of a favourable zone bounded by a difference of 15 per cent.

OM: I should like to see one or two examples of the way in which the size factor principle can be used.

YS: Suppose we consider the solid solutions of the elements of the *B* Sub Groups in copper and silver—we will regard the elements of the two Short Periods as analogous to those of the *B* Sub Groups for this purpose. The atomic diameters of copper and silver are 2.54 *kX* and 2.88 *kX* respectively. If we multiply these values by 15 per cent we obtain 0.38 *kX* and 0.43 *kX* respectively as the limits of the zones of favourable size factor for these two metals. In Fig. 127 I have drawn dotted lines 0.38 *kX* units above and below the point for copper, and 0.43 *kX* units above and below the point for silver, and these lines define the zones of favourable size factor. You will see that the two zones overlap, and in this way many apparent anomalies are accounted for.

Let us consider first the elements of Group II. Here you will see that beryllium is outside the favourable zone for silver, but inside that for copper. We are therefore led to expect a restricted solid solution of beryllium in silver, in agreement with the facts, and we can understand why there is a considerable solid solution (*ca* 18 atomic per cent) of beryllium in copper. With magnesium the position is reversed, and the size factor is favourable for silver but not for copper—we can thus understand why the solubility of magnesium in copper is restricted, and why there is a wide solid solution (*ca* 30 atomic per cent) of magnesium in silver. When we turn to zinc, you will see that the size factor is favourable for both copper and silver, and here wide solid solutions (*ca* 40 atomic per cent) are formed in both metals. Cadmium is just outside the favourable zone for copper, but within that for silver, and here the solubility in copper is small, and that in silver is large (*ca* 40 atomic per cent).

OM: The principle seems to go wrong for mercury, because there is a considerable solid solution of mercury in copper (*ca* 9 atomic per cent) although Fig. 127 shows the point for mercury to be just outside the favourable zone.

YS: In the system copper-mercury the data are not yet conclusively established. The value of 9 atomic per cent which you quote was obtained by a very indirect method—the temperatures were noted at which drops of mercury appeared on heating different amalgams; a very much smaller solubility has been claimed by an X-ray method. In this case further work is undoubtedly needed, but even if the value of 9 atomic per cent which you quoted were confirmed, it would only be a fraction of the normal solubilities of the Group II Elements in systems where the size factors are favourable. It is only right to say that the example chosen—the solubilities of the Group II Elements in silver and copper—is an extremely simple one, and things don't always work out so nicely when the size factors are favourable. When

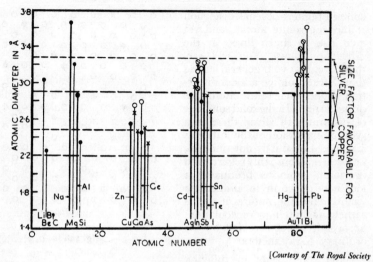

[*Courtesy of The Royal Society*

Fig. 127

one considers alloys of a given metal one should, however, always begin by drawing up a diagram analogous to Fig. 127 and when the size factor is unfavourable the solid solutions are nearly always restricted. But in many alloys where the size factors are favourable wide solid solutions are not formed, and we shall consider the reasons for this later.

OM: In Fig. 126 you have shown X-ray diffraction films of the solid solutions of cadmium in silver. These have quite sharp lines, and their displacement relative to the lines for pure silver indicates that the formation of the solid solution is accompanied by an expansion of the lattice. This is a point which always puzzles me. The sharpness of the lines suggests that the lattice spacing is perfectly uniform throughout the alloy, but I find it very difficult to understand how solute atoms can produce a lattice distortion which is not to some extent localised round each foreign atom.

YS: That is a point on which there is a great deal of misunderstanding, and it is important to realise that in such a case a sharp diffraction line does not indicate a perfectly uniform lattice spacing throughout the alloy. The lattice spacings of solid solutions measured by X-ray methods are mean values for the alloy as a whole, but local distortions can occur round solute atoms without producing fuzzy diffraction lines. The phenomenon is, roughly speaking, the three-dimensional analogue to the effects observed when an optical diffraction grating contains irregularities. In the latter case quite sharp lines can be obtained even though the grating is known to contain errors, and by analogy we can understand how a metallic solid solution may contain regions of local distortion round the solute atoms, and yet give rise to sharp lines on the diffraction films. You will see, therefore, that your general feeling that there would be a local distortion round each solute atom was quite correct. In the solid solutions of cadmium in silver there is a general expansion of the lattice as a whole, but this is not uniform, and you may probably regard each cadmium atom as producing a localised effect in its immediate vicinity, but the nature of this is rather a matter of speculation, because it is not revealed by the ordinary X-ray methods.

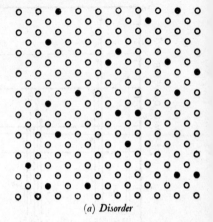

(a) Disorder

Fig. 128 [a, b, c]

OM: Am I right in thinking that in ordinary primary solid solutions the solute atoms are arranged quite at random throughout the common lattice? This is what seems to be implied by the expression " random solid solution," or "disordered solid solution" which I have often come across.

YS: That's another very difficult point. In the ordinary primary solid solution, it is quite certain that there is no *long-range order*, in the sense of a regular arrangement of solute atoms which persists over distances large compared with the size of the unit cell. If long-range order existed it would be revealed by the appearance of extra lines in the diffraction films—this effect is in fact sometimes found, and we shall consider it later when we deal with superlattice structures. The ordinary solid solution shows no long-range order, and is usually described as random or disordered, but it is I think fairly certain that a *short-range order* exists, in the sense that solute atoms tend to avoid being closest neighbours to an extent greater than that which would result from a purely random arrangement. You will understand that even in a dilute solid solution, a purely random arrangement of atoms would result occasionally in two solute atoms being closest neighbours. There is a certain amount of evidence that solute atoms tend to avoid being closest neighbours, and that this is accomplished by some kind of short-range order, that is, an order which is not maintained over long ranges. Fig. 128 may help you to understand how short-range order can occur without long-range order. You might at first imagine that both Figs. 128(a) and 128(b) showed completely random arrangements of the full circles relative to the open circles; but a more careful examination will reveal that in Fig. 128(b), no two full circles are either closest, or next closest neighbours, whereas in Fig. 128(a) the arrangement is completely random; the relative numbers of open and full

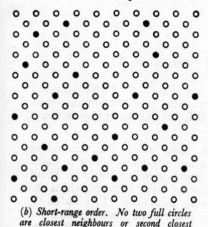

(b) *Short-range order. No two full circles are closest neighbours or second closest neighbours*

(c) *Long-range order. The relative arrangement of full and open circles is regular, and the full circles are as far away from each other as is possible for a ratio of 1 full to 8 open circles*

circles are the same in these two figures. Fig. 128(c) shows an arrangement in which a definite pattern or long-range order exists. In copper-gold alloys the solid solution of gold in copper containing 25 atomic per cent of gold is commonly said to have a disordered structure at high temperatures, but more advanced methods of X-ray crystal analysis (including a study of the relative intensities of the diffraction lines and the background) have given evidence for the existence of short-range order, and a great deal of theoretical work has been carried out on this problem. The above alloy is of course a concentrated solid solution, but I think it is fairly probable that short range order exists in most of what are commonly called disordered solid solutions. For a given atomic percentage of solute in a given solvent, the degree of short-range order may be expected to increase with difference in atomic diameters of solvent and solute, and with the difference in the electro-chemical nature of the two metals (see Chapter 39), but this statement is not one for which there is yet any definite experimental proof. The whole subject of short-range order is of great interest and importance, and it is unfortunate that the experimental evidence is as yet so meagre. You should note, however, that whereas short-range order effects are usually such that solute atoms tend to avoid each other, the opposite tendency is sometimes found, and the solute atoms tend to cluster together more than would be expected from a random arrangement. The solid solution of zinc in aluminium is an example of this kind.

34—Primary Solid Solutions, II

OLDER METALLURGIST: It seems to me that most of what you said last time about the size factor principle is only common sense. One wouldn't expect atoms of widely different sizes to fit together on a common lattice.

YOUNG SCIENTIST: The interesting thing about the size factor principle is that the effect of unfavourable size factor seems to come into play rather suddenly when the atomic diameters differ by about 15 per cent. As we shall see later there are some alloys in which the solid solubility limits follow fairly simple principles. In such cases, the relative atomic diameters of the two metals always affect the solubility limits to some extent but it seems that when the difference reaches about 15 per cent, there is a marked increase in the difficulty with which the two kinds of atom will fit together on a common lattice. It is as though metallic lattices can tolerate differences up to about 15 per cent fairly easily, but then find an enormously increased difficulty in accommodating larger differences.

OM: You have emphasized that a favourable size factor does not necessarily imply that a wide solid solution is formed. This suggests that the relative size of the atoms is only one of the factors concerned in the formation of solid solutions.

YS: That's quite right, and the next principle can be put very simply by saying that if we deal with an alloy of two metals which differ widely in electro-chemical characteristics—that is an alloy where one metal is very electropositive compared to the other—there is always a tendency to form stable intermediate phases or intermetallic compounds at the expense of the primary solid solutions. In such a case you may regard the solute atoms as having a choice of entering the solid solution or the intermetallic compound, and the tendency to enter the compound increases as the two metals differ more widely in their electrochemical characteristics. For example, the alkali metals are very electropositive compared with most if not all other metals, and it is unusual for an alkali metal to form a solid solution in or with an element of another group. Lithium is to some extent an exception to this rule, and it is of course the least electropositive of the alkali metals.

OM: Then do the alkali metals form solid solutions with one another when the size factors are favourable?

YS: Oh, certainly, yes! Rubidium and caesium, potassium and caesium, and potassium and rubidium form continuous series of solid solutions extending from 100 per cent of one metal to 100 per cent of the other—Fig. 129 shows the equilibrium diagrams. There is nothing in an alkali metal *per se* which prevents it from forming solid

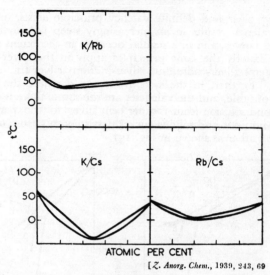

[*Z. Anorg. Chem.*, 1939, 243, 69

Fig. 129—Equilibrium diagrams of the systems K-Rb, K-Cs and Rb-Cs

solutions. It is the combination of the alkali metal with a relatively electronegative metal which prevents the formation of the solid solution. In the same way if you take an electronegative element such as antimony, and alloy it with an electropositive element such as magnesium, the solid solution in antimony will be restricted by what we may call the *electro-chemical factor*.

OM: If I understand you rightly, we are now in a position to say that an unfavourable size factor will prevent the formation of any considerable primary solid solution, and that a combination of an electropositive and an electronegative metal will have the same effect. This suggests that if we are to find any further general principles about solid solutions we must examine systems where the size factors are favourable, and the electrochemical factors are small.

YS: That is how the problem was actually approached. If you refer to Fig. 99 (page 220) you will see that if we take copper as the solvent metal, the succeeding elements zinc, gallium, germanium and arsenic are all of favourable size factor. Similarly with silver as solvent, cadmium, indium, tin and antimony are of favourable size factor. Further, in these metals the electrochemical differences are not too pronounced. Of course, zinc is electropositive compared with copper, but the differences are much smaller than in a combination such as silver-magnesium. In Fig. 130 I have drawn the equilibrium diagrams of the copper-rich alloys of the systems copper-zinc, copper-gallium, copper-germanium, and copper-arsenic. You will now see that a very clear and definite valency principle exists, and that increasing valency results in an increasingly steep fall in the liquidus and solidus curves, and in a regular decrease in the extent of the solid solution. Exactly the same principles apply in the silver-rich alloys of the systems silver-cadmium, silver-indium, silver-tin, and silver-antimony. Further, in the system silver-gold where the size factor is very favourable, and the valencies are the same, there is a complete range of solid solution from 100 per cent silver to 100 per cent gold, whilst the liquidus and solidus curves pass smoothly from one melting point to the other as shown in Fig. 131.

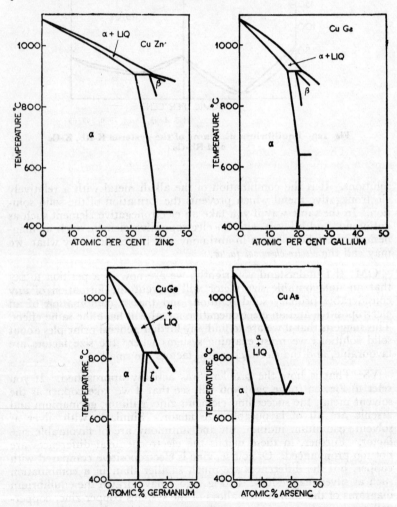

Fig. 130

286

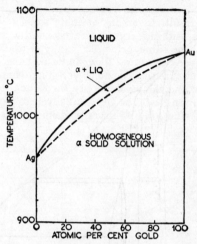

[*Courtesy The Institute of Metals*

Fig. 131—Equilibrium diagram of the system silver-gold

OM: The general principle is certainly very clear, and it might, I suppose, be due either to the increased charge on the ions of the solute, or to the fact that increasing valency means that for a given atomic percentage of solute an increasing number of electrons is being added to the lattice.

YS: Those are the two obvious alternatives, and the second of these was indicated by the fact that to a first approximation the solubility limits of the α-solid solutions occur at roughly the same *electron concentration*. By electron concentration is meant the ratio of valency electrons to atoms.

In the systems copper-zinc, and silver-cadmium, the maximum solubilities of zinc and cadmium are of the order of 40 atomic per cent. Since these are divalent solutes, you can readily see that in the alloy containing 40 atomic per cent cadmium, there will be:

40 cadmium atoms contributing $40 \times 2 = 80$ valency electrons
60 silver atoms contributing $\ \ 60 \times 1 = 60$ valency electrons

Total 100 atoms $\qquad$ and $\qquad$ 140 valency electrons

The electron concentration is thus $\frac{140}{100} = 1.40$.

In the system copper-gallium and silver-indium, the maximum solubilities of gallium and indium are of the order 20 atomic per cent and here we have:

20 atoms of trivalent indium $= 60$ valency electrons
80 atoms of univalent silver $= 80$ valency electrons

100 atoms $\qquad$ to $\qquad$ 140 valency electrons

287

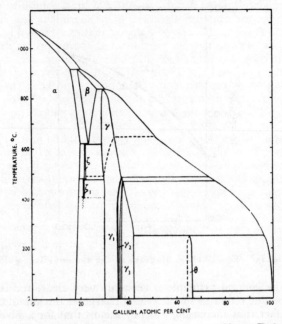

[*Courtesy The Institute of Metals*]

Fig. 132—Equilibrium diagram of the system copper-gallium

The electron concentration is thus again 1.40. You can readily see that if this principle held exactly, the solubilities of the tetra-valent and penta-valent elements should be 13.3 atomic per cent and 10 atomic per cent respectively, whereas actually they are only about 12 atomic per cent and 7 atomic per cent respectively. The general tendency is, however, clear, and the electron concentration principle holds fairly accurately for the divalent and trivalent solutes.

OM: What you say is very interesting, but it seems to me that you are going too fast. The α-solubility curve is a curve which gives the composition of the saturated α-solid solution in equilibrium with a second phase. Surely, therefore, the α-solubility curve must depend on the nature of the second phase, and it is unjustifiable to consider the one curve alone?

YS: You are quite correct in saying that the full story must involve the nature of the second phase, but you will see that the general empirical valency effect is shown very clearly by the above curves. If you examine the copper-zinc diagram, you will see that at high temperatures the α-solid solubility curve has the rather curious characteristic that the solubility increases as the temperature falls. In general one expects the solubility to increase with rising temperature, because one expects that at high temperatures the greater amplitude of the thermal vibrations will make it more easy for the lattice to accommodate foreign atoms. In the α/β brass solubility curve the tendency is in the opposite direction, and experiment has shown that the β-phase has a body-centred cubic structure. From Fig. 132 you will see that the copper-rich portion of the equilibrium diagram of the system copper-gallium has the same characteristics, and X-ray crystal structure work has shown that in this system the β-phase again has a body-centred cubic structure. In these two systems, therefore, your requirements are satisfied because in each case the second phase has the same structure. Fig. 133 shows the α/(α + β) solubility curves for these two systems drawn in both atomic percentages and in terms of electron concentration, and you will see that when drawn in terms of electron concentration the curves are very nearly superposed, and this clearly suggests that electron concentration is the predominant factor in determining these solid solubility curves. The fact that the two curves are not exactly superposed is the result of the lattice distortion being different in the two systems.

OM: When you say that electron concentration is predominant in determining this kind of equilibrium, do you mean that the nature of the atoms doesn't matter, and that the whole effect is due to electron concentration?

YS: To a first approximation, yes. In this particular class of alloy where the size factors are favourable and the electrochemical factors are small, you may regard the substitution of each atom of zinc for one of copper as simply resulting in an increase of one valency electron

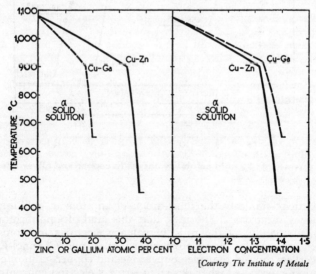

[*Courtesy The Institute of Metals*

Fig. 133—Solidus and solid solubility curves for the systems copper-zinc and copper-gallium in terms of atomic percentages and electron concentration

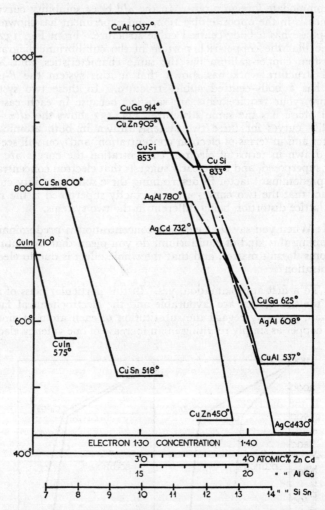

Fig. 134—$\alpha/(\alpha + \beta)$ solid solubility curves in copper and silver alloys

to the lattice—similarly the substitution of an atom of gallium adds two valency electrons. The idea that this kind of equilibrium was determined mainly by the ratio of valency electrons to atoms was advanced in 1934 by Hume-Rothery, Mabbott and Channel-Evans. These workers showed that the copper-zinc and copper-gallium curves were almost superposed when drawn in terms of electron concentration as in Fig. 133, and they also showed that the corresponding $\alpha(/\alpha + \beta)$ boundaries from other copper and silver alloys (for example, copper-aluminium, silver-aluminium, silver-cadmium, silver-zinc) were all roughly superposed when drawn in terms of electron concentration. These were all systems where the size factors were favourable, but in the system copper-tin where the same kind of equilibrium is found, the solubility of tin is only about three-quarters of that to be expected from this simple principle, and as you will see from Fig. 127, tin is on the extreme edge of the zone of favourable size factor for copper. Later work showed that the $\alpha/(\alpha + \beta)$ boundary in the system copper-indium is at a very much lower atomic percentage of indium than would be expected from the simple electron concentration principle, and the size factor for indium is again on the borderline of the unfavourable zone. These results are summarised in Fig. 134 in which the solubility curves are drawn in terms of electron concentration. You will see how the curves for copper-indium and copper-tin are clearly distinguished from those where the size factors are favourable. From this it was concluded that the simple principle of electron concentration held only in the absence of lattice distortion, and that the effect of the latter was relatively small within the favourable zone, but became overwhelmingly important as the unfavourable zone was approached. The general idea of an equilibrium determined by electron concentration was then developed by H. Jones on the basis of the Brillouin zone theories in 1937. You will understand that when once the idea had been gained that this α/β equilibrium was determined mainly by electron concentration, it was natural to try to calculate the energies of the valency electrons in the different crystal lattices.

OM: The general valency sequences shown in Fig. 130 are very fascinating, but you have not explained whether they refer to copper and silver alloys only or whether alloys of other metals show similar relations.

YS: If the interpretation of Fig. 127 on the basis of electron concentration is correct, it implies that when solid solutions are formed we have to consider the relative numbers of valency electrons and atoms. Put very naïvely we may say that when we fit atoms together to form solid solutions we have to consider not merely the sizes of the atoms, but also the numbers of valency electrons which they contain. Atoms of the same size fit together most easily if they contain the same number of valency electrons. From this it follows that if we consider alloys of elements in the same group of the Periodic Table, there is a general tendency for wide solid solutions to be formed if the size factors are favourable. You will see that this principle is satisfied for the alkali metals of Fig. 129, and also for the alloys of silver and gold (Fig. 131). Similarly in Group II, the size factor is favourable in the system magnesium-cadmium, and here the equilibrium diagram (Fig. 135) shows a continuous series of solid solutions at high temperatures, although there are transformations at low temperatures which involve the formation of superlattices (Chapter 39). In the system calcium-strontium the size factor is favourable, and there is again a continuous series of solid solutions. The principle does not

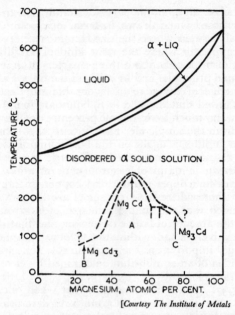

Fig. 135—Equilibrium diagram of the system magnesium-cadmium

[*Courtesy The Institute of Metals*]

always hold, but there are undoubtedly many cases in which continuous solid solutions are formed between two metals in the same Group of the Periodic Table if the size factor is favourable.

OM: In the alloys of Fig. 130 the solute metal always has a higher valency than the solvent, and so the formation of the solid solution increases the electron concentration. Reference to Fig. 125 shows that whilst there is a wide solid solution of zinc in copper, the solid solution of copper in zinc is very restricted. This suggests that as regards the formation of solid solutions a decrease in the number of electrons is more serious than an increase. Is this in any way a general principle for alloys as a whole?

YS: That is a very difficult point. If one considers the alloys of copper, silver and gold with elements of higher valency, it is a quite general principle that the solid solution in the element of high valency is smaller than that in copper, silver or gold. But with combinations of two elements of higher valency, no very general principles have yet been discovered. For example, the solid solubility of zinc in aluminium is greater than that of aluminium in zinc, so that here the solubility in the element of higher valency is the greater, in contrast to the behaviour in the copper and silver alloys. These complications are probably connected with the form of the $N(E)$ curves which we discussed in Chapter 23. In copper, silver and gold there is only one electron per atom, and this corresponds to a point before the first peak on the $\mathcal{N}(E)$ curve,[1] and hence to a region where the $\mathcal{N}(E)$ curve and the energy relations are relatively simple. With the 2-, 3-, and 4-valent elements the numbers of electrons per atom are so great that they correspond to points among the peaks and valleys of the $\mathcal{N}(E)$ curve, and here the energy relations are naturally much more complicated, and so no simple general principles are found.

You should, however, note that when we are dealing with structures involving co-valent bonds, we may expect the substitution of an element of lower valency to be less probable than one of higher valency. In the case of germanium, for example, each atom has four valency electrons and four close neighbours. It shares one valency electron with each neighbour, and so builds up an octet, and it is clear that if we replace a germanium atom by one of lower valency we shall have insufficient electrons to form the co-valent bonds, and in this kind of structure we may expect it to be more serious to have too few electrons than to have too many. But with normal metallic elements it is not yet possible to generalise in this way, although the effect in copper, silver and gold alloys is very clear.

[1] The text of the original has here been left unaltered, but as will be appreciated from the Epilogue on p. 293a, later work has shown that the Fermi surface is so distorted that it has touched the face of the zone at an electron concentration of *ca* 1.0. The whole theory is now more complicated.

35—Primary Solid Solutions, III: The α/β Brass Equilibrium

[*NOTE: For the sake of historical interest, the present chapter has been reprinted without alteration, but as explained in the Epilogue on p. 302a, later work has shown the whole position to be much more complicated than was thought in 1948.—1961*]

OLDER METALLURGIST: You explained last time how it had been discovered empirically that when the size factor was favourable, the α/(α + β) solubility curves in systems such as copper-zinc, copper-gallium, and copper-aluminium were determined mainly by electron concentration. But I'm afraid I find it very difficult to visualise what is going on, particularly in view of what you have said before about electrons being in motion throughout the crystal. If the valency electrons were fixed on the points of a lattice interpenetrating that of the atoms I could understand how there might be only so many lattice points available, and how the lattice might be able to accommodate only so many additional electrons, but if I understand you rightly, this is what does not happen.

YOUNG SCIENTIST: You are quite right in saying that the valency electrons are all in motion in the lattice, and the process which determines the limit of the solid solution may be understood by considering the relative energies of different structures. Strictly speaking we should say that the equilibrium state of an alloy is characterised by a minimum value of the *free energy*.[1] In developing the electron theories of alloys it is customary to begin by considering the state of affairs at the absolute zero. At this temperature the free energy is equal to the total energy, and we can simply say that the equilibrium structure of an alloy is the structure which has the lowest energy. Now we saw in Chapter 29 that in copper and silver the face-centred cubic structure was more stable (that is, had a lower energy) than the body-centred cube because of the interaction of the outermost electrons of the Cu^+ or Ag^+ ions. You will remember that so far as the valency electrons were concerned there was no appreciable difference between the stabilities of the face-centred cubic and body-centred cubic structures at an electron concentration of 1.0. When we dissolve zinc in copper, we increase the number of valency electrons per atom, and consequently we increase the energy of the electrons. If this process is continued, it is quite possible that a stage will be reached at which the electrons will have a lower energy in some other type of crystal structure, and in this case the face-centred cubic structure may no longer be the stable form. It is not possible to give any mechanical

---

[1] In general an alloy in equilibrium takes up the structure for which the free energy G is a minimum, where G is defined by the relation

$$G = U - TS + PV$$

In this expression, U is the total internal energy, T the absolute temperature, S the entropy, P the pressure, and V the volume. In condensed systems the terms PV can usually be neglected, in which case the condition for equilibrium is a minimum value of $U - TS$.

picture of why the face-centred cubic structure becomes unstable when the electron concentration exceeds about 1.4. It is, however, quite easy to show that when the electron concentration reaches a value of about 1.4, the addition of further electrons to the face-centred cubic structure results in a relatively rapid increase in the energy, and this leads us to expect a tendency for some other structure to appear, that is for the a solubility limit to be exceeded.

OM: I can see the general idea, but surely one must need a lot of elaborate information before the $N(E)$ curve and other energy characteristics of the electrons can be calculated.

YS: The full calculation is naturally very complicated, but fortunately drastic simplifications can be made which enable one to obtain a rough estimate very easily. You will remember that (Fig. 57, page 166) the first Brillouin zone of the face-centred cubic structure is bounded by a combination of octahedral and cube faces, and as the electron states are gradually filled up, the Fermi surface first touches the octahedral faces; these faces correspond with Bragg reflection in the (111) planes of the lattice. The first simplifying assumption we may make is that the *Fermi surfaces are spheres*. This means that with increasing numbers of electrons the occupied states in k-space lie within spheres of continually increasing diameter, and we may now calculate the electron concentration at which a spherical Fermi surface first touches the octahedral face of the zone—this electron concentration will correspond with the first peak on the $N(E)$ curve, that is, the peak A in Fig. 136. Since we are assuming the Fermi surfaces to be spherical we may use the free electron theory approximation. The momentum p is then equal to h/λ where λ is the wave length, and if we denote by p_{max} the momentum of an electron on the surface of the sphere, we shall have as in Chapter 20:

$$\frac{4}{3}\pi\, p^3\,_{max} = \frac{4}{3}\pi\, \frac{h^3}{\lambda^3} = \frac{Nh^3}{2V}$$

and hence for an assembly of N electrons in a volume V

$$\lambda = \left(\frac{8\pi}{3}\frac{V}{N}\right)^{\frac{1}{3}}$$

In this way for the electron states corresponding to the first peak on the $N(E)$ curve, we obtain one equation connecting the wave length λ, of the highest occupied state, with the number of electrons, N, and the volume V. It is now possible to obtain another relation connecting λ and V with the number of atoms N_a, and this may be done as follows.

For the electron states on the surface of a zone, the wave length satisfies the Bragg equation

$$n\lambda = 2d \sin\theta$$

For the face-centred cubic structure the first peak on the $N(E)$ curve corresponds with Bragg reflections from the (111) planes, and the interplanar spacing, d, of these is equal to $\dfrac{a\sqrt{3}}{3}$ where a is the side

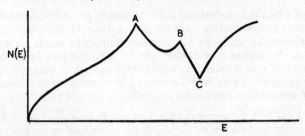

Fig. 136—N(E) curve for face-centred cubic structure

[*Courtesy The Institute of Metals*]

The points A and B represent the stages at which the Fermi surface of occupied states first touches the octahedral and cube faces of the first Brillouin zone. The curve is from calculations by N. F. Mott and H. Jones, and assumes the energy gaps at the zone boundaries to be those deduced for copper from its optical properties

of the unit cell. Where the Fermi surface first touches the zone, the first order reflection is such that $n = 1$, and $\theta = 90°$ in the Bragg equation, and we may therefore write:

$$\text{for} \quad n\lambda = 2d \sin \theta$$

$$\lambda = 2a \frac{\sqrt{3}}{3}$$

Since the unit cell contains 4 atoms, we may write

$$\frac{N_a}{V} = \frac{4}{a^3}$$

where N_a is the number of atoms in volume V. Substituting this in the above expression for λ we have

$$\lambda = \frac{2\sqrt{3}}{3} \left(\frac{4V}{N_a} \right)^{\frac{1}{3}}$$

If this expression is now united with the previous equation connecting λ and N we obtain

$$\left(\frac{8\pi V}{3N} \right)^{\frac{1}{3}} = \frac{2\sqrt{3}}{3} \left(\frac{4V}{N_a} \right)^{\frac{1}{3}}$$

and hence

$$\frac{N}{N_a} = 1.36.$$

You will see that by combining our knowledge of the real form of the Brillouin zone with the simplifying assumption of spherical Fermi surfaces, we conclude that the first peak A (Fig. 136) on the $N(E)$ curve of the face-centred cubic structure will correspond to an electron concentration of about 1.36, that is, 36 atomic per cent of zinc, 18 atomic per cent of gallium, 12 per cent of germanium, or 9 per cent of arsenic in the copper alloys.

Now a high $N(E)$ curve means that a given number of electrons can be accommodated with a relatively low energy, and conversely a low $N(E)$ curve means that the energy of a given number of electrons is high (Chapter 19, page 137). You will see therefore that if we increase the electron concentration beyond 1.36, for example if we increase the zinc content beyond 36 atomic per cent, then the addition of further electrons (or more zinc atoms) will mean a relatively rapid increase in the energy of the electrons. This conclusion refers to the $N(E)$ curve of the face-centred cubic structure, but you will realize that there is a large number of alternative possible crystal structures. If one of these has an $N(E)$ curve which continues rising beyond an electron concentration of 1.36, then so far as the electronic energy is concerned we shall expect this structure to become relatively more stable than the face-centred cubic structure as the electron concentration increases beyond 1.36, because the higher $N(E)$ curve means that the electrons can be accommodated with a lower energy. The calculation of an electron concentration of approximately 1.36 for the first peak on the $N(E)$ curve of the face-centred cubic structure enables us to say that when the electron concentration increases beyond 1.36 we may expect the face-centred cubic structure to become less stable than some other structures, and you will see that it is just about this electron concentration that the maximum solubilities of zinc, gallium, and germanium in copper are found.

OM: That would imply that the exact details of the process should depend on the crystal structure of the phase with which the a solid solution is in equilibrium, since each structure has its own characteristic $N(E)$ curve.

YS: That's quite right. The theory has not yet reached the stage of predicting what happens in a given alloy system, but if we know the crystal structure of the second phase, then we can compare the $N(E)$ curves of the two structures, and see how the relative energies of the valency electrons are related.

OM: In the $a\beta$ brass kind of equilibrium we know the β-phase has a body-centred cubic structure, so it should be fairly easy to calculate the position of the first peak on its $N(E)$ curve.

YS: That can be done quite simply. The first Brillouin zone of the body-centred cubic structure is the rhombic dodecahedron of Fig. 58 (page 167), and its surfaces correspond with Bragg reflections from the (110) planes of the lattice, whose interplanar spacing is equal to $\frac{a\sqrt{2}}{2}$ where a is the side of the unit cell. The unit cell contains 2 atoms so that we may write $\frac{N_a}{V} = \frac{2}{a^3}$ where N_a is the number of atoms in volume V. These expressions have to be used in place of the corresponding expressions for the face-centred cubic structure, but otherwise the calculation is exactly the same as the one detailed above and you will readily find that

$$\frac{N}{N_a} = 1.48$$

So the first peak on the $N(E)$ curve for the body-centred cubic structure

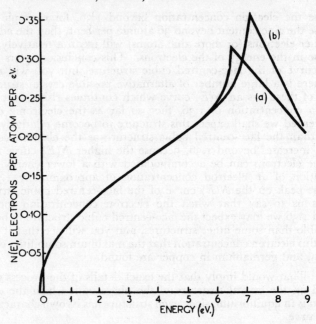

*Curves showing the number of states per unit energy range as a function of the energy (a) For
the face-centred cubic structure; (b) for the body-centred cubic structure*

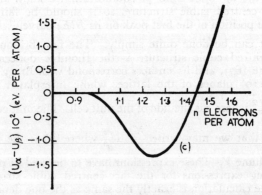

[*Proc. Phys. Soc.*, 1937, 49, 253]

*(c) The difference between the Fermi energies of the face-centred and body-centred structures as a
function of the number of electrons per atom*

Fig. 137 [a, b, c]

occurs at an electron concentration of approximately 1.48, for example 48 atomic per cent of zinc in a copper-zinc alloy.

OM: Oh, I see! So if the first peak on the $N(E)$ curve for the face-centred cubic structure is at an electron concentration of 1.36, and that on the curve for the body-centred cubic structure is at an electron concentration of 1.48, there will be a range between these two values where the curve for the face-centred cubic structure is falling, whilst that for the body-centred cube is continuing to rise. And over this range, so far as the electronic energy is concerned, the body-centred cubic structure will become increasingly stable.

YS: Exactly! And you will see that it is in this range that the brasses change from the a to the β type. So in spite of our drastic simplification of the problem, we have produced a theory of the a/β brass equilibrium diagram, which predicts the approximate composition at which the alloys change from the face-centred to the body-centred cubic structure. For a complete theory we have to replace the assumption of spherical Fermi surfaces by something which is nearer to the truth, and also to include the effect of temperature, since the above very simple arguments naturally refer to the absolute zero where there is a sharp bounding surface between the occupied and unoccupied states. This more detailed work has been done by H. Jones, and Fig. 137 shows the $N(E)$ curves which he calculated for the two structures. These are to be interpreted just as in the above description, and you will see that there is again a region where the $N(E)$ curve for the body-centred cubic structure is continuing to rise, whilst that for the face-centred cube is falling, and it is in this region that the change from the a to the β alloys occurs. Fig. 137(c) shows the difference between the Fermi energies of electrons in the two structures.

OM: That's very striking, and is all right for the absolute zero, but now we want the effect of temperature in particular, can the theory explain the curious effect which makes the solubility of zinc in copper diminish with rising temperature?

YS: There, I am afraid, the theory has not yet been successful. The original paper[1] of H. Jones included an approximate calculation for the effect of temperature on the $a/(a + \beta)$ and $(a + \beta)/\beta$ phase boundaries, and this claimed to indicate the correct dependence on temperature. But later work by Zener[2] suggests that a mistake occurred in the original calculations, and that the calculated boundaries are not really in agreement with the facts. For the present, therefore, one can only say that the electron theory predicts the approximate composition at which the change from the a to the β occurs—and after all that's something to have done!

OM: I notice that in the Cu-Ga diagram (Fig. 132) the a-solubility

---

[1] The original work of H. Jones is in the Proceedings of the Physical Society of London, 1937, 49, 249.
[2] The paper by Zener is in the *Physical Review*, 1947, 71, 846.

curve has a quite different shape below the temperature of the β-eutectoid point. I suppose that is due to the fact that below this temperature the α-phase is no longer in equilibrium with a body-centred cubic phase.

YS: That's quite correct. The Jones theory has only been applied to the equilibrium between body-centred and face-centred cubic phases. In principle the same kind of calculation could be applied to equilibrium between phases of any two given structures, but so far the mathematical difficulties have proved too great.

OM: Then if I understand you rightly, what one may call the simple Jones theory of the α/β brass equilibrium applies only when the size factors are favourable and the full theory must take the effect of lattice distortion into account.

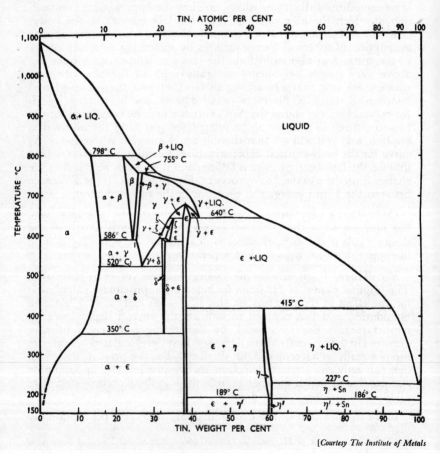

[Courtesy The Institute of Metals

Fig. 138—Equilibrium diagram of the system copper-tin

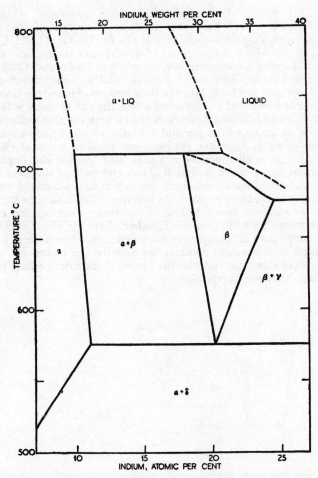

Fig. 139—Equilibrium diagram of the system copper-indium in the α/β region

[*Courtesy The Institute of Metals*

YS: Yes, from the point of view of the electron theory, nothing has yet been calculated, but a little progress has been made empirically. The systems Cu-In and Cu-Sn are the two systems in which the α/β brass kind of equilibrium is found for a solute element whose atomic diameter is on the borderline of the favourable zone. The equilibrium diagrams of these two systems are shown in Figs. 138 and 139. Examination of Fig. 139 (Cu-In) will show that the α/α + β and α + β/β phase boundaries have been displaced to lower percentages of the solute element compared with the corresponding boundaries in the system

Cu-Ga (Fig. 132) where the size factors are favourable, whilst the $(\alpha + \beta)$ area is wider. Systematic examination has shown that when the equilibrium diagrams of the system Cu-Zn, Cu-Ga, Cu-Al, Cu-In, and Cu-Sn, in which the α/β kind of equilibrium occurs, are drawn in terms of electron concentration, the systems Cu-In and Cu-Sn are characterised by a wider $(\alpha + \beta)$ area, and a displacement of the $\alpha/\alpha + \beta$ and $\alpha + \beta/\beta$ boundaries in the direction of lower electron concentration as compared with systems where the size factors are favourable. Empirical relations have been traced between these effects and the lattice distortions in the α and β phases of the different systems, but these relations have not yet been explained in terms of electron theory, and we shall therefore not deal with them. The important thing about Jones' work is that it shows clearly that the idea of an electron concentration equilibrium, which was first advanced empirically, finds a satisfactory explanation in terms of Brillouin zone theories, so that the electron concentration is one factor affecting the equilibrium between metallic phases. In other alloys the electron concentration factor may be completely outweighed by other factors and to understand these we must consider not only the size factors etc. of the primary solid solutions, but also the nature of the intermediate phases with which they are in equilibrium.

Epilogue to Chapter 35

The reader is asked to imagine the following conversation as taking place sixteen years after the conversation in the foregoing chapter, that is, sometime in 1961 or 1962. The participants are our friends the Older Metallurgist and the Young Scientist, but the former has recently retired and the latter must now be designated a Middle-Aged Scientist. They have met by chance while attending a conference and take the opportunity to consider the bearing of later work on their original discussion.

RETIRED METALLURGIST: From what I've been hearing at this conference, there is a great deal of confusion about the α/β brass theory, and much of what you told me sixteen years ago is no longer valid.

MIDDLE-AGED SCIENTIST: I'm afraid that is true, and the theory of copper and silver, and that of their alloys is now in a state of great confusion.

RM: Let us go back to the beginning and consider the first Brillouin Zone of the face-centred cubic structure which you showed in Fig. 57. Then this contains two electron states per atom, and since copper, silver, and gold are univalent, the occupied states will fill just one half the zone. You said that, under these conditions, the Fermi surface was nearly spherical and, although you did not give a diagram, I have often met Fig. 139(a) which expresses this condition of affairs.

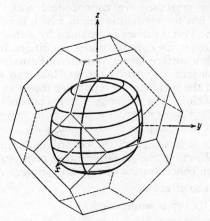

[*From "The Theory of the Properties of Metals and Alloys," Mott and Jones, Dover Publications, Inc.*

Fig. 139(a)

302a

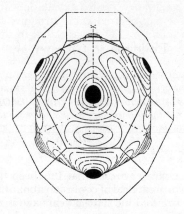

[*Courtesy Royal Society*

Fig. 139(b)—Fermi surface for copper according to Pippard

MAS: That is where the first mistake was made. The actual Fermi surfaces in copper, silver, and gold are greatly distorted from the spherical, and are in fact so distorted that they have already touched the octahedral face of the zone at the electron concentration of 1.0, characteristic of the pure metals. Fig. 139(b) shows the Fermi surface for copper which Pippard deduced from a study of the anomalous skin effect in single crystals. We cannot deal with the experimental methods here, but the method is one in which information about the curvature of the Fermi surface is obtained by a study of the conductivity for high-frequency currents under conditions in which these are carried by a thin surface layer. Further information about the area of the Fermi surface is given by the de Haas–van Alphen effect—an effect in which the magnetic susceptibility shows an oscillatory variation with the field. The evidence is now conclusive that for copper the Fermi surface has touched the face of the zone, and it is almost certain that the same applies to silver and gold.

RM: So this means that all the beautifully simple theories which showed an $\mathcal{N}(E)$ curve for the face-centred cubic structure rising to a peak at electron concentration of 1.36 are wrong.

MAS: Yes, I'm afraid so.

RM: And Fig. 137 is wrong too?

MAS: That's where things got in such a muddle, and I am as guilty as any one. I told you that in Fig. 137 the $\mathcal{N}(E)$ curve for the body-centred cubic structure continued to rise after that for the face-centred cubic structure was falling, and that these curves gave the correct position for the α/β brass boundaries. This was correct, but what nearly all of us failed to notice at the time—I didn't realise it until later—was that Jones' more detailed calculations had shifted the peak on the curve for the face-centred cubic structure back to an electron concentration of about 1.0. This was stated in the paper, but as the diagram was in terms of electron volts, most of us imagined that the curve was only slightly different from that for free electrons. Further, although it wasn't stated in the paper, integration of the curves shows that the peak for the b.c. cubic structure is an electron concentration of about 1.2, and so this peak cannot be the cause of the stability of the β-phases at e.c. 1.5.

RM: Still, as regards the curve for the face-centred cube, Jones' calculations in 1937 seem to have been a remarkable forecast of the experimental work on Fermi surfaces some 21 years later.

MAS: Yes; but if you leave it like that the price paid is a very heavy one. The previously supposed close correspondence between the position of peaks on $N(E)$ curves, and the compositions of phases has now gone.

RM: I gather there have been attempts to save the theory.

MAS: Broadly speaking, two lines of approach have been adopted. One group of theoretical physicists has argued that the successes of the earlier theories based on nearly spherical Fermi surfaces were so striking that they must have contained a certain amount of truth. They have therefore sought for mechanisms by which the Fermi surface, which is highly distorted in copper, might become more spherical as copper atoms are replaced by those of zinc. This work is due mainly to M. Cohen and V. Heine,[1] and their argument may be summarised as follows:

In the free atom of copper, the $4s$ level is lower than the $4p$ level by about 3.8 e.v., and we may represent the position

$$\left.\begin{array}{l} 4p \\ \\ 4s \end{array}\right\} 3.8 \text{ e.v.}$$

Various physical properties of solid copper suggest that at the centres of the octahedral faces of the zone, the electron states are almost purely p-like inside the zone, and s-like outside the zone. The energy gap at the zone boundary is about 4 e.v., and so for the electron states at the centres of the octahedral zone faces the position is

$$\left.\begin{array}{l} 4s \\ \\ 4p \end{array}\right\} 4 \text{ e.v.} = \Delta$$

For these states in the zone, the effect of compressing the atoms to form the solid crystal has been to lower the $4p$ states relatively to the $4s$ states, and the effect has been considerable. If we denote the energy gap at the centre of the octahedral zone face as Δ, it is the large value of Δ which corresponds with the highly distorted Fermi surface. Now, if

[1] *Advances in Physics*, M. Cohen and V. Heine. 1958, vol. 7, 395.

you consider the free atom of zinc, you find that the $4s$ level is below the $4p$ level by a greater amount than the difference between the corresponding levels in the free atom of copper. Cohen and Heine, therefore, argue that the substitution of zinc for copper will tend to lower s-states relatively to p-states and will thus reduce the energy gap $\varDelta$ at the surface of the zone. This reduction in the energy gap will make the Fermi surface more nearly spherical. The picture presented is, thus, one in which in pure copper the Fermi surface is highly distorted and touches the face of the zone. On alloying with zinc the Fermi surface becomes more nearly spherical and shrinks away from the zone face and then, as more electrons are added, it swells out again and touches the zone face at roughly the value for a spherical surface. The form of the $\mathcal{N}(E)$ curve for *solid solutions in copper* is thus imagined to be as in Fig. 139(*c*).

RM: That's ingenious, but what did Cohen and Heine say about silver?

MAS: For silver, they imagined the Fermi surface to be nearly spherical and the energy gap at the face of the zone to be very small so that the older simple theory applied.

RM: Surely that's illogical. If the solution of zinc, etc., makes the highly distorted Fermi surface of copper spherical, then the solution of cadmium or zinc in silver should make the initially spherical Fermi surface become distorted.

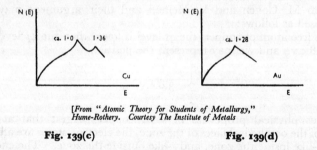

[*From "Atomic Theory for Students of Metallurgy,"*
Hume-Rothery. *Courtesy The Institute of Metals*

Fig. 139(c)   **Fig. 139(d)**

MAS: That is a reasonable objection and, apart from that, later experimental work on the de Haas–van Alphen effect shows that the Fermi surface in pure silver has already touched the octahedral zone face.

RM: If the electron states inside the centres of the zone faces were p-like, then might not the same argument apply as for copper?

MAS: That is possible. But as the energy gaps at the faces of the zone are so different in silver and copper, it would be very curious that things worked out in such a way that the same answer was obtained. Actually, as you will know, the α-solid solutions in copper and silver alloys resemble one another remarkably.

RM: Yes. But the solid solutions in gold are more restricted. They only reach an electron concentration of about 1.28, and you didn't explain this in our earlier talks.

MAS: In gold, there is strong evidence that the electron states are of an s-like nature inside the centres of the octahedral faces of the zone, and of a p-like nature outside. Cohen and Heine, therefore, argued that the solution of zinc, cadmium, etc., in gold would increase the energy gap and make the Fermi surface more distorted. They thought, therefore, that the form of the $N(E)$ curve for gold would be that of Fig. 139(d), with the peak occurring at electron concentration slightly less than 1.28.

RM: But if the new work has shown the Fermi surface to be touching the zone face in pure gold, then that figure must be wrong.

MAS: I'm afraid you are right, but some of Cohen and Heine's idea may still apply.

RM: How can that be?

MAS: The Cohen and Heine approach was one in which they try to make the Fermi surface spherical. Now consider the alternative line of keeping the Fermi surface distorted.

RM: That reminds me of one thing you haven't made clear. So far you have been considering only the first peak on the $N(E)$ curve. Now the full $N(E)$ curve for the face-centred cubic structure is of the form of Fig. 136; the first peak is where the Fermi surface touches the octahedral faces of the zone, and the second peak corresponds to contact with the cube faces. Then the new work has shifted the first peak back by an electron concentration of about 0.4, as compared with the value for a spherical surface, but you haven't told me where the second peak occurs.

MAS: If you consider a spherical Fermi surface to touch the octahedral faces of the zone at an electron concentration of 1.36, and then to continue spreading out within the zone so that the Fermi surfaces remain spherical, these will eventually touch the cube faces of the zone at an electron concentration of 1.88.

RM: So if the distortion of the Fermi surface shifted the second peak in the same proportion as the first, you wouldn't be so far from the empirical electron concentration of 1.4.

MAS: That is the line of approach adopted by Hume-Rothery and Roaf.[1] These authors suggest that the a-solid solubility limit in copper and silver alloys corresponds to the fall in the $N(E)$ curve after the second rather than the first peak, and they point out that the fall after the second peak will be steeper than that after the first, because two sets of zone faces are now cutting off the available states. Unfortunately it is not possible to make any accurate calculation, although it is possible to show that the suggestion is not unreasonable.

[1] Ref. W. Hume-Rothery and D. J. Roaf. *Phil. Mag.* 1961, vol. 6, 55.

RM: So that suggestion would mean that the Jones line of argument could still be adopted.

MAS: Yes.   Furthermore, if—as is quite likely from what is known of the atoms in the Third Long Period—the states inside the cube faces of the zone for gold are *s*-like, then the suggestion of Cohen and Heine referred to above might explain the lower solubility limits in gold alloys, because the formation of the solid solution in gold would increase the energy gap and increase the distortion of the Fermi surface.

RM: The position doesn't seem to be too bad.

MAS: For the α-solid solutions, perhaps not.   But you can see that we are still in a muddle about the β-phases.   Here the first Brillouin Zone is the dodecahedron, and we have no second peak to which we can appeal (see p. 167).

36—Intermediate Phases in Alloy Systems, I

OLDER METALLURGIST: It seems to me that if one reviews the equilibrium diagrams of alloys as a whole, the first great characteristic is that the compositions of the intermediate phases usually do not correspond with those to be expected from the normal valencies. I seem to remember early attempts to write the formulae of some of these compounds in such a way as to satisfy their normal valencies. Thus $CuAl_2$ might be written

$$\begin{array}{ccc} Cu\backslash & & /Al \\ & Al\text{---}Al & \| \\ Cu/ & & \backslash Al \end{array}$$

so that copper and aluminium atoms have one and three bonds respectively. But somehow this kind of thing never struck me as being too convincing.

YOUNG SCIENTIST: You're quite right, and it is now generally recognised that such an approach to the problem is usually wrong. You can begin to understand this if you bear in mind that most of the intermediate phases in alloy systems are conductors of electricity, whereas the ordinary normal valency compounds of inorganic chemistry are nearly always non-conductors. In the ordinary valency compounds, the valency electrons of the constituent atoms rearrange themselves so as to form stable groupings (usually octets). The ordinary valency principles are the result of each atom having a definite number of valency electrons, since this naturally means that atoms have to unite in definite ratios if the stable group of electrons is to be built up. When the valency electrons build up a complete group the electrical conductivity disappears because an external electric field cannot produce a resultant flow of electrons in any one direction. Consequently if intermetallic compounds exhibit electrical conductivity, we shall in general expect their formulae to be different from those required by the normal valency principles.

OM: The general idea is quite clear, but it seems to me that one would expect to find a gradual transition from the normal compounds of inorganic chemistry to purely metallic compounds. For example, in the elements of Groups V and VI, which are shown below, the electronegative nature becomes less pronounced as one goes down the Periodic Table, whilst the general electronic structures in each Period are similar, except for the increase in the quantum number of the valency electrons. I should therefore expect antimony, tellurium, and bismuth to form normal valency compounds, even though they were not so stable as the corresponding compounds of phosphorus and sulphur, or of nitrogen and oxygen.

YS: What you say is perfectly correct, and the first generalisation which may be made about intermetallic compounds is that when we deal with alloys of metals with the weakly electronegative elements of Groups IV, V, and VI, we tend to find intermetallic compounds whose formulae agree with those to be expected from normal valency principles. This tendency is greater the more electropositive the metal

$$
\begin{array}{ccc}
N & — & O & — & F \\
| & & | & & | \\
P & — & S & — & Cl \\
| & & | & & | \\
As & — & Se & — & Br \\
| & & | & & | \\
Sb & — & Te & — & I \\
| & & & & \\
Bi & & & &
\end{array}
$$

with which the element of Group IV, V or VI is alloyed. We find, for example, compounds such as Mg_2Sn, Mg_3Sb_2, and $Mg\,Te$ in which the very electropositive magnesium is forming a normal valency compound with the more electronegative tin, antimony, or tellurium.

OM: Then, in those compounds, are the atoms held together by electron-sharing as in the $(8 — \mathcal{N})$ rule crystals of the elements (Chapter 24)?

YS: In some cases yes, but not in the particular ones referred to above. When one comes to deal with combinations of unlike atoms, one meets a new type of interatomic bond, the so-called *ionic bond*. In the case of sodium chloride, for example, each sodium atom has a loosely bound valency electron outside a stable octet. Each chlorine atom has seven valency electrons, and so needs one more electron to complete an octet. Chemical combination then occurs by the sodium atom giving up its valency electrons to the chlorine atom, so that each is left with an outer group of 8 electrons. Since the sodium atom gives up an electron it becomes a univalent Na^+ ion with a charge of $+e$, whilst the chlorine atom becomes a univalent Cl^- ion with a charge of $-e$. The crystal structure of sodium chloride is shown in Fig. 140, from which you will see that all trace of diatomic molecules has vanished, and the crystal is built up of Na^+ and Cl^- ions in regular array. This a typical ionic or polar crystal in which the structure is held together by the electrostatic attraction between oppositely charged ions, and this electrostatic attraction pulls the ions together until their electron clouds overlap to such an extent that the resulting repulsion balances the attraction.

The same crystal structure is formed by magnesium oxide, MgO. Here each magnesium atom in the free state has two valency electrons outside an octet, and each oxygen atom has six valency electrons, and so needs two more to build up an octet. Each magnesium atom then

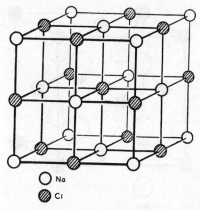

○ Na

◐ Cl

[*Courtesy The Institute of Metals*

Fig. 140—Crystal structure of sodium chloride

gives its two valency electrons to an oxygen atom, so that divalent Mg^{++} and O^{--} ions are formed, and these form the same kind of crystal structure as sodium chloride (Fig. 140), in which the whole structure is held together by the electrostatic attraction of oppositely charged ions.

OM: That would suggest that the cohesion should be stronger in MgO than in NaCl, because there are divalent ions in the one, and univalent ions in the other.

YS: Exactly. That is why magnesia has a very much higher melting point than sodium chloride.

OM: From Fig. 140 it would seem that the sodium chloride structure can be formed only if there are equal numbers of the two kinds of ion. So one would expect compounds such as MgO, MgS, MgSe and MgTe to crystallise in this structure, but not compounds such as Mg_3Sb_2 and Mg_2Sn.

YS: That's quite right. The sodium chloride structure can be formed only if the compound has a formula of the type AB. Actually there is a large number of sulphides, selenides, and tellurides which crystallise in the NaCl structure, and so if you regard the system magnesium-tellurium as a metallic system, you may regard the compound MgTe as an extension of the ordinary ionic or salt-like compounds into the region of the weakly electronegative elements such as tellurium.

When one deals with ionic compounds with formulae of the type AB_2, one of the commonest crystal structures is the CaF_2 type which is shown in Fig. 141. In this case the structure is built up of divalent Ca^{++} ions, and univalent F^- ions; each calcium atom has given up

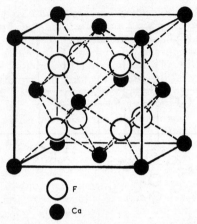

[*Courtesy The Institute of Metals*

Fig. 141—Crysta structure of calcium fluoride

two valency electrons, and each fluorine atom has received one extra electron, and in this way the outer shell of each ion contains eight electrons. This kind of crystal structure is formed by the compounds Mg_2Si, Mg_2Ge, Mg_2Sn, and Mg_2Pb, and these are said to be *anti-isomorphous* with CaF_2 because the metallic Mg^{++} ions in Mg_2Sn occupy the places of the non-metallic F^- ions in CaF_2. It is a general principle that this kind of compound becomes more stable as the difference in the electrochemical characteristics of the two metals becomes greater. In the series of compounds Mg_2Si, Mg_2Ge, Mg_2Sn, and Mg_2Pb, the magnesium is the electropositive constituent and is constant throughout the series. The electronegative nature of the Group IV elements decreases as we go down the Periodic Table, so that silicon is the most, and lead the least electronegative of these elements. We therefore expect the stabilities of these compounds to be in the order

$$Mg_2Si > Mg_2Ge > Mg_2Sn > Mg_2Pb$$

In Fig. 142 I have reproduced the equilibrium diagrams of the systems Mg-Si, Mg-Sn and Mg-Pb, and you will see how the melting points diminish on passing from Mg_2Si to Mg_2Pb. In the system Mg-Pb the liquidus curve of the compound is very flat and rounded, and this indicates extensive decomposition on melting.

OM: The general sequence is quite clear, but it is surely not justifiable to argue that a high melting point means a stable compound. Water is a very stable compound of hydrogen and oxygen, but the melting point is quite low.

YS: That depends entirely on the structure of the crystal. If the crystal contains definite compound molecules as in the case of water, H_2O, or iodine, I_2 (see Fig. 65, page 179), then the melting point depends on the intermolecular forces, and is not a measure of the stability of the compound molecule. On the other hand, in salt-like or ionic crystals where there are no molecules, but simply a regular arrangement of oppositely charged ions, the melting point is an indication of the stability of the compound, because the electrostatic attraction holding the crystal together is the force of chemical combination. The principle shown by Fig. 142 is a very general one, and can be seen in many alloy systems. For example, in the system magnesium-antimony, the magnesium is very electropositive compared with the antimony, and there is an extremely stable compound, Mg_3Sb_2, which melts above 1200° C. If we replace the magnesium by the less electropositive zinc, there is still a normal valency compound Zn_3Sb_2, but this has a melting point of only 568° C, and has a very flat maximum to its liquidus curve—you will see the contrast between the systems in Fig. 143. If we now replace antimony by the less electronegative element tin, what we may call the *electrochemical factor* is no longer sufficient to produce a compound in the system zinc-tin, but in the system magnesium-tin, the magnesium is so much more electropositive than tin that as we have already seen in Fig. 142 the normal valency compound Mg_2Sn is formed. It is right to warn you, however, that the concept of these compounds as an extension of the normal ionic

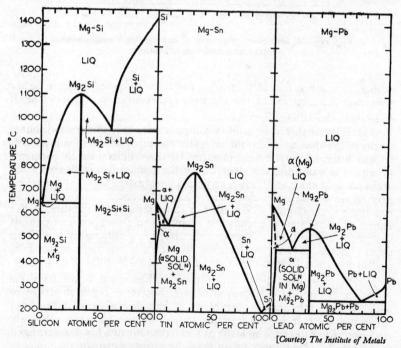

[Courtesy The Institute of Metals

Fig. 142—Equilibrium diagrams of the systems magnesium-silicon, magnesium-tin and magnesium-lead

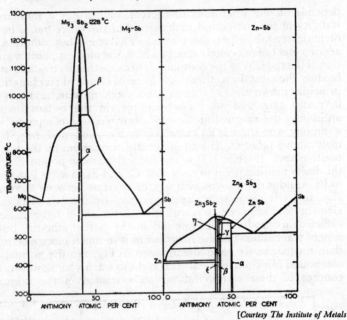

[Courtesy The Institute of Metals

Fig. 143—Equilibrium diagram of the systems magnesium-antimony and zinc-antimony

compounds is not the whole truth. For some purposes they are better regarded as examples of the electron compounds to which we shall refer later (Chapters 37 and 38).

OM: The weakly ionic kind of compound is easily understood, but it seems to me that there should be a corresponding series of compounds in which the atoms are held together by shared electrons in co-valent bonds. For example, the structure of the diamond is such that each atom has four close neighbours arranged tetrahedrally so that the atoms exert their normal valencies. There seems no reason why one should not have a compound CSi with the same structure. Further, if the characteristic is four electrons per atom, we might expect compounds such as GaAs to form the same structure, since although the gallium atom contains only three electrons, the atom of arsenic contains five, and so there would be an average of four.

YS: Your general idea is quite correct, although in some cases one finds not the actual diamond structure, but some other structure in which the tetrahedral arrangement of the atoms exists. Fig. 144 shows the zinc blende and wurtzite structures—these are two relatively common structures in which the atoms have four neighbours arranged tetrahedrally. Now suppose we take the series of elements:

Cu—Zn—Ga—Ge—As—Se—Br

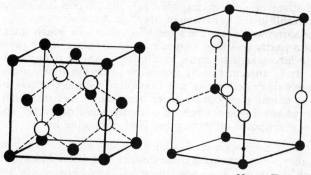

[*Courtesy The Institute of Metal*]

Fig. 144—Crystal structures of zinc blende [left] and wurtzite [right]

then of these, germanium crystallises in the diamond type of structure so that each atom has four neighbours. As you have pointed out, a compound GaAs would have eight valency electrons to two atoms, and hence an average of four valency electrons per atom, and this compound crystallises in the zinc blende structure in which a tetrahedral arrangement of neighbours is maintained. This principle can be extended further, because you will readily see that in the combinations:

$$GaAs, \quad ZnSe, \quad CuBr$$

the numbers of valency electrons are $(3 + 5)$, $(2 + 6)$ and $(1 + 7)$, respectively, and in the whole series we have thus eight electrons to two atoms, and an average of $4 : 1$. Actually, all these compounds crystallise in the zinc blende structure, and you can see how beautifully the general principle works out. You will appreciate, therefore, that just as the typical salt-like or ionic compounds extend into alloys where the electro-chemical factor is high (for example, Mg_3Sb_2, Mg_2Si), so co-valency compounds may extend into alloy systems such as zinc-selenium. In the co-valency compounds you are to regard the electron clouds as being drawn out in the directions of the bonds in the same general way that we discussed in connection with the structure of $(8 - \mathcal{N})$ rule elements (Chapter 24).

A further point which you should notice is that in a system where the electrochemical factor is high, even though a normal valency compound is not formed, the intermediate phases and even the primary solid solutions may involve forces which are of a partly ionic nature. Thus in the systems silver-magnesium and gold-magnesium, the magnesium is strongly electropositive compared with the gold or silver. In these cases there are no purely ionic compounds, but as we shall see later it is very probable that the intermediate phases involve forces which are more or less of an ionic nature—that is to say there is an interatomic attraction which is partly an electrostatic attraction between electropositively charged magnesium, and electronegatively charged silver or gold atoms, although the process has not gone so far as to result in the formation of Mg^{++} or Au^- ions.

In the same way there are some alloy phases in which interatomic forces of a partly co-valent nature may exist although the process has not gone far enough to result in the formation of definite co-valent bonds. It is, therefore, very necessary to realise that although the compounds described above are examples of almost purely ionic or purely co-valent compounds, there are many cases in which inter-metallic phases involve forces of a partly ionic or partly co-valent nature superimposed on some other kind of binding force.

OM: You have spoken about ionic and co-valent compounds as though they were something quite distinct, but I should have thought one might quite well have something half-way between the two. By this I mean that the bonding electrons might be shared between the two atoms, whilst being much more associated with the one than with the other.

YS: That is perfectly true. You will remember that in our des-cription of the H_2 molecule (page 184), we saw how the exchange forces came into being as a result of the principle that if a system can exist in more than one configuration, the lowest energy is obtained not by one configuration alone, but by a condition which may be described by the superposition of the wave-functions which characterise the two configurations. In the previous description we really over-simplified the problem because we considered only the two systems:

$$\left\{\begin{array}{l}\text{Electron No. 1 associated with atom No. 1}\\\text{Electron No. 2 associated with atom No. 2}\end{array}\right\}$$

and

$$\left\{\begin{array}{l}\text{Electron No. 1 associated with atom No. 2}\\\text{Electron No. 2 associated with atom No. 1}\end{array}\right\}$$

We saw that these systems were quite indistinguishable, and that this favoured strong resonance. Apart from these two systems, there is a further alternative, namely, the existence of ionised molecules

$$H_A^+ H_B^- \text{ or } H_A^- H_B^+$$

where the symbols H_A and H_B are used to distinguish the two hydrogen atoms. In these molecules the one hydrogen atom has given up its valency electron to the other, so that a complete $(1s)^2$ group is built up. Resonance then occurs between these structures, and the structures of the normal co-valent form. In this way a further lowering of energy takes place, and calculation shows that about 5 per cent of the bond energy of the H_2 molecule results from the ionic form. In other words, the actual hydrogen molecule involves not only the normal $H-H$ co-valent modification, but also the ionised modification, in which one atom has given its electron to the other. In this case the co-valent form is very much more stable, and so the actual molecule has the properties of the co-valent rather than of the ionised form, and the resonance with the ionised form has little effect. On the other hand, in the case of a molecule of hydrofluoric acid, the stabilities of the ionised form

$$H^+ \; F^-$$

and the co-valent form

$$H - F$$

are much more nearly equal. The conditions for resonance are thus favoured, and the resonance process results in a firmer binding and a shorter interatomic distance.

OM: Do you mean that resonance can occur between any two forms of a molecule?

YS: Resonance can occur only if the two forms have the same number of unpaired electrons. You will see that this condition is satisfied in the above examples—in $H - H$ and $F - F$ there are no unpaired electrons because the two electrons in the co-valent bonds have paired off, whilst in $H^+ \; H^-$ and $H^+ \; F^-$ there are again no unpaired electrons, because the H^+ ion has no electrons, whilst the H^- and F^- ions have complete groups of two and eight electrons respectively.

OM: This is all rather confusing—I see that you are getting at something intermediate between the two forms, but do you mean that I should regard an actual sample of hydrogen as consisting of 95 per cent $H - H$, and 5 per cent $H^+ \; H^-$ molecules, and hydrofluoric acid as consisting of more nearly equal proportions of $H - F$ and $H^+ \; F^-$?

YS: No. That's quite wrong. It is not a question of two kinds of molecule existing in equilibrium with one another. In a sense the effect is one which can really only be described in terms of wave-mechanics, but you may perhaps regard the resonance process as involving a rapid oscillation between the two structures—the frequency is of the order 10^{18} per second. If the one structure is much more stable than the other, the electronic configuration will not differ greatly from that of the stable form—this is the case in the H_2 molecule where the $H - H$ form is predominant. As the resonance becomes more pronounced, the average electronic configuration will become different from that of either form, and the molecule may develop properties which are characteristic of the resonance process, and are different from those of the structures between which resonance is occurring. It is essential to realise that we are not dealing with an equilibrium between two kinds of molecule, but with a process which may give rise to a new electronic configuration. Many authors describe the resonance as equivalent to a rapid oscillation between two forms, but it is perhaps better not to attempt to look within the process, and to say rather that when there is a strong resonance, the electrons spend most of their time in a state which is that of neither the one structure nor of the other, but is characteristic of the resonance process. In this way wave-mechanics has led to a quite new idea, and has explained why in some cases a substance seems to behave as though its molecules possessed several different formulae, none of which is by itself entirely satisfactory. A very interesting example of this kind is in connection with the structure of benzene. As you will know, the formula of this is C_6H_6, and the six carbon atoms form a ring

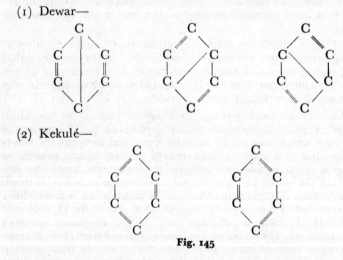

In this way it is easy to see how three out of the four valencies of each carbon atom are satisfied, but there was a great deal of dispute as to the disposal of the fourth valency. The formulae shown in Fig. 145 were suggested by Kekule and Dewar.

(1) Dewar—

(2) Kekulé—

Fig. 145

Each of these seemed to account for some of the properties of benzene, but none was completely satisfactory, and from the new view-point the actual structure results from resonance between the two Kekulé and three Dewar structures. Of these the Kekulé structure plays the most important part, but the resonance is considerable so that the substance benzene has properties which are not those of any one single structure, but are characteristic of the resonance process.

OM: If I remember rightly there were other structures besides those suggested by Kekulé and Dewar.

YS: That is true, but it can be shown that some of those (for example, the Armstrong-Baeyer structure) are really equivalent to a combination of the five shown above, so that we may consider only the resonance between these five. The resulting structure may be described partly by saying that of the 30 valency electrons present in the molecule (four from each carbon atom, and one from each hydrogen atom), 12 electrons are used to form the six co-valent bonds which bind the hydrogen atoms to the carbon atoms, whilst a further 12 may be regarded as associated with the six single bonds within the ring. This leaves six electrons to be accounted for, and as a result of the resonance process these are associated with the benzene ring as a whole, and move freely in this ring. The number of electrons available is not sufficient to produce double bonds between each two adjacent carbon atoms, but the six electrons which are there are associated with the ring as a whole. You will see how interesting this is, because it clearly suggests a means by which the atoms can be held together when there are insufficient electrons to form co-valent bonds, and so suggests what might happen in a metallic crystal. It has, in fact, been suggested by Pauling that metallic bonding is a form of resonance bonding. For example, in the crystal of an alkali metal (body-centred cube) each atom has eight close neighbours, but only one valency electron. Pauling's suggestion is that the resulting condition of affairs is equivalent to a resonance between all the structures which might be obtained by placing the electrons in one-electron or two-electron bonds between the different neighbouring atoms.

OM: That seems to be only a rather heavy way of saying that the electrons are shared throughout the crystal.

YS: To some extent that is true, but Pauling's views are supported by the fact that the interatomic distances in metallic crystals are of the same order as those in compounds of the same elements involving resonating co-valent bonds. This is something which could not have been predicted from a mere concept of shared electrons. It also enables us to understand the difference between the elements of the First Two Short Periods and of the B Sub-groups, and the elements of the Transition series. In the elements of the Short Periods and of the B Sub-groups there are only four orbitals available for bond formation and resonance, and so we can understand why $(8 - N)$ rule type structures begin at Group IV (C, Si, Ge, grey Sn). In the transition elements the d-orbitals are also available, and so the possibilities are far greater, and the metallic bonding continues beyond Group IV.

Suggestions for further reading.

For general work on the crystal structure of alloys reference may be made to *The Structure of Metals* by C. S. Barrett, McGraw Hill. *X-Ray Metallography* by A. Taylor, Chapman and Hall, also gives much information.

37—Intermediate Phases in Alloy Systems, II
Electron Compounds

OLDER METALLURGIST: The compounds which you were describing last time were all such that one constituent was of a relatively electronegative nature. It would seem that totally different principles must hold when both constituents are normal metals. There is one point which has always given me a great deal of difficulty, and that is whether every intermediate phase in an alloy system is to be looked on as a definite chemical compound. For example, in the system copper-zinc (Fig. 146) we have the β, γ and ϵ phases. These are all of variable composition, and in a sense this is contradictory to the usual definition of a chemical compound. Every schoolboy is taught that fixity of composition is what distinguishes a chemical compound from a mixture, but I seem to remember being told that β-brass could be looked upon as a compound CuZn, which was able to take up a certain amount of copper or zinc into solid solution.

YOUNG SCIENTIST: There used to be a great deal of argument about that point, but now that we know so much more about the nature of interatomic bonding, I think it is rather a waste of time. The schoolboy has to be taught simple things first, and we may as well admit frankly that the ordinary school book distinction between chemical compounds and physical mixtures fails to consider the possibility of a compound dissolving an excess of one of its constituents—it also ignores the possibility of a certain proportion of one kind of atom dropping out of a crystal lattice, and so leaving " holes " or " vacant sites," with a resulting variation of composition. Actually a large number of well-accepted chemical compounds, such as certain oxides, show a slight but quite definite variation in composition, and the name " defect structure " is sometimes used to describe crystals with vacant lattice sites.

OM: It seems to me that the distinction between chemical combination and mere physical mixture must still be a very real one.

YS: Oh, certainly yes. The essential point is that you have got to define your terms more precisely, and to consider the nature of the atomic binding process. When, for example, carbon combines with hydrogen to form methane, the process results in the formation of definite *molecules* of CH_4, in which the hydrogen atoms are bound to the carbon atom by simple co-valent bonds, analogous to those which we described in Chapter 24. If we now consider a crystal of carbon in the form of diamond—or one of silicon, germanium or grey tin which crystallize in the same structure—the atoms in the crystal are held together by co-valent bonds (Chapter 24), so that the interatomic forces in the crystal are of the same nature as those in the molecule

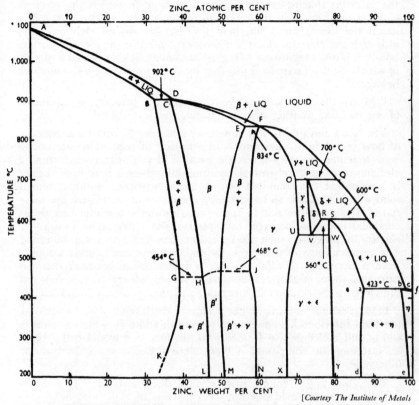

ZINC. ATOMIC PER CENT

ZINC. WEIGHT PER CENT

[*Courtesy The Institute of Metals*]

Fig. 146—Equilibrium diagram of the system copper-zinc

of CH_4. You may regard the whole crystal of diamond as an immense molecule, or giant molecule—the German term is Riesenmolekül. Now suppose we had a solid solution of silicon in germanium—the interatomic forces would be of the same general nature (co-valent bonding), and it would be purely a matter of definition whether we called each crystal of the solid solution a giant molecule in which the atoms were held together by chemical combination, or regarded it as a mixture of silicon and germanium atoms on a common lattice. But if we adopted the latter point of view, the " mixture " would clearly be quite different from a mechanical mixture of individual particles of germanium and silicon.

OM: That's quite clear, but again you are dealing with electro-negative elements, whereas I am concerned mainly with metals in which there are no co-valent bonds.

YS: If you consider what we have discussed before, I think you will agree that we cannot draw any hard and sharp line. In a crystal of the diamond type the atoms are held together by shared electrons—

the electron sharing is of the co-valent type in which the electron cloud is most dense in the direction of the bonds. In the crystal of a metal the atoms are again held together by shared electrons, and although the electron cloud is not concentrated in the direction of the bonds, it is quite legitimate to regard each metallic crystal as a molecule in which the atoms are held together by electrons giving rise to metallic linkages.

OM: In that case you will have to regard a primary solid solution of one metal in another as a compound, which is absurd.

YS: No, I don't think you should say it is absurd. It is just a question of how you define your terms. In a crystal of copper the atoms are held together by the shared electrons. If you regard this kind of electron-sharing as chemical combination, then a crystal of copper is a chemical compound of copper atoms with one another, and a solid solution of zinc in copper involves forces of essentially the same type. If you prefer not to regard the ordinary metallic linkage as chemical combination, you may reserve the latter term for specific electronic processes such as co-valent bonding, or ionic bonding. The disadvantage of this policy is that in some compounds we may have a condition of affairs which is intermediate between the two extremes—also, of course, it assumes a very considerable knowledge of the electron distribution in a crystal, and this is usually unknown.

OM: Perhaps one might get a clearer distinction if one restricted the term intermetallic compound to combinations in which a definite compound molecule was formed. In this case one would call β-brass an intermetallic compound if there were a CuZn molecule, but not otherwise.

YS: That policy suffers from several disadvantages. It is often difficult to obtain evidence for the existence of a definite molecule, particularly if the latter decomposes, or is accompanied by other molecules. Most of the methods for identifying molecules involve a study of the liquid or gaseous state, and with alloys the temperatures are so high that extensive decomposition may occur—you must also remember the experimental difficulties.

OM: I've read some attempts to restrict the term intermetallic compound to phases of fixed composition, but as far as I can see this is impracticable, because there seems to be a continuous series ranging from phases like β-brass which are of widely varying composition, to phases like Mg_3Sb_2 which are usually described as being of fixed composition.

YS: That's quite right. On the whole I think it is better not to use the term intermetallic compound, but to remember that the electron-sharing processes which take place in normal metals, or in crystals such as the diamond, are all examples of chemical combination in some sense of the term.

OM: If you do adopt that policy it would seem that there may well be intermediate phases in alloy systems in which, although the crystal structure is different from that of the parent metal, the interatomic forces are still essentially those of a metallic nature, and involve no more " intermetallic combination " than is present in the primary solid solution.

YS: That's perfectly true, and β-brass is in fact an example of that kind. As we have already seen in the system copper-zinc (Fig. 146) the β-phase lies roughly in the equiatomic region, and at the higher temperature it has a random body-centred cubic structure. Here the crystal structure is different from that of either copper (face-centred cube) or zinc (close-packed hexagonal), but it is now generally accepted that the interatomic forces are of a purely metallic nature, and that there is no more " chemical combination " in β-brass than there is in the α-solid solution of zinc in copper.

OM: The copper-zinc diagram with a β (body-centred cubic) phase following on an α-solid solution (face-centred cubic) seems to be a very general type. The copper-aluminium (Fig. 147), copper-gallium (Fig. 132), and copper-tin (Fig. 135) equilibrium diagrams show the same general characteristic, and from what you said before about the α/β brass equilibrium, I should imagine this means the β-phases are in some way related to the electron concentration. I can see from Figures 146, 147 and 138 that just as the α-solid solubility curves move to lower atomic percentages of the solute as the valency of the latter increases, so the compositions of the β-phases move in the same direction.

YS: That's quite right, and it was in fact by the study of those particular phases that one of the factors controlling the structure of alloys was discovered. In the system copper-zinc the β-phase lies in the equiatomic region, and its composition may be represented roughly by the formula CnZn, although this does not imply that any definite molecular species exists. In the system copper-aluminium, the corresponding β-phase with a body-centred cubic structure is stable only at high temperatures, and its composition lies roughly in the region Cu_3Al, whilst in the system copper-tin the β-phase lies in the region Cu_5Sn. You will now see that if we give the elements copper zinc, aluminium, and tin their usual valencies of 1, 2, 3, and 4 respectively, these three formulae CuZn, Cu_3Al, and Cu_5Sn all correspond with a ratio of 3 valency electrons to 2 atoms, that is to an electron concentration of $3/2 = 1.5$. This was first pointed out in 1926 by Hume-Rothery, when it was also shown that the equilibrium diagrams of other copper and silver alloys had the same characteristics, although only a few of the crystal structures were then known. The idea that the crystal structure of a phase might sometimes be determined by the ratio of valency electrons to atoms was then taken up enthusiastically by Westgren, Bradley and others, and the rapid development of X-ray crystal structure work showed that in a large number of alloys of copper, silver, and gold with elements of higher valency, phases of the same crystal structure tended to occur at the same ratio of valency electrons to atoms.

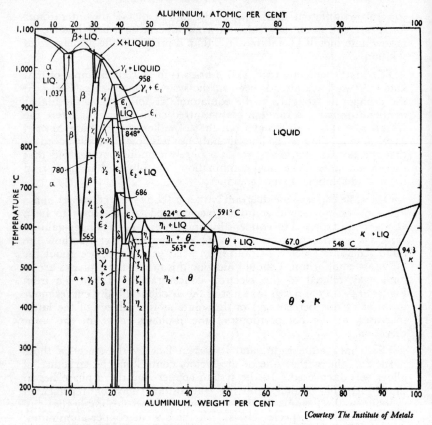

[*Courtesy The Institute of Metals*

Fig. 147—Equilibrium diagram of the system copper-aluminium

The following main groups were recognised:—

Electron: Atom Ratio	Crystal Structure of Phase
3/2	Body-centred cube
	β-manganese type
	Close-packed hexagonal
21/13	γ-brass type
7/4	Close-packed hexagonal

You will see that the electron concentration 3/2 gives rise to more than one type of structure. In the system copper-zinc, for example, there is only a body-centred cubic phase—ordered at low temperatures and disordered at high temperatures—at the composition CuZn. In the system copper-gallium an electron concentration of 3/2 corresponds with the formula Cu_3Ga because gallium is trivalent. Here, as you

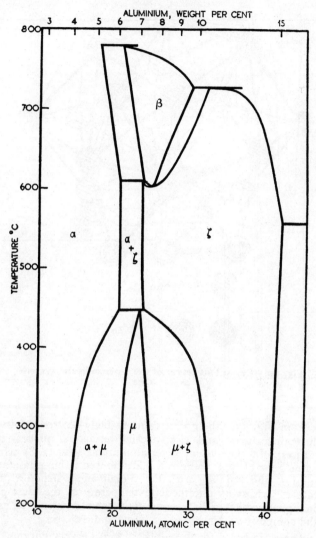

[*Courtesy The Institute of Metals*

Fig. 148—Part of the equilibrium diagram of the system silver-aluminium

The α-phase is the face-centred cubic solid solution of aluminium in silver. The β and ζ-phases have body-centred cubic and close-packed hexagonal structures respectively, whilst the μ-phase has a β-manganese structure

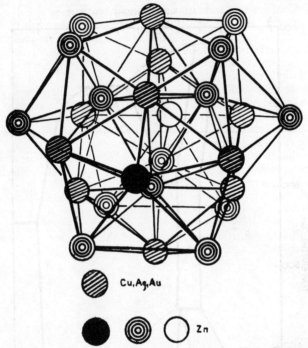

Cu,Ag,Au

Zn

Fig. 149—Crystal structure of the γ-phase in the system copper-zinc

will see from Fig. 132, there is a random body-centred cubic phase at high temperatures, and close-packed hexagonal phases at low temperatures. In the system silver-aluminium (Fig. 148) which is of the same general type, there is a body-centred cubic phase at high temperatures, and a phase with the β-manganese structure at low temperatures, whilst at intermediate temperatures the close-packed hexagonal phase which exists over a wide range of composition extends up to the composition Ag_3Al.

OM: The ratio 21/13 for the γ-phases seems a very curious one.

YS: The ratio 21/13 was deduced by the X-ray crystallographers, who showed that in the system copper-zinc the γ-phase could be regarded as based on the composition Cu_5Zn_8 (Fig. 149), whilst in the system copper-aluminium the phase with the same structure includes the composition Cu_9Al_4—you should note that this phase is usually called δ in the diagram. Both these compositions correspond with a ratio of 21 valency electrons to 13 atoms, and the corresponding phase in the system copper-tin has a composition $Cu_{31}Sn_8$ which gives 63 valency electrons to 39 atoms, and so again a ratio of 21 : 13. In the systems copper-zinc and copper-aluminium the phases with the γ-brass structure are of variable composition, and tend to lie more on the side of higher electron-concentration than the characteristic ratio 21/13, but the general tendency for the γ-phase to occur at this electron concentration is clear.

It was also shown by Bradley and Gregory that in the ternary system copper-aluminium-zinc, ternary alloys with the γ structure could be obtained provided that the atoms were in such proportions that the characteristic ratio of 21 valency electrons to 13 atoms was retained. In other words, with these particular elements one could jumble the different kinds of atom together, and obtain a phase with the same structure provided that the characteristic ratio of valency electrons to atoms was maintained.

All this suggested that in some cases the structure of an intermediate phase in an alloy system depended not on the nature of the individual atoms, but simply on the relative number of valency electrons and atoms. Intermetallic phases of this kind may conveniently be called *electron compounds*.

38—More About Electron Compounds

OLDER METALLURGIST: You explained last time that in some copper and silver alloys with elements of higher valency, phases with particular structures tended to occur at definite ratios of valency electrons to atoms. This suggests clearly that the electron concentration is what determines the stability of the phases in question, and in view of what you said before (Chapter 35) about the α/β brass equilibrium, I should expect there to be a close connection between the characteristic electron/atom ratio and the $N(E)$ curve for the crystal structure concerned. You have explained (page 136) that a high $N(E)$ curve means that a given number of electrons is accommodated with a relatively low energy. If therefore the electronic energies are determining the stabilities of the phases, one would expect that when the $N(E)$ curve could be calculated for a given structure, the characteristic electron/atom ratio would include the electron states up to a high peak on the $N(E)$ curve, and would avoid deep troughs or valleys.

YOUNG SCIENTIST: That is perfectly correct and is, in fact, more or less what was claimed by H. Jones in his development of the theory. Let us deal first with the body-centred cubic structure. You will remember that the first Brillouin zone for the body-centred cubic structure is a rhombic dodecahedron, whose faces include the wave numbers which satisfy the condition for reflection from the (110) planes of the lattice. You will also remember that our simplified calculation (Chapter 35, page 297) showed that the first peak on the $N(E)$ curve of the body-centred cubic structure occurred at an electron/atom ratio of 1.48, which is very near to the empirical value $3/2 = 1.5$ for the β-phases we discussed last time. The more complete calculations of Jones lead to the same conclusion, and so the electron theory gives a satisfactory explanation of why the β-phases occur at an electron concentration of $3/2$.[1]

OM: That doesn't seem quite correct. The peak on the curve is at an electron concentration of 1.48, and beyond this point the $N(E)$ curve falls. Consequently, your previous argument would lead us to expect that the β-phase would become unstable beyond this point, that is, beyond 48 atomic per cent of zinc, whereas actually the β-phase in Fig. 146 extends considerably beyond the equiatomic composition.

YS: Your general idea is right, but you must remember that the calculation which led to the value 1.48 was of a very approximate nature. The simplifying assumptions introduced are such that an agreement to within a few atomic per cent is all that can be hoped for. In the second place, the fact that the $N(E)$ curve begins to fall

[1] The Younger Scientist's statement here is incorrect. As explained in the Epilogue on p. 302a, the more detailed calculations of Jones gave a peak on the $N(E)$ curve of the b.c. cubic structure at an electron concentration of about 1.2, and did not, therefore, explain the existence of β-phase at e.c. 1.5. It was the simple, and not the more detailed theory which appeared to provide the explanation.

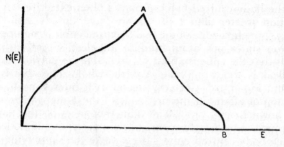

Fig. 150

after an electron concentration of 1.48, only enables us to say that we may expect a tendency for the body-centred cubic phase to become unstable compared with some other structure whose $N(E)$ curve continues to rise. The details will depend on the $N(E)$ curve of the second phase, and we shall not expect the body-centred cubic phase to become unstable immediately the electron concentration of 1.48 is exceeded.

OM: If that is so, it seems to me that one can draw a general conclusion. Let us suppose that Fig. 150 shows the $N(E)$ curve for a particular structure, and that there is a peak at A, whilst the zone ends at B. Then it would seem that the more rapid the fall from A to B, the sooner the phase will tend to become unstable when the electron concentration exceeds A.

YS: That's quite right, and it is perhaps another reason for the

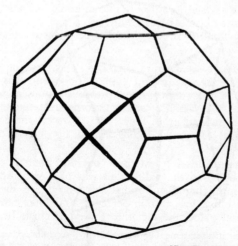

[*From* Properties of Metals and Alloys, Mott and Jones. Oxford University Press

Fig. 151—Zone for β-manganese structure

fact that the body-centred cubic β-phases often extend to an electron concentration greater than 1.48. As we have already seen (Chapter 23, page 174) the first zone of the body-centred cubic structure contains two electron states per atom, and so an electron concentration of 1.48 means that the zone is about 3/4 full, and the portion of the zone after the peak is about one quarter of the whole zone, that is, the fall from A–B in Fig. 150 is not very steep. It is interesting to compare the condition of affairs in the first zone of the β-manganese structure which is shown in Fig. 151. The numerous faces on this zone mean that it is much more nearly spherical than the rhombic dodecahedral zone for the body-centred cube. If we make the simplifying assumption of spherical energy contours, a calculation similar to that on page 296 shows that the first peak on the $\mathcal{N}(E)$ curve for the β-Mn structure occurs at an electron concentration of 1.41, whereas the completely filled zone corresponds with the electron concentration of 1.62. When compared with the values 1.48 and 2.0 for the body-centred cube, it is clear that the fall from A to B (Fig. 150) is much more rapid for the β-Mn structure, and it is perhaps significant that the compositions of the β-Mn phases do not greatly exceed the electron concentration of 1.5.

OM: That is interesting and I understand the principle as you have described it, but I am in a muddle about the γ-phases, because I have seen it stated that Jones' theory of the γ-phases requires full zone structures to be stable, and this seems improbable because when the zone is filled the $\mathcal{N}(E)$ curve has sunk to zero, and one would expect the phase to be unstable.

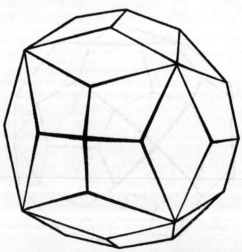

[*From* Properties of Metals and Alloys,
Mott and Jones. Oxford University Press

Fig. 152—Zone for γ-brass structure

YS: That difficulty often arises, and is the result of the fact that the zone for the γ-structure, like that for the β-Mn structure, is one with numerous symmetrical faces which make it very nearly spherical—see Fig. 152. This means that the electron concentration corresponding with the peak A is only slightly less than that for the completely filled zone (point B in Fig. 150). The correct statement of Jones' theory is that a phase tends to be stable at the electron concentration corresponding to the peak A, and this is the way you should always think of the theory. In the case of the γ-phases it just happens that the electron concentration of the point A is not very different from that of the completely filled zone, and that was why some people concluded that a full zone was stable.

OM: Then, do the zone theories account for all the intermediate phases in the copper and silver alloys?

YS: The zone theories enable one to understand why body-centred cubic and β-Mn structures occur at an electron concentration of 1.5 and γ-phase and close-packed hexagonal structures at electron concentrations of 21/13 and 7/4 respectively. They have also given an understanding of the way in which the axial ratios of the close-packed hexagonal structures—both at e.c. 1.5 and 1.75—vary with composition.

OM: The examples you have described have all been alloys of univalent copper or silver with elements of higher valency, and the electron concentration of the phases lie between 1 and 2. It would seem possible therefore that if we started with a divalent or trivalent element, and alloyed it with some element which tended to absorb electrons we might arrange things so that an electron concentration of, say, 21/13 resulted.

YS: That's quite correct. If you take an element such as zinc, and alloy it with a very electro-negative element like selenium, you obtain a stable salt-like compound ZnSe—this is because the atoms of selenium have such an affinity for electrons that they absorb both the valency electrons of each zinc atom to form Se^{--} ions with complete octets. But if you alloy zinc with some of the transition elements such as iron, you do sometimes obtain electron compounds analogous to those of the copper and silver alloys. There is for example an iron-zinc γ-phase of composition Fe_5Zn_{21}, and you will see that this has the characteristic ratio of valency electrons to atoms if the iron is assumed to have a zero valency—there are then 26 atoms to 42 valency electrons.

OM: That's not quite what I was suggesting because a zero valency would imply that the iron atoms neither absorbed nor contributed electrons.

YS: I don't think that follows. It is probably more correct to say that the iron atoms both contribute and absorb electrons. Some of the $4s$ valency electrons of the iron atoms are contributed to the structure, but the fact that the iron atoms have incomplete $3d$ shells means that they tend to take up electrons from the relatively electro-positive zinc. The two processes more or less cancel each other out so that the iron behaves as though it had a zero valency. Several of the transition elements behave like this, and γ-structures such as Fe_5Zn_{21} and Ni_5Zn_{21} were discovered by Ekman.

OM: The general character of electron compounds is clear, but you have not made it clear whether they are quite distinct from other classes of compound, or whether the various classes merge into one another.

YS: When we deal with systems such as copper-zinc, the size factors are favourable, and the electro-chemical factor is small. Under these conditions the electron concentration effect is clearly predominant, but if we take systems in which the electrochemical factor is larger, we can often see how this factor begins to affect the process. For example, if we compare the systems silver-magnesium and gold-magnesium with the system copper-zinc, we see that silver and gold are more electro-negative than copper, whilst magnesium is more electro-positive than zinc. The electrochemical factor is thus considerably greater in the systems Ag-Mg and Au-Mg. In both systems there are β-phases with a body-centred cubic structure, but these now have an ordered structure of the caesium chloride type (Fig. 153), and, further, their liquidus and solidus curves rise to maxima at the equiatomic composition, as you will see from Fig. 154, which gives the Ag-Mg diagram. In these two cases, therefore, increasing electro-chemical factor has clearly modified what we may call the typical Cu-Zn diagram, and has produced a β-phase with some of the characteristics (maximum freezing point and ordered structure) usually associated with " ordinary compounds."

OM: If that is so, it would seem that there may well be a continuous transition from pure electron compounds on the one hand, to ionic compounds on the other.

YS: Oh, certainly! The β-phases of the Ag-Mg diagram are clearly a kind of half-way house between an electron compound and a salt-like compound. The electrochemical difference is not sufficiently great to produce definite Mg^{++} and Ag^- ions, but it is highly probable that in the solid β Ag-Mg phase the silver and magnesium atoms have acquired negative and positive charges to some extent. The same process can sometimes be seen to a larger degree in other systems. In Figs. 155 and 156, for example, I have contrasted the silver-rich portions of the equilibrium diagrams of the systems silver-zinc and silver-cadmium. Zinc is more electro-positive than cadmium, and so the electrochemical factor is much more pronounced for the system silver-zinc, and you will see that in this system the change in direction of the liquidus curve at the temperature of the $\alpha + liq \rightleftharpoons \beta$ peritectic is much greater than in the system silver-cadmium. In the system silver-zinc the electrochemical factor is not sufficiently great to produce a maximum in the liquidus curve for the β-phase such as is found in the system silver-magnesium, but the effect in the system silver-zinc

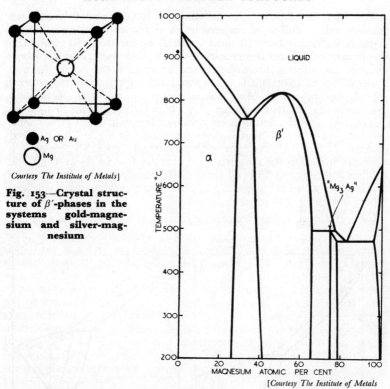

Courtesy The Institute of Metals]

Fig. 153—Crystal structure of β'-phases in the systems gold-magnesium and silver-magnesium

[Courtesy The Institute of Metals

Fig. 154—The equilibrium diagram of the system silver-magnesium. Recent work has shown that at low temperatures superlattice structures exist in the α-solid solution at compositions in the region of Ag_3Mg. This is in agreement with the high electrochemical factor.

is clearly a kind of half-way stage between that of a high (AgMg) and a low (AgCd) electrochemical factor. The same effect is seen on comparing the equilibrium diagrams of the systems silver-aluminium and silver-indium, where the former has the higher electrochemical factor.

OM: If that is so, there seems no reason why we should not obtain the same kind of effect in primary solid solutions if the two metals differ considerably in electro-chemical properties. You have said (page 317) that a typical β-phase may involve no more " chemical combination " than is found in the primary α-solid solution. So if the β-phases show an increasing effect of the electrochemical factor in the order Ag Cd > Ag Zn > Ag Mg, the same tendency should be found in the α-solid solutions.

YS: That is quite true, and I think it is very probable that the primary solid solution of magnesium in silver does involve forces of a partly ionic or electrochemical nature. So far this effect has been rather ignored by the theoretical physicists, although considered empirically the effect of increasing electrochemical factor on the form of the equilibrium diagrams is very clear for the β-phases of the systems Ag-Cd, Ag-Zn, and Ag-Mg. It is interesting to note that recent work has shown that in the system Ag-Mg, where the electrochemical factor is high, the α-solid solution takes up an ordered structure at low temperatures in a composition range including Ag₃Mg. This ordered structure is of the Cu₃Au type which we shall describe later—it is a structure in which the magnesium atoms keep as far away from one another as they can. This, of course, can readily be understood if the two kinds of atom are acquiring opposite charges, since we shall then expect like charges to repel one another.

OM: If there is to be a continuous transition from what one may call

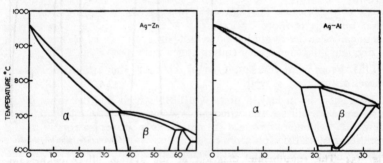

Fig. 155—Silver-rich portions of the equilibrium diagrams of the systems silver-zinc and silver-aluminium

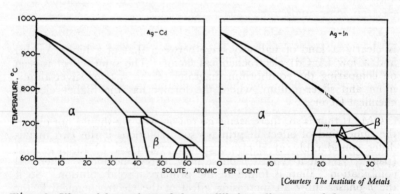

[Courtesy The Institute of Metals

Fig. 156—Silver-rich portions of the equilibrium diagrams of the systems silver-cadmium and silver-indium

pure electron compounds to compounds of an ionic nature, is it not possible that some of what you have called normal valency compounds may also be looked upon as electron compounds?

YS: Sometimes that is so. You will remember that (page 306) we regarded compounds like Mg_2Sn as being of an ionic nature, anti-isomorphous with CaF_2. It can be shown that this structure gives rise to a Brillouin zone with 8/3 electron states per atom, and this is the exact electron concentration of Mg_2Sn, if magnesium and tin are divalent and tetravalent, respectively. The electrical properties suggest that Mg_2Sn is an intrinsic semi-conductor, whereas Mg_2Pb is more like a pure metal. In such cases it is legitimate to regard both the zone picture and the normal valency concept as expressing part of the truth.

OM: This is most suggestive, because Al_2Ca has the same structure, and this can't be a normal valency compound, but it has an electron atom ratio of 8/3, if calcium and aluminium are divalent and trivalent respectively.

YS: That's right. There is also a phase $AuAl_2$ with the same structure, but this is more difficult to understand, because the normal chemical valencies of gold are one and three, and an *ad hoc* assumption of divalent gold is not very convincing.

OM: From what you say, it would seem that there might be ternary phases of this type as well.

YS: There is, in fact, a phase CuBiMg which has the same structure, but you will see that this can be looked on from either point of view. The valencies of one, two, and five for copper, magnesium and bismuth give an electron/atom ratio of 8/3, whilst one can also imagine positively charged copper and magnesium, and negatively charged bismuth.

OM: If there is no sharp distinction between electron compounds and ionic compounds, one would expect a similar transition from electron compounds to co-valent compounds.

YS: That is true, and it is probable that some intermetallic phases exist in which the forces are partly of a co-valent nature. In the early development of the science of alloys it was suggested by J. D. Bernal that, in the γ-phases which are of variable composition, there was a general tendency for the solid solution to extend farther on the side of high electron concentration than on that of low electron concentration. It was suggested that this might be because, with co-valent bonds, it would be more serious to have too few electrons than to have too many. A more recent examination[1] shows that the γ-phases as a whole do not show this characteristic, but the general idea that in some alloys a deficiency in electrons is more serious than a surplus may well be right.

OM: These electronic effects are very fascinating, and I think I

[1] See references at the end of this chapter.

understand the general principle that, when other factors are favourable, the crystal takes up the structure which accommodates the electrons with the lowest energy. But if one considers the variation of composition of a phase with an $N(E)$ curve such as that of Fig. 150, is it not possible that on increasing the electron concentration beyond that of the point A, the structure might undergo some slight modification so that, without a real change of phase, the $N(E)$ curve remained high, and so made the phase stable?

YS: In general that does not seem to happen, but in some alloys most curious effects are found in which, on increasing the percentage of one metal, a limit is reached beyond which further change in composition is achieved, not by atomic substitution, but by one kind of atom dropping out of the structure so that a defect lattice is formed. In the nickel-aluminium alloys, for example, there is a body-centred cubic β-phase Ni Al, with the characteristic electron/atom ratio of 3/2 —assuming nickel to be zero-valent. This phase is of variable composition, and on increasing the aluminium content beyond 50 atomic per cent, atoms drop out of the structure in such a way as to maintain a constant number, namely *three electrons per unit cell*. You will see that, as long as the body-centred cubic structure has all its lattice points occupied, this is equivalent to an electron/atom ratio of 3/2, but when vacant lattice sites occur the electron/atom ratio may increase whilst the number of electrons per unit cell remains constant.

The same kind of effect is found in the γ-phases of the system copper-gallium—in Fig. 132 you will see that there are three modifications of the γ-phase, denoted γ_1, γ_2, and γ_3, and in the last two of these, increasing percentage of gallium results in a dropping out of atoms so that a constant number of electrons per unit cell is maintained. A similar effect is found in the phases of the copper-aluminium system with the general γ-brass type of structure.

OM: That suggests that the number of electrons per unit cell is more fundamental than the number per atom.

YS: Certainly. The $N(E)$ curves depend on the Brillouin zones, and these, as we saw in Chapter 35, are determined by the crystal structure, and so depend on the unit cell. When all the lattice points are occupied, the number of electrons per unit cell is a simple multiple of the number per atom, but when there are vacant sites this simple proportionality no longer holds, and the number per unit cell is the fundamental quantity. The empirical discovery of the electron concentration principle was possible only because most structures contain relatively few lattice defects. In these curious structures where defects are formed, you may say that increasing the number of electrons per unit cell would produce such a great increase in energy that the lattice prefers to drop atoms in order to avoid the increase in energy.

OM: That is very striking, but I suppose it applies mainly when the size-factors are favourable. What I should like to know now is how electron compounds are affected by size-factor. You have explained before (page 302) how the $\alpha/\alpha + \beta$ phase boundaries in the systems copper-tin and copper-indium are displaced on account of the relatively large atomic diameters of tin and indium, and one would expect that when one dealt with complicated crystal structures, the effects of atomic diameter might affect the way in which the atoms fitted together.

YS: That is perfectly correct, and the effect was shown by the very beautiful work of A. J. Bradley on the crystal structure of the γ-phases Cu_5Zn_8 and Cu_5Cd_8. In the system copper-cadmium the size factor is unfavourable, although only just so. There is a very restricted primary solid solution of cadmium in copper, and no body-centred cubic β-phase exists, but there is a γ-phase Cu_5Cd_8. This phase has a structure which is of the same general type as that of Cu_5Zn_8, but as shown in Fig. 157, the detailed atomic arrangements are different, and can readily be explained by the relatively large size of the cadmium atom. You can understand how from this effect there can be a regular transition until one reaches phases whose structures are determined primarily by the relative sizes of the atoms, and we shall consider some of these later (Chapter 39).

OM: If I have understood you rightly, each general type of electron compound has got its characteristic electron concentration, but the details may be affected by both the size factor and the electro-chemical factor of the different systems. The problem must be extremely complicated, and I don't see how you can get much farther.

YS: From the point of view of pure theory you are correct, but systematic empirical examination of the equilibrium diagrams of the different systems has revealed some of the principles very clearly. You will readily understand that if progress is to be made, the first requirement is to redraw the equilibrium diagrams of the different systems in terms of electron concentration. Now we have already seen that at the electron concentration of 3/2, there is a tendency to form body-centred cubic (ordered or disordered), β-manganese, or close-packed hexagonal structures—sometimes the last named is found in a partly ordered form. For convenience we may use the symbols β and β' for the body-centred cube, μ for the β-manganese, and ζ and ζ' for the close-packed hexagonal structures, a dash denoting an ordered structure. In Fig. 158 I have shown the extent of these phases in all the systems for which data were available in 1940, and the systems are arranged so that those for which the size factor is favourable are in the centre, and the size factor becomes increasingly unfavourable as one moves outwards. Systems to the right are those for which the size factor is positive (that is the solute atom is larger than that of the solvent), and those to the left are those for which the size factor is negative (that is the solute has the smaller atom). It should be emphasized that the systems are only arranged in a rough *order* of size factors, there is no attempt to give an accurate scale of size factor—the whole concept of size factor is too approximate to justify attempts at drawing a scale.

This diagram therefore shows in a general way the effect of size

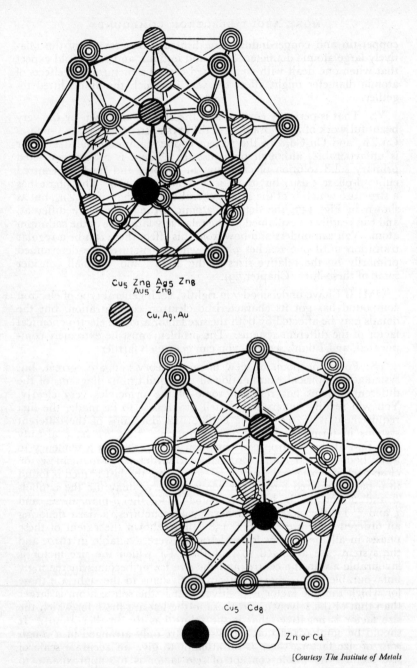

Cu₅ Zn₈ Ag₅ Zn₈
Au₅ Zn₈

Cu, Ag, Au

Cu₅ Cd₈

Zn or Cd

[Courtesy The Institute of Metals

Fig. 157—Crystal structures of the γ-phases in the systems copper-zinc and copper-cadmium

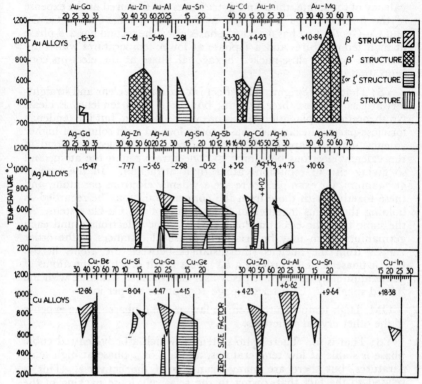

[Courtesy The Institute of Metals]

Fig. 158

factor on electron concentration. In comparing the three series of alloys you must remember that gold is the most, and copper the least electro-negative of the three elements copper, silver, gold. It follows therefore that in alloys with electro-positive elements such as zinc or magnesium, the electrochemical factor increases in the order

$$Cu < Ag < Au$$

With electro-negative elements, the electrochemical factor will be in the reverse order. In proceeding along a series of elements such as

$$Zn \rightarrow Ga \rightarrow Ge \rightarrow As \rightarrow Se$$

the elements of Groups V and VI are weakly electro-negative. It follows therefore that in their alloys with zinc, the metals copper, silver and gold are the electro-negative components of the system, whereas in alloys with selenium they are the electro-positive component. There is thus a point somewhere in the region of Group IV and V where the electrochemical factor is very small.

OM: Examination of that diagram suggests that on increasing the valency of the solute, the μ and ζ structures are favoured at the expense of the β structure. For example in the alloy systems Cu-Zn, Cu-Ga and Cu-Ge, the first has β-and β'-phases only, the second has a β-phase at high temperatures and a ζ-phase at lower temperatures whilst the third has only a close-packed hexagonal phase at the electron concentration 3/2.

YS: That's quite right. The effect isn't always so clear and straightforward as in those three systems, but the general tendency is clear. No theoretical explanation of this has yet been given, but the tendency for close-packed hexagonal phases to be formed with solutes of higher valency may perhaps be the result of part of the electron cloud of the valency electrons beginning to concentrate round the atom, and so giving rise to repulsion rather than attraction. In the case of germanium, for example, there are 4 valency electrons per atom, and these together with those from the copper atoms may be regarded as holding the atoms together in the ζ-phase of the Cu-Ge system. At the same time the electron cloud of the valency electrons round each germanium atom may be relatively dense at distances of the order $1.25kX$ from the nucleus (the distances between the atoms in the Cu-Ge phases is of the order $2.5\ kX$), as a result of which the atoms of germanium may fit together easily as a close-packed structure with the " hard spheres " (Chapter 26, page 195) of the copper ions.

OM: High temperatures seem to favour the β-phases at the expense of the other crystal structures.

YS: That is so. There is no system in which a body-centred cubic phase is stable at low temperatures, and a ζ-or μ-phase at high temperatures, but there are many examples of the converse. This is related to the fact that, owing to the relatively loose packing of the body-centred cubic structure, there is an abnormally large amplitude of thermal vibration of the atoms in one direction relative to the crystal axes. This means a correspondingly large entropy of vibration, and since the free-energy $G = U - TS + PV$ (p. 294), the term $-TS$ becomes large at high temperatures; thus the free energy is lowered and the phase made more stable.

OM: One can also see that in a general way increasing positive size factor shifts the composition of the β-phases to a lower electron concentration. In fact, in the system Cu-In the β-phase lies wholly to the low electron concentration side of the value 3/2, and I think I have seen this phase described as Cu_4In rather than Cu_3In.

YS: That is a very interesting phenomenon, and it has been suggested that it is due to the existence of short range order in the β-phase. The experimental work shows conclusively that in the system Cu-In, the β-phase extends just up to the composition 25 atomic per cent indium (Cu_3In) but does not exceed this value. It has been suggested that if one tries to fit copper and indium atoms together on a common body-centred cubic lattice with short range order, the composition 25 atomic per cent represents a critical value beyond which there is a marked increase in the number of indium atoms which are relatively close neighbours. This is only speculation, but there is a number of cases in alloy diagrams where phase boundaries of what are commonly called random solid solutions tend to approach but not to exceed simple whole number ratios of atoms, and several people have suggested that this indicates short range structures in the phases concerned.

OM: One thing seems to be very clear in Fig. 158, namely that the ordered body-centred cubic phases are favoured by high electro-chemical factor and to a lesser extent by high size factor. The relation between the ordered and disordered phases must be very interesting. and I should like to consider this next, but perhaps you would just explain to what extent the conclusions of Fig. 158 are general conclusions affecting all alloys.

YS: Fig. 158 refers only to the 3/2 electron compounds of copper, silver and gold alloys, and the conclusions refer only to these alloys. Since these include the well-known β-brass alloys the conclusions are of some practical value, but the main interest of Fig. 158 is that it shows how when a whole series of phases of a given structure is examined systematically from the point of view of valency, size factor, and electrochemical factor, definite principles become apparent in a general qualitative way, and it is by this kind of systematic examination that we may hope to lay the foundations of a science of alloy structures.

Suggestions for further reading.

Elementary:

An Introduction to the Electron Theory of Alloys, G. V. Raynor. Institute of Metals Monograph Series.
Atomic Theory for Students of Metallurgy, W. Hume-Rothery. Institute of Metals Monograph Series.
G. V. Raynor, Progress in Metal Physics, Vol. p. 1.
For a general survey of γ-brass phases, see:
W. Hume-Rothery, J. O. Betterton, and J. Reynolds, J. Inst. Metals, 1952, 80, 609.

More Advanced:

The Theory of the Properties of Metals and Alloys, N. F. Mott and H. Jones. Oxford Clarendon Press.

Epilogue to Chapter 38

The reader is asked to imagine the following conversation as taking place sixteen years after the conversation in the foregoing chapter, that is, sometime in 1961 or 1962. The participants are our friends the Older Metallurgist and the Young Scientist, but the former has recently retired and the latter must now be designated a Middle-Aged Scientist. They have met by chance while attending a conference and take the opportunity to consider the bearing of later work on their original discussion.

RETIRED METALLURGIST: From what you told me before (p. 302a) it would seem that a good deal of the original simple theory of electron compounds is now incorrect—in particular the theory of β-brass where, for a spherical Fermi surface, the peak on the $\mathcal{N}(E)$ curve was at an electron concentration of 1.48.

MIDDLE-AGED SCIENTIST: The position is really one of very great difficulty. You are quite right in saying that the revised calculations of Jones (p. 302a and Fig. 137) gave a peak at an electron concentration of 1.22 for the $\mathcal{N}(E)$ curve of the body-centred cubic structure. But as regards this, two comments may be made:

Firstly, the calculations of Jones assumed the energy gap at the surface of the zone for the β-phase to be the same as that for pure copper. This was a purely arbitrary assumption and was always a weak part of the theory.

Secondly, nobody really knows how to calculate the behaviour of an electron in the field of a random solid solution with two kinds of atom mixed up. The X-ray diffraction patterns show that a periodicity of the structure remains. But it is clearly not a simple periodic potential, and any rigorous solution of the problem is at present too difficult.

RM: But the agreement with the simple theory was surely too striking to have been coincidental.

MAS: That is the line of argument which Cohen and Heine took (p. 302b) in their theory of the α-solubility limits.

RM: It would seem, therefore, that even though Cohen and Heine were wrong about silver and gold they may have been right about the alloys.

MAS: The difficulty there is to see how their ideas could hold for the whole range of α-, β-, γ- and ϵ-phases. It is the essence of Cohen and Heine's view that the substitution of, say, zinc for copper lowers the energy gap at the zinc boundary to such an extent that the markedly unsymmetrical Fermi surface in pure copper becomes almost spherical at the composition of the α-boundary. This would be a very marked effect, and we should expect that with increasing zinc content the energy gaps would begin to increase again in the opposite sense—s-states inside, and p-states outside the centres of the zone faces.   Further-more, as you yourself pointed out (p. 302c), it would be difficult to understand why the same electron concentrations held for copper and silver alloys.

RM: Then do you mean to say that there is no theory?

MAS: One can only answer that, if you are willing to accept the idea of an approximately spherical Fermi surface, then a lot of facts seem to fall into line.   But nobody has yet given any proof of why the Fermi surface should be mainly spherical.

RM: You explained some of the empirical principles underlying the relative stabilities of the different 3/2 electron compounds (p. 334).   Is there any explanation of these effects?   In particular, why are the β-phases favoured by high temperatures?

MAS: That can be understood.   The relatively loose packing of the body-centred cubic structure means that the amplitudes of the atomic vibrations in certain directions are relatively large, and the correspond-ing entropy of vibration is correspondingly large.   Now the free-energy G (p. 294) contains the entropy S in the form:

$$G = U - TS + PV$$

For the body-centred cubic structure, the term $-TS$ becomes large at high temperatures, and so the free energy is reduced, and the phase becomes relatively more stable.   This may be the reason for the characteristic shape of the β-phase regions in the equilibrium dia-grams, where the phase covers a much wider range of concentration at high temperatures.

RM: If you are going to argue like that, it would seem that a larger solute atom would be accommodated more easily in the loosely-packed β-phase than in the close-packed α-phase, and so the free-energy of the β-phase would not increase so much as that of the α-phase.   The β-phase would, thus, have a lower free energy, and the phase-boundaries would be displaced in the direction of lower percentage of solute—which is what happens.

MAS: That's quite right.   In many cases these empirical principles can be seen quite clearly, but they are empirical and qualitative, and not quantitative.   That's the tragedy—there is no quantitative theory, as yet.

39—Superlattice Structures and Interstitial Compounds in Alloys

OLDER METALLURGIST: You have already spoken several times about the development of short range in alloy phases, and have told me to regard this as a process in which solute atoms tend to avoid being close neighbours, with the result that the energy of the structure is lowered because there are no longer regions where groups of close -solute neighbours produce intense local strains. It seems to me that if short range order can lower the energy in this way, it should some-times be possible to lower the energy still further by a long range order in which the solvent and solute atoms occupy regular positions relative to one another, the regular arrangement persisting throughout the whole crystal. I imagine this is what you meant when you referred to the ordered structures of the β-phase (Chapter 38, page 331), but there would seem to be no reason why the same effect should not be observed in primary solid solutions.

YOUNG SCIENTIST: In some systems changes of that kind do occur, and alloys are found which at high temperatures possess a random —or more probably a short range order—structure, but which on slow cooling or annealing at a low temperature undergo an atomic re-arrangement in which, whilst the crystal structure as a whole remains unchanged[1] the two kinds of atom take up regular positions relative to one another, forming a long range ordered structure which is usually known as a *superlattice*.

The history of the subject is very interesting. There are some alloy systems where at high temperatures a continuous series of solid solu-tions is formed. The system copper-gold is an example of this kind, and in the early work on the subject it was found that on taking cooling curves of alloys with compositions in the region 25 or 50 atomic per cent of gold, thermal arrests—sometimes rather ill-defined—occurred at low temperatures, and suggested that a change in structure was taking place. Measurements of electrical conductivity then showed that whereas alloys quenched from high temperatures gave the typical U-shaped conductivity-composition curve (Fig. 159), the slowly-cooled alloys, or alloys annealed at low temperatures, gave curves in which the conductivities rose to maxima at the compositions corresponding to the formulae Cu_3Au and $CuAu$. The temperature coefficients of resistance showed corresponding variations. These facts were first taken to indicate that definite compounds Cu_3Au and $CuAu$ were crystallizing out of the solid solution, and could take up a certain

[1] In some cases a cubic structure may become tetragonal with an axial ratio very nearly 1.0. Here the structure as a whole is very slightly changed, but the process is often clearly of the superlattice type.

amount of gold and copper into solid solution. There were, however, many difficulties in this interpretation, and it was not until 1928 that the X-ray crystal analysis of Borelius, Johannsson and Linde showed the true nature of the change.

In the case of the Cu₃Au alloy, the structure at high temperature is a more or less random face-centred cubic structure with some kind of short range order. Direct evidence for the short range order was obtained by Wilchinsky who showed that Debye-Scherrer X-ray diffraction films exhibited variations in the density of the general scattering—that is the general background of the film as distinct from the sharp diffraction lines—which indicated a short range order effect. The structure of the same alloy after slow cooling, or annealing at a low temperature, is shown in Fig. 160. Here you will see that the structure as a whole remains face-centred cubic, but the two kinds of atom now occupy regular positions relative to one another. The gold atoms are at the corners of the cube, and the copper atoms at the centres of

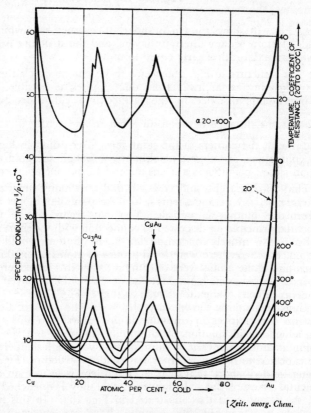

[*Zeits. anorg. Chem.*

Fig. 159—Conductivity curves of copper-gold alloys after annealing at the temperatures indicated

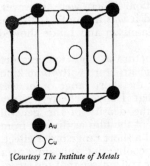

Au

Cu

[*Courtesy The Institute of Metals*]

Fig. 160—The Cu₃Au structure

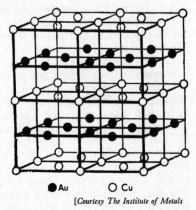

Au   Cu

[*Courtesy The Institute of Metals*]

Fig. 161—The CuAu superlattice structure

the faces. Fig. 161 shows the CuAu superlattice structure in which the two kinds of atom occupy alternate layers, and the structure is tetragonal with an axial ratio nearly equal to unity.

OM: The structure of Fig. 160 seems to be one in which the gold atoms are keeping as far away from one another as possible. The closest interatomic distance in the face-centred cubic structure is $\frac{a\sqrt{2}}{2}$, that is the distance between an atom in the centre of a cube face and one at the corners of the same face. According to Fig. 160 no two gold atoms are closest neighbours, although the gold atoms are second closest neighbours at a distance of a from one another.

YS: That is quite right, and you will find that many superlattices are characterised by arrangements which keep similar atoms as far apart from one another as possible. You may regard this as an extension of the principle we discussed in connection with the short range order effects. An entirely random arrangement of atoms would result in some places where there were local groups of atoms of one kind or the other, and if the atoms were of different sizes this would produce intense local strains, which might to some extent be removed by a regular arrangement of the atoms such as that of Fig. 160.

The same principle is shown very clearly by the work of Bradley and Jay on superlattices in iron-aluminium alloys. In this system there is a wide solid solution of aluminium in iron, and the alloy containing 25 atomic per cent of aluminium at very high temperatures may be expected to have a more or less random structure (Fig. 162) with some kind of short range order, but there is as yet no direct experimental proof of this.[1] If, however, the alloy is quenched from 700° C, the structure is that illustrated in Fig. 163. In this figure, 8 units of the body-centred cubic structure have been shown, and the

[1] Experimental evidence of this has now (1962) been obtained.

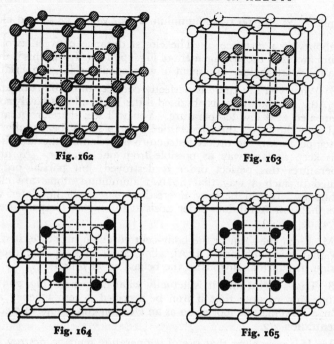

Fig. 162   Fig. 163

Fig. 164   Fig. 165

open circles represent positions which are occupied by iron atoms, whilst the cross-hatched positions are occupied by iron or aluminium atoms at random. You will see that in this arrangement, if we ignore the difference between the two kinds of atom, the structure is body-centred cubic, but there is now a definite long range order in the sense that some sites are occupied by iron atoms only, whilst others may contain atoms of either iron or aluminium.

OM: That is a very interesting arrangement, and it seems to bear out what you said before. In the body-centred cubic structure the closest distance of approach of the atoms is equal to $\dfrac{a\sqrt{3}}{2}$ where a is the side of one of the small cubes in Fig. 160. The arrangement you have shown in Fig. 163 is such that no two aluminium atoms are closest neighbours at a distance $\dfrac{a\sqrt{3}}{2}$. On the other hand a random arrangement of the two kinds of atom among the cross-hatched sites will mean that some aluminium atoms are second closest neighbours at a distance a from one another. Now it seems to me that I could improve on the arrangement of Fig. 163. If the two kinds of atom were arranged as in Fig. 164 where the full circles represent aluminium atoms, no two aluminium atoms would be closest neighbours at a distance $\frac{a\sqrt{3}}{2}$, and no two aluminium atoms would be second closest neighbours at a distance a. The closest distance between two aluminium atoms in the arrangement of Fig. 164 is $a\sqrt{2}$, and this is therefore a more satisfactory fulfilment of your condition for a superlattice.

YS: What you say there is perfectly correct, and the arrangement of Fig. 164 is in fact what is obtained if the Fe_3Al alloy is slowly cooled or annealed at a low temperature. You will see, therefore, that the Fe_3Al alloy illustrates the superlattice principle very beautifully. At low temperatures, the ordered structure is such that the aluminium atoms keep as far away as possible from one another. At higher temperatures this perfect order is destroyed, but partial order is retained in such a way that no two aluminium atoms are closest neighbours. It will be very interesting to see whether later work shows that a more random order exists at still higher temperatures, as I have suggested.

OM: From the form of the body-centred cubic structure, it would seem that the equiatomic, FeAl, alloy could take up the caesium chloride structure analogous to the behaviour of β-brass.

YS: That's right, and it is actually what happened (Fig. 165). It is interesting to note that if iron be ascribed a zero valency as in Fe_3Zn_{21}, FeAl may be looked on as an electron compound of electron concentration 3/2.

OM: It is very clear that rise of temperature tends to destroy these ordered structures, and in view of what you said about thermal arrests in copper-gold alloys, it would seem that the process is like that of a phase change.

YS: That is rather a confusing point, and it is not necessarily the case. The change from the ordered to the disordered state is usually regarded as a co-operative phenomenon, and in some ways it is analogous to the change from the magnetized to the unmagnetized state of a ferromagnetic substance. Suppose for example we consider the ordered structure of Fig. 165, and that we call the open circles the " right " and the full circles the " wrong " positions for the iron atoms. In this case the full circles will be the right positions for the aluminium atoms, and the open circles will be the wrong ones. If we now consider the average energy necessary to place one iron atom and one aluminium atom into the wrong positions, the energy will become smaller as the disorder increases. In other words when there is perfect order, the creation of disorder is opposed by the whole order of the assembly, and the less perfect the order, the more easy it is to create further disorder. When this idea is developed mathematically, it is found that on raising the temperature, the order is destroyed, at first very gradually and then with a sudden rush over a comparatively short range of temperature, just as ferromagnetism is destroyed over a short range in the region of the Curie point. Some writers have in fact used the expression " Curie point " to describe the temperature at which most of the superlattice order is suddenly destroyed, but on the whole this procedure is rather confusing, and it is not to be recommended.

OM: If the order is destroyed over a range of temperature, the process is different from that of the melting of a pure metal or compound, which takes place at a constant temperature. I suppose this means that if there are thermal arrests, they will also extend over a range of temperature?

YS: The change from order to disorder is always accompanied by the absorption of energy, and this appears as a rise in the specific heat in the region where the order/disorder change takes place. The exact details depend on the particular superlattice concerned. Thus, in the β-brass order/disorder change there is an abnormally large specific heat over a considerable range but there is no definite latent heat at any one temperature. On the other hand in the Cu_3Au superlattice there is a definite latent heat (that is the specific heat becomes infinite) at one point. There was much discussion as to whether superlattice changes should be classed as phase-changes or not, and for a time many of them were called phase-changes of the second-order, to distinguish them from ordinary phase-changes of the solid⇌liquid type whose principles are summarised in the well-known Phase Rule. More detailed examination has shown that many superlattice changes are properly regarded as ordinary phase-changes, and in some cases (e.g., Cu_3Au) 2-phase structures have been obtained with ordered and disordered phases in equilibrium. For the present we may ignore these details, and regard the formation of a superlattice as a process in which the free energy is lowered by the production of an ordered arrangement of the atoms.

OM: I can see that in a superlattice change, the structure of an alloy as a whole remains unaltered, and this seems to introduce some complications which you have not discussed. For simplicity in drawing, let us consider a 2-dimensional square-centred lattice with two kinds of atom as I have shown in Fig. 166, where the upper figure represents a random arrangement of the two kinds of atom. Now suppose a superlattice is formed in which one kind of atom occupies the centres, and the other the corners of the squares. This will prevent like atoms from becoming closest neighbours, and will satisfy your condition for a superlattice. Examination now shows that this can happen in two ways as illustrated in the lower figure of Fig. 166, but these two arrangements won't fit together, because the centres of the squares in the one arrangement are the corners in the other, and vice versa. In such a case, how does the crystal know how to start?

YS: That effect has actually been found in the case of Cu_3Au. In this superlattice the structure (Fig. 160) is face-centred cubic, and it may be looked on as formed by the interpenetration of four simple cubic lattices, just as your structure Fig. 166 is equivalent to two interpenetrating square lattices. In the case of Cu_3Au, the ordered state corresponds with one of these lattices being occupied entirely by gold atoms, and the other three by copper atoms. The ordering can

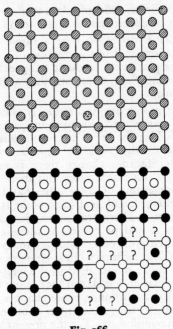

Fig. 166

thus occur in four ways in any one crystal—just as your structure Fig. 166 gave two ways—and by cooling under suitable conditions it is possible to obtain structures in which each crystal has begun ordering in four ways, with the production of what are called " anti-phase nuclei." These grow outwards until they meet, but they cannot coalesce for reasons similar to those which apply to your Fig. 166. This effect was studied by C. Sykes who was able to obtain specimens with small anti-phase domains of remarkable stability. This stability is the result of there being four alternative ways of ordering. In the general case, such as your structure (Fig. 166), the tendency would be for one small anti-phase domain gradually to grow at the expense of another with the production, first of a coarse anti-phase structure, and ultimately of a single ordered structure. But with four ways of ordering, a small anti-phase structure is stabilised for reasons similar to those which make a foam structure stable in spite of its great surface area.

OM: If the formation of a superlattice is due to the relief of the strain which results when two like atoms are closest neighbours, it would seem that the stability of a superlattice would increase with increasing difference between the sizes of the atoms concerned. If the atoms are of the same size there will be no strain to relieve. On the other hand, if the atoms are too different in size, they will not fit together to form a solid solution. So it seems likely that superlattices will usually be found in systems where the size factors are neither too favourable nor too unfavourable.

YS: That's perfectly right. You will see that in the system copper-gold the size factors are on the borderline of the favourable zone—the atomic diameters are 2.54 kX and 2.88 kX for copper and gold respectively. The values for iron and aluminium are about 2.5 and 2.8 kX respectively.

OM: It would seem to me therefore that one might carry the process a stage farther, and obtain alloy structures which were determined primarily by the sizes of the constituent atoms, even though these differed too greatly for solid solutions to be formed.

YS: That's perfectly true, and many examples have now been found. The first of these to be discovered was the so-called Cu_2Mg structure which is shown in Fig. 167(a). This structure is formed by the compounds

$$Cu_2Mg, \quad Au_2Bi, \quad KBi_2.$$

All of these are characterised by containing atoms whose diameters are roughly in the same ratio. You will see the interesting way in which the bismuth atom is the smaller atom in the compound KBi_2, but the larger atom in Au_2Bi. From Fig. 167(a) you will see that the small copper atoms from tetrahedra which are linked together, and Fig. 167(b) shows this skeleton of copper atoms, in the holes of which lie the larger atoms of magnesium. In the $MgNi_2$ and $MgZn_2$ types of structure there are again tetrahedral skeletons of the smaller atoms which fit together as shown in Fig. 167(c) and 167(d). These are called *Laves' Phases* because they were discovered by Laves who also recognised their dependence on a roughly constant ratio of the atomic diameters of the constituent atoms.

OM: All those are examples of binary phases, but could one not have structures in which one kind of large atom was mixed with more than one kind of small atom, provided that the ratio of large: small was maintained?

YS: Examples of that kind are known. One of these is the isomorphism of the two compounds

$$Al_6 Cu Mg_4 \quad \text{and} \quad Al_2 Mg_3 Zn_3$$

which occur in the ternary systems Al-Cu-Mg and Al-Mg-Zn respectively. At first sight it might seem that there was little connection between these two formulae, but if you remember that the magnesium atom is considerably larger than any of the others, you will see that we may re-write the formulae:

$$Al_6Cu Mg_4 = Mg_{12}Al_{18}Cu_3$$
$$Al_2Mg_3Zn_3 = Mg_{12}Al_8Zn_{12}$$

There are, thus, 12 large magnesium atoms to 21 or 20 smaller atoms, and this is the characteristic of the structure. Other examples of this

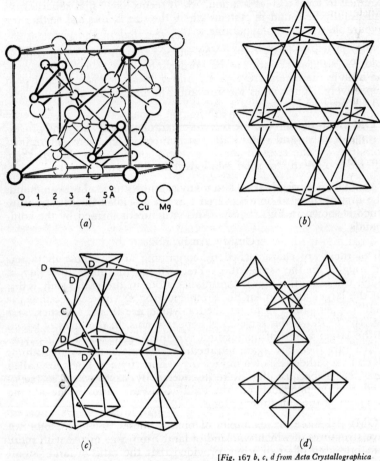

[Fig. 167 b, c, d from Acta Crystallographica

Fig. 167

(a) shows the structure of Cu₂Mg in which the small Cu atoms form tetrahedra which are re-arranged relatively to one another as shown in (b). The large Mg atoms lie in the holes between the small tetrahedra. In MgZn₂ the small Zn atoms again form tetrahedra which are arranged as shown in (c), and the large Mg atoms lie in the holes between the tetrahedra. In MgNi₂ the small Ni atoms form tetrahedra arranged as shown in (d), and the large Mg atoms again occupy the holes between the tetrahedra.

kind have been encountered, and the work is associated particularly with the name of Laves.

OM: It seems, therefore, that we have a continual transition from compounds such as Cu_5Cd_8 where the increasing difference in atomic diameters has modified the details of the Cu_5Zn_8 structure, although retaining the main structure, to compounds such as those you have described above in which the size factor is predominant and actually determines the structure.

YS: That's quite right. You will see that in the wide range of alloy structures which we have discussed, what we may call the size factor is one of the most important factors affecting the structure of an alloy. The electro-chemical factor is also of general importance in most alloy systems, and the electron concentration clearly plays a vital part in many alloys. In the general case, these three factors, and probably others which are not yet understood, are all concerned, and it is their interplay which makes the science of alloy structures so difficult to understand.

OM: That I can quite understand, but there is one further possibility which you have not considered. You explained how primary solid solutions could be of two kinds—substitutional and interstitial. It would seem therefore that if we can have an interstitial solid solution, we might also have an interstitial compound in which, if one kind of atom were very small compared with the other, the smaller atoms fitted into the holes or empty spaces between the larger atoms.

YS: That is perfectly correct, and some of the metallic carbides and nitrides are of that type. If you examine the sodium-chloride structure of Fig. 140 you will see that each kind of ion by itself forms a face-centred cubic structure. The X-ray work has shown that in some metallic carbides of formula MC, where M is a metal, the metallic M atoms occupy a face-centred cubic lattice, and the carbon atoms occupy the holes in this lattice, so that the structure as a whole is of the sodium-chloride type with the metallic atoms " in contact."

OM: You mean that the carbon atoms are, as it were, rattling about loose in the holes between the metallic atoms?

YS: No. The interesting thing is that structures are apparently not formed so that one kind of atom is " loose " in the holes between the other atoms. You will understand from Fig. 140 that in sodium chloride the electrostatic attraction pulls the positive and negative ions together until they " touch " (that is, their electron clouds overlap), and the process is brought to a stop by the " contact " of oppositely charged ions, and each ion has six neighbours of the opposite kind. In the MC metallic carbides, we have the same kind of structure, and if we regard the two kinds of atom as spheres, it is easy to show that if the atomic diameter of the one kind of atom is 0.41 times that of the other, the smaller atoms exactly fill the spaces between the larger atoms, and the MC sodium-chloride type of structure becomes one in which the larger M atoms touch each other as well as the smaller C atoms. Experiment then shows that in systems where the diameter of the carbon atom is less than 0.41 times that of the metal atom, a sodium-chloride type of structure is not produced, whereas if the " radius ratio " is slightly greater than 0.41, the sodium-chloride structure may be formed.

OM: You mean that in these MC carbides the metal atoms occupy a face-centred cubic lattice with the carbon atoms at the centres of the edges of the unit cube—there will also I suppose (Fig. 140) be a carbon atom at the centre of the unit cube.

YS: Yes. That is what happens if the radius ratio is greater than 0.41.

OM: If you look at the structure of the face-centred cube (Fig. 77) the atoms form tetrahedra in which one atom rests on the triangle formed by three others. In MC carbides where the metal atoms are so much larger than the carbon atoms that the latter are loose in the " holes " of the sodium-chloride structure, it seems that there are smaller " holes " in the middle of the tetrahedra formed by the metal atoms. One might therefore expect compounds in which the metal atoms occupied the points of a face-centred cubic lattice, with the smaller atoms in what might be called the tetrahedral holes of the structure.

YS: That is quite true, and in some interstitial compounds, that kind of atomic arrangement is found. Speaking generally for the transition elements, hydrogen is only element for which the radius ratio is sufficiently small for the " tetrahedral holes " to be preferred. As we have already seen, when the radius ratio is 0.41, the smaller atoms just fill the sodium-chloride type of hole in the face-centred cubic structure, and experiment has shown that with radius ratios between 0.41 and 0.59 interstitial compounds of the sodium-chloride type are often formed. In the same way with the metal atoms occupying a close-packed hexagonal structure, it is possible to insert interstitial atoms into " holes " so that each has six metal atom neighbours (analogously to the sodium-chloride structure) or into tetrahedral holes so that each interstitial atom has four metal atom neighbours. These very simple ideas have explained the structures of many carbides, nitrides, and hydrides, and the work is associated mainly with the name of G. Hägg. You should also note that in this class of compound variation in composition is very common, and not all the " holes " may be filled by the smaller atoms. This is why carbides and nitrides of elements like titanium are often of variable composition.

OM: In view of the electrochemical nature of carbon, it seems rather strange that these compounds can be regarded as consisting of spheres in contact. I should have expected some kind of definite chemical combination between the metallic and carbon atoms.

YS: There you are certainly right, and the idea of large and small spheres is now admitted to be much too simple, although it did serve to generalise a great many facts. I think you may take it as fairly certain that something like co-valent bonding exists between the metallic and carbon atoms, although the number of electrons present is insufficient to form normal bonds with two electrons held in common. You will notice that, in the sodium-chloride structure of the MC carbides, each M atom has six carbon atoms, and that the bonds are mutually perpendicular. The six atoms form the corners of an octahedron, and octahedral bonds of this kind are known to result from d^2sp^3 hybridisation of the orbitals of transition elements; and it is very probable that this kind of bonding is present in these carbides. The co-valent bond radius of carbon is small compared with atomic radii in metals, and so we can understand why the simple early concept of large and small spheres did permit some generalisation.

OM: On the whole it seems that the atomic size factor is the most important factor in determining the structure of an alloy.

YS: There I agree with you. The atomic size factor is the first and most important factor in determining the structure of an alloy, and that is why it must always be considered before the effect of valency, electron concentration, or electrochemical factor can be seen.

Suggestions for further reading.

The Crystal Structure of Metals, C. S. Barrett.
The Structure of Metals and Alloys, W. Hume-Rothery and G. V. Raynor. Institute of Metals.
Superlattice Structures, H. Lipson. Progress in Metal Physics, Vol. 2, p. 1.

PART IV—THE STRUCTURE
OF THE NUCLEUS

40—Radioactivity and Natural Disintegration

OLDER METALLURGIST: In an earlier chapter (Chapter 2, page 20)
you implied that the structure of the nucleus was generally
unimportant from the metallurgists' point of view. But with all this
new work on atomic energy, I imagine that many new metallurgical
problems will arise, and that the metallurgist must know some of
the underlying ideas. If I remember rightly, it was the study of radioactive substances which gave the first evidence that atoms were not
indestructible.

YOUNG SCIENTIST: That's quite right. The study of radioactivity
in the years 1896 to 1920 led gradually to the conclusion that radioactive changes involved not a mere rearrangement of the extra-
nuclear electrons, but changes in the actual nuclei of the atoms. This
was indicated by the magnitude of the energy changes, and also by the
fact that in some changes it was possible to show that the emission
of radiation was accompanied by the transformation of one element
into another. This was of course in complete contrast with ordinary
chemical changes, in which although compounds may be formed
or decomposed, each atom concerned remains an atom of the same
element. For example, hydrogen may combine with oxygen to form
water, and the water may combine with a salt to form a hydrated
crystal, and this may be decomposed by heating, with the production
of water, which may then be split up into hydrogen and oxygen by
electrolysis. In all this sequence, although the configuration of its
outer electrons may be altered, a given atom of oxygen remains an
oxygen atom, and similarly with the hydrogen. In contrast to this,
when radium gives off the so-called α-rays, the divalent alkaline earth
element radium of atomic number 88 disappears, and a new inert
gas " radon," or " emanation," of atomic number 86 is formed.

OM: You have explained before that an element of atomic number
Z contains a nucleus with a charge of $+Ze$, surrounded by Z electrons
It seems, therefore, that if an element of atomic number 88 changes
to one of atomic number 86, the nucleus must somehow get rid of a
charge of $+2e$.

YS: Actually that is what happens, and the so-called radiation
consists of a stream of what are called α-particles. These are helium
nuclei, or He^{++} ions, and as they carry away a charge of $+2e$ from
the nucleus, the emission produces a new element which is two places
earlier in the Periodic Table. You may, if you like, say that the atom
of radium has disintegrated with the emission of an α-particle, and the

production of a new element lying two places back in the Periodic Table.

OM: If the α-particles are doubly charged ions, they could I suppose be deflected by electric and magnetic fields, and this might give a way of measuring their charge and mass.

YS: The nature of α-particles was in fact established in that way, and the identification was later confirmed by detection of the helium. The fact that the α-particles are charged means that they possess strong powers of ionisation when passed through a gas, and this has led to various methods by which their paths can be studied. In the Geiger-Nuttall type of instrument the α-particles are led into a partly evacuated chamber containing two electrodes between which a potential difference is maintained. The entrance of the α-particle produces a number of ions, and in one type of instrument the ionisation produced by the α-particle serves to produce an electric discharge; in this way each individual α-particle which enters the chamber can be counted. In another modification of the instrument the ions first produced by the α-particle produce further ions by collision, and the resulting current between the electrodes can be measured.

Another instrument which has been of very great value is the expansion chamber of C. T. R. Wilson. This makes use of the fact that if the α-particles pass through air which is supersaturated with water-vapour, the ions which are produced form nuclei on which water condenses, and the minute droplets can be illuminated by a strong beam of light, and can then be photographed. The supersaturation is produced by suddenly expanding moist air, when the cooling caused by the expansion tends to condense the water. In this way the passage of an α-particle leaves a trail of minute droplets which can be photographed; Fig. 168 is an example of this kind.

OM: In Fig. 168 the tracks of the α-particles seem to be of two kinds, each being roughly of the same length. If the bright lines represent the ranges over which individual α-particles have produced ions, the photograph suggests that there are α-particles of two distinct energies, which are absorbed after travelling through different distances in air.

YS: That's quite right. In general each type of disintegration process produces α-particles of definite energy,[1] and these can penetrate air for different distances before they are slowed down to such an extent that they no longer produce ionisation. This range is reasonably although not absolutely sharp, and may be used as a characteristic constant of a particular series of α-particle. If α-particles are passed through a metal foil, they are retarded, and the range of the transmitted particles in air is reduced by what is called the stopping power of the sheet, which is defined as the equivalent air path by which the normal range has been reduced. The stopping power of course increases with the thickness of the sheet, and for a given thickness it increases with the density and atomic weight.

[1] To a higher degree of accuracy the energy distribution may show a fine structure.

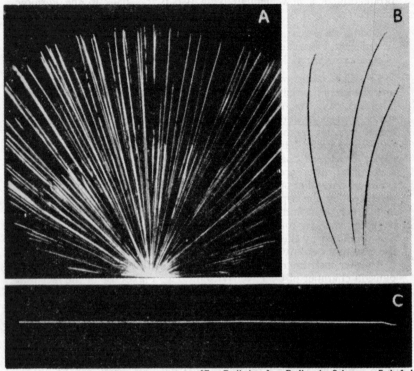

[*From* Radiations from Radioactive Substances, *Rutherford, Chadwick and Ellis. Courtesy of Cambridge University Press*

Fig. 168

A—Tracks of α-particles from thorium (C + C′) in a Wilson chamber, showing the two ranges. B—Curved tracks of α-particles in a magnetic field of 43,000 gauss. C—Complete track of α-particle ejected from atom of radon in air

In some studies of absorption of α-particles (see Chapter 42), the results are expressed in terms of what is called the effective collision radius, r, or more commonly the " cross sections " $\sigma = \pi r^2$ where r is the value which has to be assigned to the sum of the radius of the particle, and the radius of the absorbing atoms, in order to account for the results on the assumption that the absorption process is one of collisions between particles treated as hard spheres. It is an unfortunate term because, as we shall see later, the process is frequently not analo-gous to a colision between spheres, but the term is often used.

OM: The fact that α-particles are emitted with a change in the nuclear charge indicates clearly that nuclei are not all indestructible, and I suppose it suggests that units of atomic weight 4 exist as such in the nuclei of the heavy atoms.

YS: This was at first believed, but it cannot be maintained nowadays. If it were true we should be hard put to explain the binding energies of nuclei (particularly why Be^8 is unstable and yet C^{12} and He^4 stable). Apart from α-ray radioactive changes, there is a second kind of change in which the so-called β-rays are emitted. These are more penetrating than α-rays, and deflection experiments in magnetic and electric fields show that they are ordinary electrons moving with very high velocities which may be as high as 2 or 3×10^{10} cm/sec. This means that they exhibit the effect required by the Theory of Relativity. The mass m is related to the velocity u by the equation

$$m = m_0 / \left(1 - \frac{u^2}{c^2} \right)^{\frac{1}{2}}$$

where m_0 is the rest mass.

OM: If we apply the argument you gave before, it would seem that when an atom of atomic number Z undergoes a β-ray emission process, it must change into an element of atomic number $(Z + 1)$, because if a nucleus loses a charge of $-e$, it is equivalent to the gain of a charge of $+e$.

YS: That's quite true. A β-ray disintegration leads to the production of a new element which is one place forward in the Periodic Table, in contrast to α-ray emission where the new element is two places back compared with the element giving rise to the emission. There is also a third kind of radioactive emission, the so-called γ-rays, and experiments show that these are not deflected by electric or magnetic fields. This means that they carry no electric charge, and they may be regarded as X-rays of very short wave length. The fact that they carry no charge means that their emission from a nucleus produces no alteration in the charge of the nucleus concerned, and so γ-ray emission does not lead to the formation of a new element.

OM: That seems very suggestive, because when a nucleus emits radiation, it must presumably lose energy, and if a new element is not produced in the change, the resulting nucleus will have the same atomic number, but a lower energy than the original nucleus—it's almost as though the nuclei concerned can exist in different energy states, just as the extra nuclear electrons can be excited, and can then fall back into the normal state with the emission of radiation.

YS: In a general way, your analogy is quite correct, and you will see that the earlier work on radioactivity was of great interest in proving first that the nuclei of heavy atoms were not indestructible, and secondly in giving evidence for a nuclear structure of some kind.

41—Artificial Disintegration of Atoms

OLDER METALLURGIST: In your description of natural radioactive disintegration, you said that the process was one which involved the nucleus, and not the outer electrons of an atom. In discussing the electronic structure of metals, you have several times emphasized that in a metal such as lead, an inner group of electrons, such as the $(1s)^2$ group, is so deep down in the atom that it is practically unaffected by the presence of adjacent atoms in a molecule or crystal. It would seem, therefore, that in a process where the nucleus itself is concerned, the state of chemical combination of the atom will have little effect.

YOUNG SCIENTIST: That is perfectly correct, and radioactive disintegration proceeds quite independently of the state of chemical combination of the atoms concerned. The disintegrating process is a process in which the nucleus alone is involved, and does not depend on any kind of reaction between the outer electrons.

OM: In that case, at a given time the total emission from a given sample should be proportional to the number of atoms which have not previously disintegrated. That is to say the number of atoms disintegrating in an interval Δt, should be proportional to $N\Delta t$ where N is the number of unchanged atoms at the beginning of the interval. This would imply that N diminished exponentially.

YS: That is in fact what is found, and if the constant of proportionality is called λ, the number of atoms disintegrating in time Δt is equal to $N\lambda\Delta t$, where λ is called the *decay constant*. In this case the number N of atoms present at time t, is given by the relation

$$N = N_0 e^{-\lambda t}$$

where N_0 is the number present at time $t = 0$. You can readily see that λ is the chance of a single atom disintegrating in unit time (1 sec.), and so a large value of λ means that the nucleus concerned is relatively unstable. The relation between N and t which corresponds with the above equation is of the form shown in Fig. 169. λ is thus a measure of the stability of the nucleus, but in many cases it is customary to consider not λ, but the *time of half life*, which is the time required for the element concerned to decay or disintegrate to one-half its original amount. This is given by the time at which the ordinate in Fig. 169 has the value of 0.5. At this point $N = \dfrac{N_0}{2}$, and we have therefore

$$t = \frac{\log_e 2}{\lambda} = \frac{0.693}{\lambda}$$

You will see, therefore, that a short half-life (i.e., large λ) means that the atom is very unstable. The actual half-lives vary enormously. For some artificial isotopes (see page 355) they may be of the order

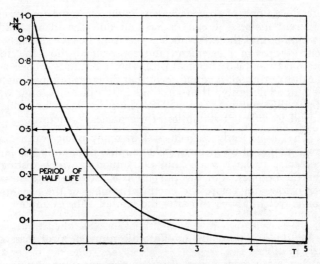

Fig. 169—To illustrate the general form of the law of radioactive disintegration

N_0 *is the number of atoms present at time* $T = 0$ *and* N *the number present at time* T. *The graph shows* $\dfrac{N}{N_0}$ *plotted against* T. *The value of* T *when* $\dfrac{N}{N_0} = 0.5$ *is called the period of half life*

10^{-6} sec, whilst for the isotope uranium, known as uranium I, the half life is several billion years.

OM: I have noticed that most of the radioactive elements to which people refer are of high atomic number. This is very interesting, and it suggests that when the accumulation of positive charge on a nucleus becomes too great, the resulting structure is unstable, and tends to disintegrate spontaneously.

YS: That is quite correct, and is the reason why the atomic numbers do not go on increasing indefinitely. Apart from establishing this point, the recognition that radioactive transformations involved the disintegration of the nuclei was of supreme importance, because it naturally led people to consider whether the nuclei of the lighter elements might not be made to disintegrate. The physicists then had the brilliant idea of using the high energy a-particles produced in natural radioactive disintegrations as projectiles for the bombardment of atoms of light elements. It was hoped that the impact between an a-particle and an atomic nucleus might be sufficiently violent to disintegrate the latter.

OM: There is one point you haven't made clear yet. You have explained (Chapter 2, page 18) how nearly all elements are mixtures of isotopes, the isotopes of a given element having the same nuclear charge, but different masses. I can understand how the identical nuclear charge implies that the extra-nuclear electrons behave similarly in the different isotopes of an element, and consequently how the different isotopes have identical chemical properties. But in a process such as nuclear disintegration, it would seem that different isotopes might well behave quite differently. If two isotopes have different atomic weights, they have different amounts of something in them, and this must surely lead to different stabilities of the nuclear structures.

YS: That is perfectly correct, and in many nuclear processes the different isotopes of an element behave quite differently. It is therefore necessary to have some kind of symbolism which distinguishes between the isotopes. For this purpose it is usual to write the atomic number below and before the chemical symbol of the element, and the atomic weight above and after the symbol. For example

$$_2He^4$$

stands for the isotope of helium (atomic number 2) of mass 4, and similarly in other cases.

The first really convincing disintegration experiments were made (1919) by Rutherford who found that when a radioactive source of α-rays was placed in nitrogen, particles were produced which could travel in air for much longer ranges than the original α-particles. Thus α-particles from radium C^1 have a range in air of 6.9 cm, but when nitrogen was exposed to the action of these α-particles, new particles with ranges up to 40 cm were obtained. Rutherford showed that this was due to the production of an isotope of fluorine which was unstable, and at once underwent a further disintegration with the production of the oxygen isotope of atomic weight 17, and a hydrogen nucleus or *proton*—it was these protons which constituted the long range particles, and the whole process may be represented:

$$_2He^4 + _7N^{14} \rightarrow (_9F^{18}) \rightarrow _8O^{17} + _1H^1$$

In this way oxygen was produced from nitrogen, and the first artificial transmutation of an element into another was achieved.

OM: I don't think you ought to say that, because radium compounds must often have been in contact with atmospheric nitrogen, and this will have led to the process you have just described.

YS: I'm sorry. I should have said that it was the first time that the transmutation had been produced under controlled conditions. Once the nature of the process had been established, similar experiments were carried out with many of the lighter elements, and a number of transmutations were found to occur. When this stage had been reached, it was natural to see whether similar disintegrations could be brought about by bombarding the light elements with protons (H^+ ions) or other ions which had been accelerated by passing through a high potential difference. In 1932 Cockroft and Walton bombarded lithium with high-speed protons, accelerated by 300,000 V, and succeeded in obtaining helium from lithium. Ordinary lithium contains two isotopes of atomic weights 6 and 7, and these underwent the following two nuclear reactions—

$$_3Li^7 + {}_1H^1 = {}_2He^4 + {}_2He^4$$
$$_3Li^6 + {}_1H^1 = {}_2He^4 + {}_2He^3$$

This is a completely artificial transmutation, because lithium does not come into contact with high-speed protons in the ordinary course of nature. The above is not the only process which can occur— sometimes a proton is captured by a lithium atom with the production of a beryllium atom in a highly excited state. This is unstable and emits a gamma ray leading to an unexcited state which is still unstable but has a longer half life. Finally, within a time of about 10^{-14} second the beryllium decays into two α-particles.

The work was rapidly extended to many other elements, and in this way the sciencies of Nuclear Physics and Nuclear Chemistry were developed and numerous transmutations brought about. In the examples described, you will have seen that the first product of the reaction is unstable and undergoes a second nuclear reaction. This is very common, and in such cases the intermediate product is said to be an artificial radioactive isotope of the element concerned. The half-lives of these artificial radioactive products vary from a very small fraction of a second to periods of many years. It is these isotopes which may be used for following processes such as diffusion in metals, and for this purpose the half-life must not be too short.

OM: In the above equations you have written the atomic weight of each atom as a whole number. This is very interesting because it reminds one of the old hypothesis of Prout according to which all atomic weights were whole number multiples of that of hydrogen. This was, of course, very soon shown to be wrong for the ordinary atomic weights, and now that most of these have been shown to result from mixtures of isotopes the non-integral values are readily understood. But your formulae suggest that the atomic weights of the individual isotopes are whole numbers, and so Prout's Hypothesis seems to have come into its own again.

YS: That is really true only to a first approximation, and to a higher degree of accuracy there are slight divergencies from exact whole numbers. For example, the atomic weights of $_3Li^7$, $_2He^4$, and $_1H^1$ are really 7.0176, 4.00395, and 1.00815, respectively, if $_8O^{16}$ is taken as 16.0000[1], and the nuclear reaction which is often written

$$_3Li^7 + {}_1H^1 = {}_2He^4 + {}_2He^4$$

is really

$$_3Li^{7.0176} + {}_1H^{1.00815} = {}_2He^{4.00395} + {}_2He^{4.00395}$$

OM: Now you've made a mistake there.

YS: What makes you say that?

---

[1] The atomic weights of isotopes are referred to the value 16.0000 for the $_8O^{16}$ isotope. The scale is thus slightly different from that of ordinary atomic weights since these are referred to a value of 16.0000 for ordinary oxygen which is a mixture of O^{16}, O^{17} and O^{18}.

OM: Well, if you add up the masses on the left-hand side of the equation, you obtain 7.0176 + 1.00815 = 8.02575, whilst for those on the right-hand side you have 2 × 4.00385 = 8.00790, so the two sides don't balance, and matter has been lost which is impossible.

YS: You have hit on a vital point, and I'm glad to say that the equations are quite all right. You have forgotten that according to the Theory of Relativity, matter and energy are interchangeable, a mass m being equivalent to an energy mc^2, where c is the velocity of light. In the ordinary reactions of chemistry, the energy changes are so small compared with c^2 that the corresponding changes in mass are undetectable by ordinary methods, and so we may say that mass is conserved. Actually, if we could measure to a sufficiently high degree of accuracy we should find that in a chemical reaction where an amount of energy E was evolved, there was a loss of mass equal to

$$\frac{E}{c^2}.$$

In nuclear disintegrations we are concerned with energy changes which are enormously greater than those in ordinary chemical reactions, and so the loss of mass is no longer negligible. The fact that in the above equation there is a lack of balance of 0.01785 on the two sides indicates not that the equation is wrong, but rather that the change is accompanied by an evolution of energy equal to $0.01785 \times xc^2$ where x is the weight of a hydrogen atom, and c is the velocity of light (3×10^{10} cm/sec). Since Avogadro's Number equals 6.02×10^{23}, the weight of a hydrogen atom is 1.66×10^{-24} g, and so the evolution of energy is equal to

$\qquad 0.01785 \times 1.66 \times 10^{-24} \times 9 \times 10^{20} = 2.7 \times 10^{-5}$ ergs.

This is the energy evolved when one single atom of hydrogen reacts with an atom of lithium according to the above equation. You can readily see that the energy evolved per gramme of reactants will be enormous.

OM: Then do you mean that the energy comes off as a quantum of radiation?

YS: The way in which the energy appears depends on the change in question. In the above case the liberated energy appears as kinetic energy of the emitted particle, and this is the most general phenomenon. There have, in fact, been extensive investigations in which reactions such as those of the above equation have been examined in detail, and it has been found that the equations are always consistent if mass and energy are related by the equation $E = mc^2$.

42—Fundamental Particles

OLDER METALLURGIST: From what you said last time about the equivalence of mass and energy, it would seem that the differences between the exact atomic weight of an isotope and the nearest whole number might be used to give an indication of the stability of the nucleus of the isotope concerned. For example, the atomic weight of the hydrogen nucleus is about 1.008 relative to that of 16.000 for oxygen, whilst the atomic weight of the helium He^4 isotope to which you referred (page 355) is 4.00395. If the helium nuclei contained 4 hydrogen nuclei, and there were no loss of energy, the mass would be $4 \times 1.008 = 4.032$. This is appreciably greater than the actual atomic weight, and so suggests that energy has been evolved.

YOUNG SCIENTIST: Your general idea is quite right, and the effect is usually expressed by what is known as the packing fraction. If we consider a particular isotope whose atomic weight to the nearest whole number is N, the actual atomic weight will differ by an amount which may be denoted δ. In this case δ/N is called the packing fraction. It would undoubtedly be simpler if the atomic weight of hydrogen were assumed to be 1.000 because in this case δ would always be negative. Actually atomic weights are referred to the value[1] 16.000 for oxygen, and so it is customary to refer the packing fraction to that of oxygen as zero. If this is done, the packing fractions for the elements immediately preceding oxygen are positive, and for those which follow the values are negative. This difference in sign of the packing fractions does not mean that the one set of atoms is stable and the other unstable. It is simply the result of the atomic weight of oxygen being taken as 16.000.

OM: It seems to me that all this idea of atoms being built out of so many hydrogen nuclei raises one fatal difficulty. If we omit the small fractions the atomic weight of oxygen is 16, whilst its atomic number is only 8. So if the oxygen nucleus is built up out of protons, there must be 16 of them, but 8 of them will have to be neutralized by negative electricity, if the nuclear charge is to be $+8e$. The nucleus will therefore have to contain 8 electrons as well as 16 protons.

YS: That's one difficulty, and there are others which are more complicated and concern spin, statistics and the Uncertainty Principle. These difficulties were not overcome until 1932, when Chadwick discovered a new kind of particle which is now called a *neutron*. The original discovery arose from the fact that when the α-particles from polonium were allowed to collide with beryllium, they produced what were at

---

[1] As explained before ordinary atomic weights are referred to the value 16.000 for ordinary oxygen, whilst isotopic atomic weights are referred to the value 16.000 for O^{16}. The two scales are thus not exactly the same because ordinary oxygen is a mixture of isotopes, and is not pure O^{16}.

first thought to be very penetrating " rays," which were later shown to be particles of the same mass as the proton, but with no electric charge—it was for this reason that they were called neutrons, and a neutron may be represented by the symbol $_0n^1$ because the charge is zero, and the atomic weight is the same as that of the proton—to a higher degree of accuracy it has been determined as 1.00895.

OM: But if the neutron has no charge, it will not be deflected by a magnetic or electric field, and so surely its mass cannot be determined?

YS: The mass cannot be determined by a deflection method, but it can be estimated indirectly by measuring the energy relations in processes in which neutrons are involved. Just as the loss of a mass m corresponds with an energy evolution of magnitude mc^2, so a loss of energy E corresponds with the appearance of a mass equal to E/c^2, and in this way the mass of the neutron has been estimated.

OM: I can understand how the absence of charge accounts for the great penetrating powers of neutrons, because they will not be attracted or repelled by electrons or positively charged ions or nuclei. But it's difficult to see what will happen to them—they can't just go on for ever!

YS: Neutrons decay spontaneously in free space

$$N \rightarrow P + \bar{e} + \nu$$

where P is the proton, $\bar{e}$ an ordinary electron, and ν is the neutrino to which we shall refer later (page 362); the half life of this is about 10 minutes. When neutrons are passed through matter, they eventually " collide " with and are absorbed by a nucleus with the production of a new isotope. As in the case of electrons in metals, the term collision is rather unfortunate, because one should not think of a head-on collision between bullet-like neutrons and nuclei.

A neutron of momentum p is associated with a wave-length $\frac{h}{p}$.

OM: You mean that the general ideas of wave mechanics apply to neutrons as well as to electrons?

YS: The ideas of wave mechanics apply to all the elementary particles, and a particle of momentum p is always associated with a wave length equal to $\frac{h}{p}$. Since a neutron is roughly 1,840 times as heavy as an electron, it follows that the momentum of a neutron is 1,840 times that of an electron moving with the same velocity,[1] and consequently the associated wave length is $\frac{1}{1,840}$ that of an electron of the same velocity. The result is that for neutrons which are not moving too fast, the associated wave length is larger than the " size " of a nucleus (*ca* 10^{-12} cm), and so the interaction between a neutron and a nucleus is analogous to the absorption of a quantum of visible light by an atom rather than to a collision between two bullet-like particles. Just as an electron exhibits some of the properties of both

[1] For simplicity the relativity correction is being ignored.

particles and waves, so a neutron has a corresponding dual nature, although the wave lengths are much smaller owing to the greater mass of the neutron. These wave-like characteristics mean that neutrons undergo diffraction by crystal lattices, and neutron diffraction methods can be used for the study of crystal structure. They are very useful[1] because atoms which have the same, or almost the same scattering power for X-rays may have widely differing scattering powers for neutrons, and so neutron diffraction may reveal superlattices which cannot be detected by X-ray methods. The neutron scattering factors also depend on magnetic spin, and neutron diffraction can distinguish between, say, a crystal of iron in which all the atoms have the same spin—this is actually the case—and a hypothetical crystal in which there is a magnetic superlattice with atoms of different spins occupying regular positions on the common lattice.

OM: It would seem that if the neutrons can be looked on as part of the nucleus of an atom, then a good deal of my previous difficulty is removed. The nucleus of an atom of atomic number Z and atomic weight W need not contain a lot of electrons—if there were some way of holding neutrons and protons together, it might contain Z protons and W-Z neutrons, and as the atomic weights are usually roughly twice the atomic numbers, the nuclei would contain roughly equal numbers of the two kinds of particle.

YS: That's right, and that's why the discovery of the neutron was of such immense importance. The discovery also threw light on the empirical fact that nuclei of even mass number are much more common than those with odd mass number. In the majority of cases a nucleus of odd mass number occurs only once in the whole Periodic Table, but nuclei of even mass number may give rise to isotopes of several adjacent elements. This clearly suggests that neutrons and protons tend to go in pairs in atomic nuclei.

OM: There will still have to be something to bind the neutrons and the protons together, and it seems difficult to see what this can be, when one of them is neutral.

YS: Yes; at first people merely said there exists a " nuclear force " —a completely unknown quantity—and tried to find out something about it. The study of the nuclear force from this phenomenological basis is still going on extensively. But Yukawa suggested another line of approach. In analogy with the photons of the electromagnetic field (see page 368), he assumed that the nuclear forces were caused by particles. The mathematical statement of this theory is possible, and although the solution of the equations has not yet been completely shown, it was possible to predict the existence of particles, known as mesons, of mass about 280 times that of the electron, and produced freely in nuclear collisions when there is enough energy to spare. These mesons were first found in the study of what are called Cosmic

---

[1] For a useful review see: G. E. Bacon and K. Lonsdale. *Reports on Progress in Physics*, 1953, **16**, 1. (Physical Society.)

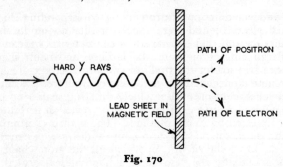

Fig. 170

Rays. The existence of these rays was first indicated by the fact that carefully insulated electroscopes showed a very gradual leakage of their charges. Elaborate experiments were carried out with electroscopes carried to high altitudes in balloons, or sunk to great depths in lakes or in the sea. These experiments all indicated that the surface of the Earth was subject to the action of a stream of very penetrating radiation. The intensity of the radiation varied in different places on the Earth, and on the assumption that this was the result of the Earth's magnetic field, it was possible to show that the cosmic rays were not homogeneous, but consisted of particles of different energies and different charges. The final conclusion was that the most penetrating component of the radiation could not be electrons, but must be particles of considerably greater mass. These were called mesons, or mesotrons—that is, particles of intermediate mass. Later the large particle accelerators built in the United States produced mesons in quantity in the laboratory. These nuclear force mesons are called π-mesons—the word pion is also used—and they can be positively or negatively charged or neutral. Other mesons called μ-mesons, or muons, have also been found in cosmic rays, but probably have nothing to do with nuclear forces. They are included in Table X.

OM: Then do you mean that the earth is being continually bombarded by streams of mesons, which are travelling through interstellar space?

YS: No, that's not right. Mesons in the free state are unstable and decay into each other, and finally into an electron; the half lives are all less than 10^{-6} second. This means that the cosmic ray particles travelling through space are not themselves mesons, but give rise to mesons when they reach the Earth's atmosphere. The actual cosmic ray particles are probably electrons and *positrons*, and the discovery of the latter was one of the great advances which resulted from the study of cosmic rays. A positron or positive electron is a particle with the same mass as an electron but with a charge of $+e$ instead of $-e$. These were discovered experimentally in cosmic radiation, and it was later found that if very hard γ-rays, that is, rays of short wave length, were passed through a sheet of thin metal (for example, lead) placed in a magnetic field, the result was sometimes to produce two particles which were deflected in opposite directions (see Fig. 170), the one being an ordinary electron, and the other a positron—similarity of the curved tracks showed that the masses of the particles were equal, and the sign of their charges opposite. It is of interest to note than just as the existence of the meson was predicted theoretically before there was any experimental evidence, so the positron was predicted by Dirac from purely theoretical considerations.

OM: That is most extraordinary, but if it can really occur, what happens to the positrons? We never seem to meet them in ordinary life.

YS: The fate of a positron, is the supreme illustration of the equivalence of matter and energy. What happens is that a positron of mass m and charge $+e$ meets an electron of mass m and charge $-e$, and the two annihilate one another as regards mass, and produce two quanta or photons of radiation each of energy mc^2. In other words matter is completely destroyed and converted into radiation. Expressed in electron volts, the mass energy mc^2 of an electron or of a positron is roughly 500,000 electron volts. It is customary to describe the energies of nuclear processes in units of 1 million electron volts for which the symbols MeV, MV or sometimes mV are used. If therefore a positron and an electron annihilate one another and form two quanta of radiation, each quantum will be of energy 0.5 MeV, and the corresponding frequency v will be given by the relation $E = hv$, and is equal to 1.2×10^{20}. Conversely if a γ-ray is to be captured by lead, and transformed into a positron and an electron, the γ-ray photon must have an energy of not less than $1 MeV$, since two particles of mass m (the electronic mass) are created. This has in fact been confirmed experimentally.

OM: I've read about that in a vague way before, but there is one thing which is never made clear. When one deals with matter—say an electron—one deals with something which is reasonably localised. Even if one takes into account all of what one may call your Heisenberg business, an electron is localised to a reasonable degree. When one spoke of radiation in the old days, one thought of expanding wave surfaces, and hence of something which was not localised. But if I understand you rightly (Chapter 5, page 38) radiant energy is now to be regarded as consisting of a stream of quanta or photons, and the wave theory is only a means by which the probable photon density can be calculated. Each individual photon is reasonably localised, and it seems to me that you shouldn't talk of annihilation. What you seem to do is to take the two reasonably localised " somethings " which we call an electron and a positron, and convert them into two reasonably localised " something elses " which we call photons.

YS: There I think I agree with you, although you must remember that apart from the question of electric charge there is a great difference between the " something " which we call a photon, and the two " somethings " which we call positrons and electrons. The latter can be slowed down and made to move with any velocity in a given medium, whereas photons can move only with the velocity of light in the medium concerned. But you are quite right in saying that a photon is almost as localised as an electron, and if you like to speak of the reaction between a positron and an electron as a conversion rather than an annihilation of matter, I have no objection, although the latter term is now generally accepted.

OM: This accumulation of fundamental particles is really rather confusing.

YS: Yes. The subject is developing rapidly and there is a continual discovery of new particles. Some of these are summarised in Table X, which includes the following in decreasing order of mass:—

Hyperons which are unstable particles with masses somewhat greater than that of a proton. These are of several kinds, and have been found in cosmic rays, and prepared artificially.

Protons and Neutrons with mass approximately 1 (in terms of the hydrogen atom), and with charges $+e$ and zero respectively. The term *nucleon* is sometimes used to include both these.

Pions or π-mesons with masses of the order 270–280 times that of an electron, and which may have charges of $+e$, $-e$, or zero. It is these which give rise to the meson field and the nuclear forces.

Muons or μ-mesons with charges of $+e$ or $-e$ and masses slightly less than those of the π-meson.

Electrons and Positrons which have the same mass (about 1/1,840th that of a proton) and charges $-e$ and $+e$ respectively.

OM: To these I suppose one might add photons as being particles of zero mass, moving with the velocity of light—you agreed with me before about photons being localised.

YS: That's rather a matter of opinion or definition, and we need not argue about it. If you like to call a photon a particle, I have no real objection, but you can hardly call it a fundamental particle, because there are innumerable kinds of photon corresponding with the innumerable frequencies, each frequency of radiant energy corresponding with photons of energy $h\nu$.

You should, however, note that apart from the fundamental particles you have mentioned above, there is indirect evidence for the existence of a further particle known as a *neutrino*. When the nuclear reactions are studied in detail, it is found that in many cases the various collision processes take place in such a way that the angular momentum is conserved as in large scale phenomena. In some nuclear reactions, however, angular momentum appears not to be conserved, and the mathematical physicists concluded therefore that a particle now called a *neutrino* was emitted, which was characterised by the possession of zero charge and zero mass, and a spin angular momentum of magnitude

$$\frac{h}{2\pi}\sqrt{s(s+1)}$$

where $s = \frac{1}{2}$. As the neutrino has neither mass nor charge, it cannot be observed, and . . .

Table X

Particle	Mass relative to that of the electron	Charge	Spin[1]	Magnetic moment in units of the Bohr magneton μ, or of the nuclear magneton $\mu_N = \mu/1830$, or of the meson magneton $\mu_M = \mu/210$
Hyperon	>1830	different kinds		
Proton	1830	$+ e$	$\frac{1}{2}$	$+ 2.8\mu_N$
Neutron	approx. 1830	0	$\frac{1}{2}$	$- 1.9\mu_N$
Pion or π meson ..	277	$+ e$ or $- e$	0	0
Pion or π meson ..	270	0	0	0
Muon or μ meson ..	210	$+ e$ or $- e$	$\frac{1}{2}$	approx. $+$ or $- 1\mu_M$
Negative electron (ordinary electron)	1	$- e$	$\frac{1}{2}$	$- 1\mu$
Positron or positive electron	1	$+ e$	$\frac{1}{2}$	$+ 1\mu$
Neutrino and Anti-neutrino ..	$<1/1000$	0	$\frac{1}{2}$	0
Photon or light quantum ..	0	0	1	0

[1] When the spin is described as x, the magnitude of the spin is $\dfrac{h}{2\pi}\sqrt{x(x+1)}$

OM: Now, that's unsound, and you are contradicting yourself. You told me (Chapter 8, page 49) that it was meaningless to speak of physical quantities or things unless one could describe experiments by means of which the quantities or things could be measured or revealed. You talked a lot about this in connection with Heisenberg's Principle, and now you are doing just what you told me I wasn't to do myself. You have found that angular momentum isn't conserved in some of your phenomena, and instead of accepting the facts—which was what you insisted on my doing in the case of the Heisenberg difficulties—you are inventing an imaginary particle in order to make your preconceived opinions hold.

YS: That objection was at first made by many people, and if it were merely a question of accounting for the angular momentum, your objection would be valid and it would be perfectly legitimate to assume that angular momentum was no longer conserved in the processes concerned. But when the neutrino hypothesis is developed mathematically, it does seem to explain some phenomena for which it is not an *ad hoc* assumption, and so the position isn't so bad as you suggest.

OM: Then if the neutrino has zero mass, has it kinetic energy, or is it more like a photon?

YS: The energy may be regarded as kinetic, and so may that of a photon. For any particle one may write E, the sum of the rest mass energy and the kinetic energy in the form

$$\frac{E^2}{c^2} = m_0 c^2 + p^2$$

where p is the momentum, and m the mass is given by

$$m = \frac{m_0}{\sqrt{1 - \dfrac{v^2}{c^2}}}$$

whilst v is the velocity, and c the velocity of light. For a photon or a neutrino, you can write $m_0 = 0$.

OM: In that case you may as well call a neutrino a photon and avoid all this worry.

YS: No. There is a difference between a neutrino and a photon as regards the spin. If you write the magnitude of the spin in the form $\frac{h}{2\pi}\sqrt{x(x+1)}$ then $x = 1$ for a photon and $x = \frac{1}{2}$ for a neutrino.

OM: That reminds me of a point which has always confused me in books and reports on nuclear structure. In Chapter 13, page 93, and also on page 362, you have said that the spin has magnitude given by a relation of the form $\frac{h}{2\pi}\sqrt{x(x+1)}$. But all the books on nuclear structure write $\frac{h}{2\pi}x$.

YS: That is just an abbreviation. When the theoretical physicist writes $\frac{h}{2\pi}x$, he really means $\frac{h}{2\pi}\sqrt{x(x+1)}$, but the latter is rather difficult to print.

OM: It seems to me that's just asking for trouble and confusion.

YS: On the whole I rather agree with you, but you must remember that nuclear physics has developed in a great hurry, and the expert often forgets that the general reader won't know these shortened abbreviations. You are quite right in suggesting that in reports for the non-expert reader, the point should be made clear.

You will see, therefore, that the list of fundamental particles is longer than you expected, and for convenience Table X summarises the properties of some of these particles, but there are others which are not included.

Suggestions for further reading.

Radiations from Radioactive Substances, E. Rutherford, J. Chadwick and C. D. Ellis.
Introduction to Atomic Physics, S. Tolansky.

43—The Structure of the Nucleus

OLDER METALLURGIST: In considering the structure of the nucle
it seems to me that the usual description of the nucleus as carryi
a charge of $+Ze$, where Z is the atomic number, must be wrong
some ways. If it were really true, one would expect a nucleus to attra
electrons, so that if a substance were bombarded by a stream of electro
one would expect the nuclei gradually to absorb electrons, and co
tinual series of transmutations would occur—each time a nucle
captured an electron, the atoms would move one place backward i
the Periodic Table.

YOUNG SCIENTIST: When you argue like that, you are really con
fusing between two different effects. The nucleus of an element o
atomic number Z undoubtedly carries a charge. Provided the distances
are not too small, this will attract a negative charge, or repel a positive
charge according to the usual inverse square law. This law is valid at
distances from the nucleus which are greater than about 10^{-12} cm. At
distances from the nucleus which are less than this, the inverse square
law breaks down, and in the immediate vicinity of the nucleus the
condition of affairs is often represented by a diagram of the type
shown in Fig. 171. In this diagram the nucleus is at the bottom of a
potential trough surrounded by a high but thin potential barrier—
the whole thing is on scale of the order 10^{-12} cm.

OM: If it is all on such a small scale as this, how can anything be
known about it? The distances are far too small to be explored by
X-rays.

YS: The general picture was obtained by considering the difficulty
which you yourself have raised. It was realized that at very smal
distances something must go wrong with the ordinary laws of attrac
tion and repulsion, and a detailed study of the scattering of a-particle
by matter suggested that the inverse square law began to break dow
at distances of the order 10^{-12} cm from the nucleus. The genera
picture presented by Fig. 171 has thrown light on both a-ray disinte
gration and on the effects when atoms are bombarded by rapidl
moving particles, as in the experiments on artificial disintegration
You will realise from Fig. 171 that the high potential barrier will ten
to prevent the particles within the nucleus from escaping, and also t
prevent particles entering the nucleus from outside. If the a-particle
concerned behave simply as " particles," they could pass across th
barrier only if their energies exceeded the value of the peak on the curv
But as the potential barrier is so very thin, wave mechanics indicate
that particles of lower energy have a chance of penetrating the barrie
the probability diminishing rapidly as their energy becomes smaller—
the effect is analogous to that we noted in connection with the passag
of electrons through very thin potential barriers.

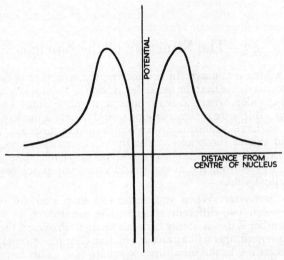

Fig. 171

OM: You explained before (Chapter 42, page 359) that the great importance of the neutron was that it enabled us to understand how the atomic weight could be so much greater than the atomic number without the nucleus containing numerous electrons. We saw that an atomic weight W and nuclear charge Z might consist of Z protons and (W-Z) neutrons. Now when we deal with elements of low atomic number (for example, C, N, O) we find that the atomic weight is about twice the atomic number, and this suggests that the numbers of neutrons and protons are approximately equal. But when we reach the heavier elements we find that the atomic weights are considerably more than twice the atomic numbers—for example, mercury has atomic number 80 and atomic weight *ca* 200. It seems, therefore, that there must be some gradual change in the relative numbers of protons and neutrons as one goes down the Periodic Table.

YS: That is quite correct, and the effect is due to the mutual repulsion which the protons exert on one another. There is no electrostatic repulsion between a proton and a neutron, or between two neutrons, but there is a repulsion between two protons, and this repulsion becomes so great that a hypothetical nucleus containing 80 protons and 80 neutrons—that is, the nucleus of a hypothetical mercury of atomic weight 160—would be quite unstable. The addition of a further 40 neutrons serves to dilute the positively charged protons, and a stable structure results.

OM: That is all right as regards the atomic weights, but it seems a rather *ad hoc* assumption, and it emphasizes an objection which I have felt all along about your neutrons, and that is how they can be held together if they possess no charge?

YS: That, of course, is the real problem of nuclear structure, and it is not yet fully solved. You should, however, note in the first place that the forces which hold the constituents of the nucleus together are not electro-magnetic forces between individual particles. Various attempts were made to develop theories of nuclear forces on such lines, and they were found to lead to quite incorrect values for the binding energies, and for the sizes of the nuclei of the heavier elements. It was realized that the nuclear forces were not electro-magnetic, and were of some quite new type. Now we have seen that the proton and neutron have almost identical masses, and differ in that the proton has a charge of $+e$, whereas a neutron is uncharged. The first suggestion was therefore that the forces between a neutron and a proton were of an exchange nature, and involved the interchange of electron, for example

$$\text{proton} + \text{electron} \rightarrow \text{neutron}$$
$$\text{neutron} - \text{electron} \rightarrow \text{proton}.$$

The process assumed was mathematically analogous to that we considered (Chapter 25, page 188) in connection with the exchange forces in the H_2 molecule but the distances involved are of the order 10^{-12} cm in the nucleus, as compared with 10^{-8} cm in the H_2 molecule. When this idea was developed mathematically, it was found to lead to a quite wrong answer, and it was first shown by Yukawa that the correct magnitudes would be obtained if the interchange involved not an electron, but a particle of about 100–200 times the mass of an electron. In this way Yukawa was led to predict the existence of the *meson* (page 360), before the latter had been observed experimentally, and although his predictions were not altogether correct, the prediction of the meson before it was observed was very striking. If, therefore, we use the symbols π^0, π^+, and π^- to denote neutral, positively charged and negatively charged pions or π-mesons (page 360) respectively, the nuclear forces may be regarded as resulting from exchange processes of the type

$$P + \pi^- = N \qquad N + \pi^+ = P \qquad N + \pi^0 = N$$
$$N - \pi^- = P \qquad P - \pi^+ = N \qquad N - \pi^0 = N$$

where N stands for a neutron and P for a proton.

In a sense we may regard the repeated exchange of the meson as converting a given proton into a neutron, and then back again into a proton, and so on. But as in the case of the H_2 molecule, this may be misleading, and it is more correct to think of the proton-neutron combination as existing in a state which is characteristic of the meson exchange process, and which differs from the extremes between which the interchange occurs. These nuclear forces are not electromagnetic in nature, but are forces of a new kind, and since action at a distance is impossible, they are regarded as the result of a new kind of field, the meson field.

OM: It seems to me that however interesting this may be historically it must be wrong because you have already (page 360) explained that the meson is unstable with a half life of the order 10^{-6} sec. If it is so very unstable, it surely cannot be responsible for the nuclear cohesion which is clearly stable over long periods?

YS: That is a very difficult point which can only be understood by going into the mathematics. You may perhaps obtain a rough analogy by considering the relation between electric force and light photons. You are quite familiar with the idea of the binding force between the electron and the proton of the neutral hydrogen atom as resulting from the attraction of opposite electric charges. You are also accustomed to the electromagnetic field of a light wave, and to the concept of a ray of light as consisting of a stream of photons, and to the detection of an individual photon in a photo-electric experiment. Now, considering formally, the binding of an electron in a hydrogen atom can be described as a process involving the continual emission and absorption of photons. But this does not usually lead one to say that a hydrogen atom contains photons—alternatively, if one did say that the hydrogen atom contained photons, they would have properties different from those of free photons. In an analogous way we have the meson or nuclear attractive forces, the meson field, and the free mesons, and the properties of mesons as free particles are not necessarily the same as those when they are responsible for the nuclear forces. The apparent contradiction to which you referred is apparent only, but the way in which it is removed can, I am afraid, be removed only by considering the mathematics. For our purpose it is probably sufficient to realize that the nuclear forces are not directed forces between individual particles in the nucleus, and that they are not of an electro-magnetic nature. They are forces of a new type which, through the meson field, are related to free mesons somewhat analogously to the way in which the electromagnetic field of a light wave involves a relation between free photons and electrostatic attraction.

OM: It seems that there will also have to be some kind of attractive force to account for the binding of one neutron to another, because in this case there is no exchange of charge.

YS: The binding of one neutron to another is supposed to take place by the exchange of a neutral meson, as is shown on the previous page. The general order of magnitude of the attraction between two neutrons is the same as that between a proton and a neutron.

44—Fission of the Nucleus

O LDER METALLURGIST: In the last chapter you explained that the forces which held the constituents of the different nuclei together were connected with mesons, and we have already seen that the nuclei of isotopes with even atomic weights are more stable than those of odd atomic weights, because the former consist of a definite number of proton-neutron and neutron-neutron pairs, whereas in the latter there must be an odd particle left over. Now in the work on artificial transmutation which you described, the result is often to produce α-particles or other particles of relatively small mass. This suggests that we can, as it were, chip little bits off the nucleus, but can never go very deeply into it.

YOUNG SCIENTIST: You are quite correct in saying that in most artificial transmutations the atoms of the element which is bombarded do not lose more than an α-particle. You should not, however, look on the process of artificial disintegration as one in which a bullet-like projectile (α-particle or neutron) hits a small particle in the nucleus, and knocks it out. The size of the nucleus is so minute that in many cases it is smaller than the wave length associated with the bombarding particle. This applies particularly to disintegrations cased by slow neutrons, and in such cases the so-called " collision " between the bombarding particle and the nucleus is analogous to the absorption of a light quantum by an atom, rather than to a collision between two bullet-like particles. The constituent particles of a nucleus are packed together so tightly that as soon as energy is absorbed from an incident particle (for example an α-particle), it is immediately distributed over the nucleus as a whole, and you may perhaps regard the whole nucleus as suddenly boiling up with excess energy, and throwing out one or more of its constituent particles. The following analogy was, I think, originally due to Bohr, and may perhaps help you to understand the general effect, although the picture is in terms of particles, and as I have explained above this is in some ways misleading.

Let us suppose we have a number of billiard balls in contact with one another whilst in rapid motion in a bowl whose walls are sufficiently high to prevent the balls from jumping out. Now imagine that a bullet is fired into the bowl, and hits one of the balls, with the result that energy is transmitted from the bullet to the ball. The close packing of the balls will result in the absorbed energy being passed on from one to another—you can verify this by shooting a marble against an assembly of balls on a billiard table—and one or more of the balls may jump out of the bowl, but the balls which escape in this way are not in general those which were originally hit by the bullet. You should not, therefore, regard an artificial disintegration as a process in which a bombarding particle chips a piece off the nucleus, but rather as a process in which the energy of the nucleus is suddenly increased so that one or more of its constituents is thrown out. The process may take place so suddenly that the resulting nucleus is left in an unstable condition, and changes later into a more stable state—which is why so many of the artificially produced isotopes are radioactive.

OM: Am I right in thinking that although all this work was very interesting, it offered little prospect of obtaining energy on a practically useful scale from artificially produced disintegrations? The disintegrations could be produced, but they were very wasteful processes, and required much more energy to set them going than was given out again.

YS: That was the position until about 1938, when a quite different kind of disintegration was discovered. Like so many discoveries of real fundamental importance, the discovery of *atomic fission* arose from work which had been carried out with a quite different intention. We have already seen that the ultimate fate of a neutron is to be absorbed by an atomic nucleus with the production of an atom whose atomic weight is one unit greater, and which may subsequently undergo a radioactive (α, β, or γ) transformation. It was therefore hoped that if neutrons were passed into uranium, there might be a chance of producing elements with atomic weights greater than that of uranium itself, and from these to prepare elements lying one or more places forward in the Periodic Table—the so-called *trans-uranic elements*. Experiments of this kind were carried out by Hahn in 1938, and some of the resulting products were found to possess properties quite different from those which had been expected. After much uncertainty it was eventually shown that atoms were present whose atomic weights were roughly one half that of the atom of uranium, and it was concluded that some of the uranium atoms had been broken up into two parts of approximately but not exactly the same weight. This *atomic fission* was accompanied by the evolution of a very large amount of energy, but the really vital point about the process was that the fission of the nucleus was accompanied by the emission of neutrons. This fact meant that there was at last the prospect of a continuous nuclear reaction which, when started by a few neutrons, could continue by itself, because each atomic fission produced more neutrons to carry on the process.

OM: The general principle is simple, but it is not clear why there were not dangerous explosions when the discovery was made.

YS: You are forgetting that the neutrons which are emitted by an atomic fission do not all produce further atomic fissions. Some of them may be absorbed by nuclei without producing fission, whilst others may simply escape from the sample. You can readily see that the chance of a neutron escaping will diminish as the size of the sample increases. With an infinitely large specimen, only neutrons produced near to the surface would have an appreciable chance of escaping, whilst with a very minute particle the chance of a neutron escaping would be very great, because the number of nuclei which it could meet would be small. From this it follows that a specimen has to be of a certain minimum size before the fission process can be self sustaining. This minimum size depends on the substance, and in the case of ordinary uranium the size has to be very considerable because the element consists of a mixture of isotopes of atomic weights 234, 235 and 238 of which U^{238} is by far the most common, as you can see from the fact that the atomic weight of ordinary uranium is 238.07. It is only the isotope 235 which is able to undergo the fission process.

OM: You mean that the different isotopes behave differently as regards nuclear processes as I had suggested before, although their chemical properties are the same?

YS: That's right. There is roughly one atom of U^{235} to every 140 atoms of U^{238}, so that only a very small proportion of the atoms is able to undergo atomic fission. In order to obtain an atomic bomb, it was therefore necessary to concentrate the atoms which were fissionable, and this was done in two entirely different ways. The first of these involved the separation of the uranium isotope 235 from ordinary uranium. It is probably not unfair to say that if such a proposal had been made ten years ago[1] it would have been dismissed as hopelessly impracticable. The possibilities arising from atomic fission were however tremendous, and they provided such a stimulus that the difficulties were overcome, and quantities of the order of a few pounds of U^{235} were made, and the material was used in one of the atomic bombs dropped on Japan at the end of the second World War.

The second way of obtaining concentrated fissionable material from uranium might at first sight appear even more fantastically impossible. We have seen how the original discovery of nuclear fission arose from attempts to prepare trans-uranic elements by submitting ordinary uranium to the action of neutrons. As we have already seen, these results showed that the uranium 235 isotope was able to undergo fission, whilst uranium 238 could not do so. Further examination showed that some of the neutrons were being absorbed by the uranium 238 with the production of a new uranium isotope 239 which was unstable (half life about 24 minutes) and underwent a β-ray disintegration with the production of a new element of atomic number 93, which has been called neptunium. This neptunium 239 isotope is again unstable (half life of the order 2 days), and undergoes a β-ray transformation with the production of a new element of mass 239 and atomic number 94, to which the name plutonium has been given. Neptunium and plutonium are thus genuine trans-uranic elements, and lie beyond uranium in the Periodic Table.

OM: If plutonium can be found like that as a stable element, it seems curious that it should not be found in nature.

YS: Plutonium 239 itself is not stable, but undergoes a gradual α-particle disintegration, as a result of which it is changed back into

[1] This discussion took place in 1947.

uranium 235, but the rate at which the change occurs is very much slower than the two β-ray disintegrations to which we have referred above. You will see, therefore, that plutonium 239 lies two places beyond uranium in the Periodic Table, and has an atomic weight 4 units greater than that of uranium 235, which is the uranium isotope capable of undergoing nuclear fission. From the general relation between isotopes of different elements it was concluded that plutonium 239 would be capable of undergoing atomic fission, and this was confirmed experimentally. In this way a second method of obtaining fissionable material has been found, because plutonium 239 can be prepared from ordinary uranium by the action of neutrons, and then the plutonium 239 can be separated from the uranium. The experimental methods are extremely difficult, because the intermediate products are highly radioactive, and give off dangerous rays. The processes have, therefore, to be carried out by remote control with the workers protected by thick walls of concrete, or other screening material, whilst elaborate precautions have to be taken to prevent the discharge of radioactive matter in the form of smoke, fumes, etc. These difficulties have, however, been overcome, and plutonium was separated and used in one of the bombs dropped on Japan.

OM: From what you said it would seem that a very small piece of fissionable material, say uranium 235, will be harmless, even if it is bombarded by neutrons. Some atomic fission processes will occur, but most of the resulting neutrons will just escape from the surface, and the reaction will not be self-sustaining.

YS: That is perfectly true, and it is for that reason that pure fissionable material can be made safely. But once the size of the sample exceeds a certain critical limit, the possibilities are tremendous. From what we saw before, you will have appreciated that the conditions for a chain reaction[1] are that when one neutron causes an atomic fission, the number of neutrons produced must be sufficiently great for at least one of them to be effective in producing a further fission, and so on. Of course, only a certain fraction of the neutrons produced are *effective* in causing further fissions. Some of the neutrons may escape through the surface of the specimen as you have suggested, whilst others may be absorbed without producing fission, and so on. It is only the number of neutrons effective in producing further fission which is important, and the condition for a chain reaction is expressed by saying that the *reproduction factor* must be greater than unity. If, for example, the reproduction factor is 1.1, then after the first fission we have sufficient neutrons to produce 1.1 fissions, and after this " second generation " of fission processes has occurred, there will be sufficient neutrons to produce $(1.1)^2$; = 1.21 atomic fissions, and after *six* generations the number of neutrons will have doubled. The speed with which this kind of process occurs is enormous—

[1] The term chain reaction is used to describe a process such as atomic fission in which the first reaction (atomic or molecular) produces what is necessary (in this case neutrons) to enable the reaction to proceed.

it is usual to describe nuclear processes on a time-scale of micro-seconds (that is, millionths of a second), and in pure uranium 235 a single generation takes only a minute fraction of a micro-second. It follows, therefore, that if we take a lump of pure fissionable material which is of sufficient size, and whose reproduction factor exceeds unity, we have the exact conditions for an explosive evolution of an enormous amount of energy.

OM: You mean that if we had two or three relatively small pieces of fissionable material, they would emit neutrons, but would be quite safe, whereas, if we placed them in contact so as to form a large lump, they would at once explode?

YS: That's the general idea, although the details are not so simple as you imply. The enormous speed of the neutron generation process would mean that as the two pieces of fissionable material were brought together the chain reaction would begin, and the heat evolved would vaporise the material, and the greatly increased volume would bring the process to a close. There would, of course, be a very considerable upheaval, but only a small fraction of the material would undergo fission. For a real " atomic explosion " it is necessary to create conditions in which nearly the whole mass undergoes fission, and the " atomic bomb " is essentially a device for bringing two or more small pieces of fissionable material into contact so that these conditions are fulfilled. But the details of this, I am afraid, are not divulged to the ordinary younger scientist.

OM: The general idea seems quite simple, and I see now why it is that we cannot get atomic explosions on a small scale, and so use nuclear energy in that way for peaceful purposes. It would seem, however, that we might control the process by diluting the fissionable material with something which absorbed neutrons, and whose concentration could be varied.

YS: That is more or less what is done in the so-called atomic piles. In these the fissionable material is divided up into lumps—the arrangement is sometimes called a lattice—and the intervening space is filled with a substance such as graphite or heavy water[1] which has the property of slowing down the neutrons without absorbing them too greatly. The reaction can then be controlled by inserting sheets of a material such as cadmium which absorbs neutrons strongly. But this kind of thing lies quite outside the scope of our present discussion, and it is sufficient to note that the use of atomic energy for peaceful purposes requires a totally different arrangement from that of an atomic bomb.

[1] Heavy water, D_2O, is the oxide of deuterium, the isotope of hydrogen of mass 2

Suggestions for further reading.

Elementary:
An interesting review is given in Part II of *Science News* (Penguin Books).

More Advanced:
Applied Nuclear Physics by E. Pollard and W. L. Davidson.
Introduction to Atomic Physics by S. Tolansky.

45—Conclusion

OLDER METALLURGIST: I've been looking over the various notes I have made about our discussions, and I must confess that I am rather disappointed. I hope I do understand a little more of what the new theories are about, and I can see how fascinating some of them are, but they don't seem to be of much practical value. I want to make stronger alloys, and better castings, and your theories don't help, and they don't seem anywhere near the stage at which they are likely to help. I don't mean to suggest that you have deliberately deceived me, but I do mean that you have taken me on a long climb, only to find at the end that the new country which has come into sight is—shall we say?—beautiful, but without any industrial prospects.

YOUNG SCIENTIST: That point of view is very common, and it is by no means easy to answer briefly. The first steps in a new Science are seldom of direct practical application, and at the present time we are only at the beginning.

OM: That's nonsense. Metallurgy is one of the oldest of the sciences.

YS: On the contrary, it is one of the oldest of the arts, but one of the youngest of the sciences. That is the point which I find it so difficult for some of my older metallurgical friends to realise. It is only those who have come into metallurgy from sciences such as chemistry and physics who can appreciate the extent to which metallurgy suffers from the lack of a proper scientific background.

OM: I don't agree with that at all. For thousands of years there has been metallurgy of a crude kind, and chemical industry of a crude kind. After all, the ancient peoples knew how to make glazes, and that was chemistry of a sort; and they knew how to refine gold and silver, and that was metallurgy of a sort. The one has got just as much background as the other.

YS: I think you would find that many people would call those early stages of applied chemistry and metallurgy the developments of arts or crafts rather than of science, but we needn't squabble about the exact terminology. I think you will agree though that however much had been learnt in early times, it was the great developments of the seventeenth, eighteenth and nineteenth centuries which put chemistry and physics on really firm scientific foundations.

OM: But that was laboratory science and not industry.

YS: Exactly! And that is just the difference between chemistry and metallurgy. In nearly every case, the processes involved in modern chemical industry are the early laboratory experiments done on a large scale. Of course it all looks very different, but that is only natural—you can heat 5 grams of a substance in a glass tube, but it needs a lot of clever engineering to heat 5 tons. I can assure you I am not exaggerating. Only a year or two ago I was shown round the synthetic ammonia plant of the Imperial Chemical Industries at Billingham, and as my friend there took me round he continually explained things and quoted simple equations such as $H_2O + C = CO + H_2$ (water-gas).

These are the reactions whose details were worked out by chemists fifty or a hundred years ago, and it is because of their sound scientific background that the immense advances in industrial chemistry have been possible.

In contrast to this, metallurgical industry has developed largely from the older metallurgical arts or crafts. It is only in comparatively recent years that any considerable fundamental work has been carried out on metals and alloys, and in all too many cases this work has lost much of its value because so-called " fundamental work " has been concentrated on alloys which appeared to be of immediate practical value.

OM: Now that's going too far. I'll grant you the difference between the developments of modern chemical industry and metallurgical industry, but I won't have you running down the fundamental work done in our universities and research associations. It's only common sense to concentrate on metals which are of practical value.

YS: That is where you are wrong. Just think of your early science lessons, and try to imagine where chemical industry would be to-day if chemical research had been concentrated on substances which appeared to be of immediate practical value. What was the immediate practical value of the discovery that two volumes of hydrogen combine with one volume of oxygen? What was the immediate practical value of the study of the rare earths or the inert gases? You know as well as I do that the answer is " none at all." The work was done to discover the general principles, and when these principles had been discovered, chemists became, as it were, so familiar with their different elements and compounds that all the wonder of modern chemistry became possible. In contrast to this, metallurgical science is still largely empirical, and very few of the fundamental principles have been discovered. You may be fairly certain that these principles will be discovered only by work on metals and alloys many of which are of no immediate industrial value. If other sciences are any guide you may expect such work to lead to many discoveries of great practical value, but the work must be planned in order to throw light on the fundamental principles, and it will often happen that the industrial metals are the least suitable for the purpose of revealing the general principles.

OM: That may be all very well for young intellectuals at universities, but it isn't of much value to my laboratory when we are worried about an unsound batch of castings. It is no good telling us to play about with copper-germanium alloys when bronzes are going wrong—we're much too busy.

YS: Oh, certainly! Your works laboratories are concerned with immediate practical problems and *ad hoc* research. That kind of work will always be wanted and will always be of great value—I'm not suggesting for a moment that it is in any way less important than what is sometimes called " pure science." But even in the *ad hoc* work you would find things much easier if metallurgy had a sound theoretical background as is the case with chemistry—it is the chemist's general familiarity with the background to his subject which gives him such great power.

OM: Well, what do you suggest?

YS: That question can't be answered shortly. So far as your own immediate study of the work is concerned, don't expect too much. There is no magic about the new developments, and little immediate practical application. The new theories are not likely to produce better castings for a long time yet, and if they do reach that stage it will be those who really understand the work who will lead the way, and not men like yourself. But everything is to be gained by your keeping in touch with what is going on, so that when the time arrives you can encourage and help those who are introducing the new theories into the practical work. Use your influence to stimulate the metallurgical societies to which you belong to keep up to date in all branches of physics and crystallography which bear on metals. The chemical and physical societies are much more active in these ways—they publish annual reports on the progress of the different branches of their sciences, and some of these are excellent. Try to persuade your metallurgical societies to do the same thing, and insist that every meeting has at least one semi-popular lecture on metal physics of some kind. Make it quite clear that you refuse to acquiesce in the position in which a metallurgist is the last man to understand what a metal is.

OM: I agree with that, but surely I can do something to get the new ideas applied to my own problem?

YS: Oh, certainly! Encourage your young men to think about alloys from the new viewpoint. After all the work has already led some way. We can begin to predict which combinations of metals will form solid solutions, and which will not. Atomic diameters and the stabilities of compounds may provide clues to the choice of metals likely to produce alloys of the precipitation-hardening or age-hardening type. Be sure that your staff contains men who will follow up these clues and think on these lines. If a young man brings you an idea for a new alloy as the result of considering valencies or sizes of atoms or electron concentrations or electro-chemical factors, then let him have his chance to make the alloy. And make sure you know enough about the general ideas to be able to take an intelligent interest in the work.

OM: I expect you are really right, and it will be the younger men who will have to lead the way in this sort of thing. It will be my son and not myself. That reminds me of one point you raised at the start of our discussions and which has worried me a great deal. You said that very few universities would give my son the right type of education, and you advised me to let him read physical chemistry, and then to turn over to metallurgy later. But do you really mean that the metallurgical departments at the different universities are unsuitable?

YS: If you had asked that question fifteen years ago[1], I should have said that from your son's point of niew, the majority of metallurgical departments were useless. I don't want to be unfair, and it takes all sorts to make up the staff of any metallurgical firm or institution, but ten or fifteen years ago the majority of metallurgical departments were teaching men technology and things of immediate industrial application, rather than giving them any real education in scientific method. Of course such men were very useful in their way—they fitted straight into works, but when they came up against new problems and new possibilities, their lack of a real scientific education was all too obvious, and both they and metallurgy as a whole suffered.

OM: I must confess there is something in that, but things are better now. I was at the metallurgical department of one of the universities this week, and the professor there emphasised how much purely scientific work his men were doing, and the professor at another university said much the same when I was there last.

YS: Whenever you see any metallurgical professor nowadays you may be quite sure he will tell you that his laboratory is the one place where metallurgists do get a sound and scientific education, but unfortunately things aren't quite so simple. There is now an increasing recognition that the old kind of metallurgical course was unsatisfactory, but things haven't straightened out properly yet. In some cases what has been done is to add elementary X-ray crystal analysis, electron theory, and theory of alloys to the syllabus of the metallurgical course, and at the same time to retain all the old subjects. The result is that the syllabus is often hopelessly overcrowded, and the wretched student has no time to do anything thoroughly. This is a bad educational method, and very seldom gives a proper training in scientific method.

OM: It seems to me that you are altogether too one-sided. Electron theory isn't the only kind of metallurgy. I've got to have men who are good technologists or the whole of my plant will get disorganised.

YS: Oh, certainly! I'm not suggesting for a moment that everyone should have the same education. What I am saying is that a smattering of a dozen subjects[2] is not a scientific education and that until the metallurgical departments have got things straightened out, you as a father had better send your son to a university where he can take a full honours course in physical chemistry. This will give him a good general background, and the subject is sufficiently wide for him to be able to develop his strong points—he can do anything from quantum mechanics to glass blowing—and at the same time get a real scientific

[1] This discussion took place in 1947.
[2] Some metallurgical courses include: Chemistry (Organic, Inorganic, Physical, and Analytical), Physics, Mathematics, Crystallography, Metallography, Strength of Materials and Mechanical Testing, Geology, General Metallurgy, Extraction-metallurgy, Electro-metallurgy, Fabrication and Production Metallurgy, Pyrometry, Refractory Materials, and Fuel Technology.

education. After he has done this you have several alternatives. If you aim at ultimately making him the director of your research department, you should let him do two years' research work on the purely scientific side of metallurgy, for a Phil. D. degree. I would emphasise the desirability of a purely scientific and not a semi-industrial problem, because a scientific attitude of mind is often acquired more readily from purely scientific work. In industrial work it is sometimes necessary to compromise between what is desirable in order to solve the problem, and what is desirable in order to obtain results quickly or without the use of expensive materials.

OM: It seems to me this is going to be a long business—at least six years.

YS: Oh, certainly! If you want to give a man a good scientific education, and research experience, you must allow at least six years. Don't be misled by the type of education which puts a man on to a research problem for a month, and calls that " research experience." No real research is done in a month.

OM: As a matter of fact I'm not sure whether my son will want to take up research.

YS: In that case you can be quite sure that a real training in scientific method will be of enormous value to him, and in the long run it will pay him better than a course in technology or a smattering of a large number of subjects with nothing really understood. Metallurgy covers such a wide range that I clearly cannot advise in detail, but unless your son wishes to go into what one may call the engineering side of metallurgy, I think you will find physical chemistry the best approach.

OM: It seems such a waste of time that he cannot work on metallurgy all along.

YS: There I agree with you entirely. It would be much better if there were degree courses in what one might call the science of metallurgy. The subject is such a wide one that a splendid degree course could be arranged so that a man obtained a real scientific background and a training in scientific method. But whether or how soon that is done will depend upon people like you!

OM: Now, look here! I quite agree that the university courses aren't what they might be, but that is the professors' fault, not mine.

YS: I don't necessarily mean you personally, but indirectly it is the fault of many of your friends who insist that metallurgical departments must produce sound practical men with a knowledge of technology. It is true that some firms are now more enlightened, but the old attitude of mind is still too common, and as long as it persists the professors feel that they must produce what is asked for, or otherwise their men won't get jobs.

OM: Then do you really mean that apart from the actual research staff, the whole staff of an industrial firm should have read what one may call the science of metallurgy rather than its technology? You must remember that I've got to have technologists somehow.

YS: The staff of an industrial firm must obviously contain experts in many branches of metallurgy, but the ideal to aim at is certainly one in which all or nearly all of the staff have received an education in the science of metallurgy. After all, the men who control chemical industry are not fools, and they are quite content to let university courses in chemistry remain purely scientific courses, without insisting that they must produce sound practically trained men with a knowledge of chemical technology. They need, of course, to have chemical engineers to deal with their engineering and constructional problems, just as you need men with a good training in engineering. But this doesn't affect my main point that if you compare the average man entering chemical industry with the average man entering metallurgical industry, you will find that the former has a much wider knowledge of the science of his subject, and a smaller knowledge of the technology—and those who share my views would say that this is why chemical industry has progressed so enormously in the last fifty years.

OM: If your suggestions are followed, there will soon be no metallurgists of the old school left. That would be a pity—after all we've done something. The alloys of the last fifty years have been good alloys and they were made by men like me.

YS: There we can both agree. The older metallurgists were great men—so were the Elizabethan sailors. But the greatness of the latter did not lie in the fact that they used boats with sails—that was the technical method of their day and it was succeeded by steam and oil. You are living at the time when the principles underlying the structure and properties of metals and alloys are at last being discovered, and you mustn't complain if this leads to a new attitude towards the work, and if the new attitude leads to new technical methods. You and your friends may well be proud to call yourselves the last of the older metallurgists. Your achievements are secure, and the alloys you made were good alloys—they were very good alloys, and time alone will show if the younger scientists are able to produce better.

Epilogue to Chapter 45

The reader is asked to imagine the following conversation as taking place sixteen years after the conversation in the foregoing chapter, that is, sometime in 1961 or 1962. The participants are our friends the Older Metallurgist and the Young Scientist, but the former has recently retired and the latter must now be designated a Middle-Aged Scientist. They have met by chance while attending a conference and take the opportunity to consider the bearing of later work on their original discussion.

RETIRED METALLURGIST: It will be interesting to know how much your views have changed in the last sixteen years. You will remember that it was one of my complaints that the work you described was scientifically interesting, but with little practical application. Have there been any cases in which you can say that the new science of metals and alloys has been of any real practical use?

MIDDLE-AGED SCIENTIST: Things haven't been so bad. You will know of the developments of nuclear metallurgy?

RM: Yes. It's been a strange subject. Uranium was, of course, known in the old days, but the amount of work done on it has been extraordinary. And that curious new metal plutonium has been even more astonishing.

MAS: There you had a case in which one new and one almost unknown metal suddenly became of great industrial importance, and it was necessary to find out as much as possible of their alloys as quickly as it could be done. The empirical alloy theory did not enable people to predict the forms of the equilibrium diagrams of the different alloy systems, but it did result in a great saving of time. The simple ideas of size-factor, and valency, and electrochemical factors did enable some idea to be formed of which metals would probably be the most suitable. In fact I was told that, if plutonium and uranium had suddenly come on the market in 1920, it would have taken at least twice as long as it has done to reach our present understanding of their alloys, assuming of course that the same methods and the same number of man-hours of work had been available. The position has been much the same with the new metals such as titanium. The simple empirical rules have been of real value.

RM: But you can't forecast the mechanical properties of an alloy.

MAS: Not yet. But they can be understood much better, and the science of dislocations is making such progress that it should soon be of real value.

RM: And all the rest of the electron theory of metals is useless?

MAS: No! No! It has been of value in many ways. There is now an immense science of semi-conductors which is simply an extension of the ideas of Chapter 27, and this is intimately connected with all the electronic devices—transistors and so on—which are such a feature of our modern life. The electron theory has, admittedly, failed in not enabling us to predict the structure of a given alloy—although empirical rules have generalised a great deal—but it has been brilliantly successful in many other spheres.

RM: And now what about education? My son is now a managing director, but we're a metallurgical family, and do you still advise me to tell my grandsons to study physical chemistry rather than metallurgy at their universities?

MAS: In that respect, the position has changed greatly. There are now many universities which give a good scientific education in metallurgy, with much less emphasis on the technological details which used to be such a feature of the subject. Some of them make the mistake of giving their students too much, and I often wonder that the students' heads don't burst with all they have to take in. But if you can find one of these good universities with physical metallurgists and metal physicists who can explain their subjects clearly, you can send your grandson there, knowing that he will get what is wanted. Physical and inorganic chemistry are still a good introduction to metallurgy, and if your grandson is mathematical he may perhaps find physics is the best approach. You may summarise the position by saying that fifteen years ago I should have said that physical chemistry or physics were better approaches to metallurgy than most metallurgical courses, but now I should say that all three were equally good—and if you get the occasional university where the metallurgical department has really good metal physicists who can both teach and do research, that may be the best of all.

RM: As a metallurgist, I'm glad to hear that. But I have one complaint to make about your new type of young science graduate— he is very seldom able to write a report clearly and concisely.

MAS: I agree with you. It is the great defect of our educational system at the moment that so few of our students learn to write clearly. I cannot speak for other countries, but in Great Britain I think the responsibility lies primarily with the school teaching of science. The description of scientific experimental work can be made a superb test of clear writing.

RM: You are a University man, and you're only passing the baby.

MAS: No, I don't think so. Unless there is a system of individual tuition such as exists at Oxford and Cambridge, there is little way by which each university student can be given the help and criticism he needs. But I agree with you that, with the immense increase in the number of scientists, the problem is of great importance.

RM: The editor would agree with us there!

MAS: Yes. And now let us drink to the editors, both English and American, who have let us put so many of our ideas on paper. (*The two drink deeply.*)

Subject Index

(Alloys are indexed with the main constituent first)

Name Index

CATALOG OF DOVER BOOKS

PHYSICS

General physics

FOUNDATIONS OF PHYSICS, R. B. Lindsay & H. Margenau. Excellent bridge between semi-popular works & technical treatises. A discussion of methods of physical description, construction of theory; valuable for physicist with elementary calculus who is interested in ideas that give meaning to data, tools of modern physics. Contents include symbolism, mathematical equations; space & time foundations of mechanics; probability; physics & continua; electron theory; special & general relativity; quantum mechanics; causality. "Thorough and yet not overdetailed. Unreservedly recommended," NATURE (London). Unabridged, corrected edition. List of recommended readings. 35 illustrations. xi + 537pp. 5⅜ x 8.
S377 Paperbound **$2.45**

FUNDAMENTAL FORMULAS OF PHYSICS, ed. by D. H. Menzel. Highly useful, fully inexpensive reference and study text, ranging from simple to highly sophisticated operations. Mathematics integrated into text—each chapter stands as short textbook of field represented. Vol. 1: Statistics, Physical Constants, Special Theory of Relativity, Hydrodynamics, Aerodynamics, Boundary Value Problems in Math. Physics; Viscosity, Electromagnetic Theory, etc. Vol. 2: Sound, Acoustics, Geometrical Optics, Electron Optics, High-Energy Phenomena, Magnetism, Biophysics, much more. Index. Total of 800pp. 5⅜ x 8. Vol. 1 S595 Paperbound **$2.00**
Vol. 2 S596 Paperbound **$2.00**

MATHEMATICAL PHYSICS, D. H. Menzel. Thorough one-volume treatment of the mathematical techniques vital for classic mechanics, electromagnetic theory, quantum theory, and relativity. Written by the Harvard Professor of Astrophysics for junior, senior, and graduate courses, it gives clear explanations of all those aspects of function theory, vectors, matrices, dyadics, tensors, partial differential equations, etc., necessary for the understanding of the various physical theories. Electron theory, relativity, and other topics seldom presented appear here in considerable detail. Scores of definitions, conversion factors, dimensional constants, etc. "More detailed than normal for an advanced text . . . excellent set of sections on Dyadics, Matrices, and Tensors," JOURNAL OF THE FRANKLIN INSTITUTE. Index. 193 problems, with answers. x + 412pp. 5⅜ x 8.
S56 Paperbound **$2.00**

THE SCIENTIFIC PAPERS OF J. WILLARD GIBBS. All the published papers of America's outstanding theoretical scientist (except for "Statistical Mechanics" and "Vector Analysis"). Vol I (thermodynamics) contains one of the most brilliant of all 19th-century scientific papers—the 300-page "On the Equilibrium of Heterogeneous Substances," which founded the science of physical chemistry, and clearly stated a number of highly important natural laws for the first time; 8 other papers complete the first volume. Vol II includes 2 papers on dynamics, 8 on vector analysis and multiple algebra, 5 on the electromagnetic theory of light, and 6 miscellaneous papers. Biographical sketch by H. A. Bumstead. Total of xxxvi + 718pp. 5⅜ x 8⅜.
S721 Vol I Paperbound **$2.00**
S722 Vol II Paperbound **$2.00**
The set **$4.00**

Relativity, quantum theory, nuclear physics

THE PRINCIPLE OF RELATIVITY, A. Einstein, H. Lorentz, M. Minkowski, H. Weyl. These are the 11 basic papers that founded the general and special theories of relativity, all translated into English. Two papers by Lorentz on the Michelson experiment, electromagnetic phenomena. Minkowski's SPACE & TIME, and Weyl's GRAVITATION & ELECTRICITY. 7 epoch-making papers by Einstein: ELECTROMAGNETICS OF MOVING BODIES, INFLUENCE OF GRAVITATION IN PROPAGATION OF LIGHT, COSMOLOGICAL CONSIDERATIONS, GENERAL THEORY, and 3 others. 7 diagrams. Special notes by A. Sommerfeld. 224pp. 5⅜ x 8.
S81 Paperbound $1.75

SPACE TIME MATTER, Hermann Weyl. "The standard treatise on the general theory of relativity," (Nature), written by a world-renowned scientist, provides a deep clear discussion of the logical coherence of the general theory, with introduction to all the mathematical tools needed: Maxwell, analytical geometry, non-Euclidean geometry, tensor calculus, etc. Basis is classical space-time, before absorption of relativity. Partial contents: Euclidean space, mathematical form, metrical continuum, relativity of time and space, general theory. 15 diagrams. Bibliography. New preface for this edition. xviii + 330pp. 5⅜ x 8.
S267 Paperbound $1.85

PRINCIPLES OF QUANTUM MECHANICS, W. V. Houston. Enables student with working knowledge of elementary mathematical physics to develop facility in use of quantum mechanics, understand published work in field. Formulates quantum mechanics in terms of Schroedinger's wave mechanics. Studies evidence for quantum theory, for inadequacy of classical mechanics, 2 postulates of quantum mechanics; numerous important, fruitful applications of quantum mechanics in spectroscopy, collision problems, electrons in solids; other topics. "One of the most rewarding features . . . is the interlacing of problems with text," Amer. J. of Physics. Corrected edition. 21 illus. Index. 296pp. 5⅜ x 8.   **S524 Paperbound $1.85**

PHYSICAL PRINCIPLES OF THE QUANTUM THEORY, Werner Heisenberg. A Nobel laureate discusses quantum theory; Heisenberg's own work, Compton, Schroedinger, Wilson, Einstein, many others. Written for physicists, chemists who are not specialists in quantum theory, only elementary formulae are considered in the text; there is a mathematical appendix for specialists. Profound without sacrifice of clarity. Translated by C. Eckart, F. Hoyt. 18 figures. 192pp. 5⅜ x 8.
S113 Paperbound $1.25

SELECTED PAPERS ON QUANTUM ELECTRODYNAMICS, edited by J. Schwinger. Facsimiles of papers which established quantum electrodynamics, from initial successes through today's position as part of the larger theory of elementary particles. First book publication in any language of these collected papers of Bethe, Bloch, Dirac, Dyson, Fermi, Feynman, Heisenberg, Kusch, Lamb, Oppenheimer, Pauli, Schwinger, Tomonoga, Weisskopf, Wigner, etc. 34 papers in all, 29 in English, 1 in French, 3 in German, 1 in Italian. Preface and historical commentary by the editor. xvii + 423pp. 6⅛ x 9¼.
S444 Paperbound $2.45

THE FUNDAMENTAL PRINCIPLES OF QUANTUM MECHANICS, WITH ELEMENTARY APPLICATIONS, E. C. Kemble. An inductive presentation, for the graduate student or specialist in some other branch of physics. Assumes some acquaintance with advanced math; apparatus necessary beyond differential equations and advanced calculus is developed as needed. Although a general exposition of principles, hundreds of individual problems are fully treated, with applications of theory being interwoven with development of the mathematical structure. The author is the Professor of Physics at Harvard Univ. "This excellent book would be of great value to every student . . . a rigorous and detailed mathematical discussion of all of the principal quantum-mechanical methods . . . has succeeded in keeping his presentations clear and understandable," Dr. Linus Pauling, J. of the American Chemical Society. Appendices: calculus of variations, math. notes, etc. Indexes. 611pp. 5⅜ x 8.
S472 Paperbound $2.95

ATOMIC SPECTRA AND ATOMIC STRUCTURE, G. Herzberg. Excellent general survey for chemists, physicists specializing in other fields. Partial contents: simplest line spectra and elements of atomic theory, building-up principle and periodic system of elements, hyperfine structure of spectral lines, some experiments and applications. Bibliography. 80 figures. Index. xii + 257pp. 5⅜ x 8.
S115 Paperbound $1.95

THE THEORY AND THE PROPERTIES OF METALS AND ALLOYS, N. F. Mott, H. Jones. Quantum methods used to develop mathematical models which show interrelationship of basic chemical phenomena with crystal structure, magnetic susceptibility, electrical, optical properties. Examines thermal properties of crystal lattice, electron motion in applied field, cohesion, electrical resistance, noble metals, para-, dia-, and ferromagnetism, etc. "Exposition . . . clear . . . mathematical treatment . . . simple," Nature. 138 figures. Bibliography. Index. xiii + 320pp. 5⅜ x 8.
S456 Paperbound $1.85

FOUNDATIONS OF NUCLEAR PHYSICS, edited by R. T. Beyer. 13 of the most important papers on nuclear physics reproduced in facsimile in the original languages of their authors: the papers most often cited in footnotes, bibliographies. Anderson, Curie, Joliot, Chadwick, Fermi, Lawrence, Cockcroft, Hahn, Yukawa. UNPARALLELED BIBLIOGRAPHY. 122 double-columned pages, over 4,000 articles, books classified. 57 figures. 288pp. 6⅛ x 9¼.
S19 Paperbound $1.75

MESON PHYSICS, R. E. Marshak. Traces the basic theory, and explicity presents results of experiments with particular emphasis on theoretical significance. Phenomena involving mesons as virtual transitions are avoided, eliminating some of the least satisfactory predictions of meson theory. Includes production and study of π mesons at nonrelativistic nucleon energies, contrasts between π and μ mesons, phenomena associated with nuclear interaction of π mesons, etc. Presents early evidence for new classes of particles and indicates theoretical difficulties created by discovery of heavy mesons and hyperons. Name and subject indices. Unabridged reprint. viii + 378pp. 5⅜ x 8.   S500 Paperbound **$1.95**

See also: STRANGE STORY OF THE QUANTUM, B. Hoffmann; FROM EUCLID TO EDDINGTON, E. Whittaker; MATTER AND LIGHT, THE NEW PHYSICS, L. de Broglie; THE EVOLUTION OF SCIENTIFIC THOUGHT FROM NEWTON TO EINSTEIN, A. d'Abro; THE RISE OF THE NEW PHYSICS, A. d'Abro; THE THEORY OF GROUPS AND QUANTUM MECHANICS, H. Weyl; SUBSTANCE AND FUNCTION, & EINSTEIN'S THEORY OF RELATIVITY, E. Cassirer; FUNDAMENTAL FORMULAS OF PHYSICS, D. H. Menzel.

Hydrodynamics

HYDRODYNAMICS, H. Dryden, F. Murnaghan, Harry Bateman. Published by the National Research Council in 1932 this enormous volume offers a complete coverage of classical hydrodynamics. Encyclopedic in quality. Partial contents: physics of fluids, motion, turbulent flow, compressible fluids, motion in 1, 2, 3 dimensions; viscous fluids rotating, laminar motion, resistance of motion through viscous fluid, eddy viscosity, hydraulic flow in channels of various shapes, discharge of gases, flow past obstacles, etc. Bibliography of over 2,900 items. Indexes. 23 figures. 634pp. 5⅜ x 8.   S303 Paperbound **$2.75**

A TREATISE ON HYDRODYNAMICS, A. B. Basset. Favorite text on hydrodynamics for 2 generations of physicists, hydrodynamical engineers, oceanographers, ship designers, etc. Clear enough for the beginning student, and thorough source for graduate students and engineers on the work of d'Alembert, Euler, Laplace, Lagrange, Poisson, Green, Clebsch, Stokes, Cauchy, Helmholtz, J. J. Thomson, Love, Hicks, Greenhill, Besant, Lamb, etc. Great amount of documentation on entire theory of classical hydrodynamics. Vol I: theory of motion of frictionless liquids, vortex, and cyclic irrotational motion, etc. 132 exercises. Bibliography. 3 Appendixes. xii + 264pp. Vol II: motion in viscous liquids, harmonic analysis, theory of tides, etc. 112 exercises. Bibliography. 4 Appendixes. xv + 328pp. Two volume set. 5⅜ x 8.

S724 Vol I Paperbound **$1.75**
S725 Vol II Paperbound **$1.75**
The set **$3.50**

HYDRODYNAMICS, Horace Lamb. Internationally famous complete coverage of standard reference work on dynamics of liquids & gases. Fundamental theorems, equations, methods, solutions, background, for classical hydrodynamics. Chapters include Equations of Motion, Integration of Equations in Special Gases, Irrotational Motion, Motion of Liquid in 2 Dimensions, Motion of Solids through Liquid-Dynamical Theory, Vortex Motion, Tidal Waves, Surface Waves, Waves of Expansion, Viscosity, Rotating Masses of liquids. Excellently planned, arranged; clear, lucid presentation. 6th enlarged, revised edition. Index. Over 900 footnotes, mostly bibliographical. 119 figures. xv + 738pp. 6⅛ x 9¼.   S256 Paperbound **$2.95**

See also: FUNDAMENTAL FORMULAS OF PHYSICS, D. H. Menzel; THEORY OF FLIGHT, R. von Mises; FUNDAMENTALS OF HYDRO- AND AEROMECHANICS, L. Prandtl and O. G. Tietjens; APPLIED HYDRO- AND AEROMECHANICS, L. Prandtl and O. G. Tietjens; HYDRAULICS AND ITS APPLICATIONS, A. H. Gibson; FLUID MECHANICS FOR HYDRAULIC ENGINEERS, H. Rouse.

Acoustics, optics, electromagnetics

ON THE SENSATIONS OF TONE, Hermann Helmholtz. This is an unmatched coordination of such fields as acoustical physics, physiology, experiment, history of music. It covers the entire gamut of musical tone. Partial contents: relation of musical science to acoustics, physical vs. physiological acoustics, composition of vibration, resonance, analysis of tones by sympathetic resonance, beats, chords, tonality, consonant chords, discords, progression of parts, etc. 33 appendixes discuss various aspects of sound, physics, acoustics, music, etc. Translated by A. J. Ellis. New introduction by Prof. Henry Margenau of Yale. 68 figures. 43 musical passages analyzed. Over 100 tables. Index. xix + 576pp. 6⅛ x 9¼.

S114 Paperbound **$2.95**

THE THEORY OF SOUND, Lord Rayleigh. Most vibrating systems likely to be encountered in practice can be tackled successfully by the methods set forth by the great Nobel laureate, Lord Rayleigh. Complete coverage of experimental, mathematical aspects of sound theory. Partial contents: Harmonic motions, vibrating systems in general, lateral vibrations of bars, curved plates or shells, applications of Laplace's functions to acoustical problems, fluid friction, plane vortex-sheet, vibrations of solid bodies, etc. This is the first inexpensive edition of this great reference and study work. Bibliography. Historical introduction by R. B. Lindsay. Total of 1040pp. 97 figures. 5⅜ x 8.
S292, S293, Two volume set, paperbound, **$4.00**

THE DYNAMICAL THEORY OF SOUND, H. Lamb. Comprehensive mathematical treatment of the physical aspects of sound, covering the theory of vibrations, the general theory of sound, and the equations of motion of strings, bars, membranes, pipes, and resonators. Includes chapters on plane, spherical, and simple harmonic waves, and the Helmholtz Theory of Audition. Complete and self-contained development for student and specialist; all fundamental differential equations solved completely. Specific mathematical details for such important phenomena as harmonics, normal modes, forced vibrations of strings, theory of reed pipes, etc. Index. Bibliography. 86 diagrams. viii + 307pp. 5⅜ x 8.
S655 Paperbound **$1.50**

WAVE PROPAGATION IN PERIODIC STRUCTURES, L. Brillouin. A general method and application to different problems: pure physics, such as scattering of X-rays of crystals, thermal vibration in crystal lattices, electronic motion in metals; and also problems of electrical engineering. Partial contents: elastic waves in 1-dimensional lattices of point masses. Propagation of waves along 1-dimensional lattices. Energy flow. 2 dimensional, 3 dimensional lattices. Mathieu's equation. Matrices and propagation of waves along an electric line. Continuous electric lines. 131 illustrations. Bibliography. Index. xii + 253pp. 5⅜ x 8.
S34 Paperbound **$1.85**

THEORY OF VIBRATIONS, N. W. McLachlan. Based on an exceptionally successful graduate course given at Brown University, this discusses linear systems having 1 degree of freedom, forced vibrations of simple linear systems, vibration of flexible strings, transverse vibrations of bars and tubes, transverse vibration of circular plate, sound waves of finite amplitude, etc. Index. 99 diagrams. 160pp. 5⅜ x 8.
S190 Paperbound **$1.35**

LOUD SPEAKERS: THEORY, PERFORMANCE, TESTING AND DESIGN, N. W. McLachlan. Most comprehensive coverage of theory, practice of loud speaker design, testing; classic reference, study manual in field. First 12 chapters deal with theory, for readers mainly concerned with math. aspects; last 7 chapters will interest reader concerned with testing, design. Partial contents: principles of sound propagation, fluid pressure on vibrators, theory of moving-coil principle, transients, driving mechanisms, response curves, design of horn type moving coil speakers, electrostatic speakers, much more. Appendix. Bibliography. Index. 165 illustrations, charts. 411pp. 5⅜ x 8.
S588 Paperbound **$2.25**

MICROWAVE TRANSMISSION, J. S. Slater. First text dealing exclusively with microwaves, brings together points of view of field, circuit theory, for graduate student in physics, electrical engineering, microwave technician. Offers valuable point of view not in most later studies. Uses Maxwell's equations to study electromagnetic field, important in this area. Partial contents: infinite line with distributed parameters, impedance of terminated line, plane waves, reflections, wave guides, coaxial line, composite transmission lines, impedance matching, etc. Introduction. Index. 76 illus. 319pp. 5⅜ x 8.
S564 Paperbound **$1.50**

THE ANALYSIS OF SENSATIONS, Ernst Mach. Great study of physiology, psychology of perception, shows Mach's ability to see material freshly, his "incorruptible skepticism and independence." (Einstein). Relation of problems of psychological perception to classical physics, supposed dualism of physical and mental, principle of continuity, evolution of senses, will as organic manifestation, scores of experiments, observations in optics, acoustics, music, graphics, etc. New introduction by T. S. Szasz, M. D. 58 illus. 300-item bibliography. Index. 404pp. 5⅜ x 8.
S525 Paperbound **$1.75**

APPLIED OPTICS AND OPTICAL DESIGN, A. E. Conrady. With publication of vol. 2, standard work for designers in optics is now complete for first time. Only work of its kind in English; only detailed work for practical designer and self-taught. Requires, for bulk of work, no math above trig. Step-by-step exposition, from fundamental concepts of geometrical, physical optics, to systematic study, design, of almost all types of optical systems. Vol. 1: all ordinary ray-tracing methods; primary aberrations; necessary higher aberration for design of telescopes, low-power microscopes, photographic equipment. Vol. 2: (Completed from author's notes by R. Kingslake, Dir. Optical Design, Eastman Kodak.) Special attention to high-power microscope, anastigmatic photographic objectives. "An indispensable work," J., Optical Soc. of Amer. "As a practical guide this book has no rival," Transactions, Optical Soc. Index. Bibliography. 193 diagrams. 852pp. 6⅛ x 9¼.
Vol. 1 T611 Paperbound **$2.95**
Vol. 2 T612 Paperbound **$2.95**

THE THEORY OF OPTICS, Paul Drude. One of finest fundamental texts in physical optics, classic offers thorough coverage, complete mathematical treatment of basic ideas. Includes fullest treatment of application of thermodynamics to optics; sine law in formation of images, transparent crystals, magnetically active substances, velocity of light, apertures, effects depending upon them, polarization, optical instruments, etc. Introduction by A. A. Michelson. Index. 110 illus. 567pp. 5⅜ x 8.
S532 Paperbound **$2.45**

OPTICKS, Sir Isaac Newton. In its discussions of light, reflection, color, refraction, theories of wave and corpuscular theories of light, this work is packed with scores of insights and discoveries. In its precise and practical discussion of construction of optical apparatus, contemporary understandings of phenomena it is truly fascinating to modern physicists, astronomers, mathematicians. Foreword by Albert Einstein. Preface by I. B. Cohen of Harvard University. 7 pages of portraits, facsimile pages, letters, etc. cxvi + 414pp. 5⅜ x 8.
S205 Paperbound **$2.00**

OPTICS AND OPTICAL INSTRUMENTS: AN INTRODUCTION WITH SPECIAL REFERENCE TO PRACTICAL APPLICATIONS, B. K. Johnson. An invaluable guide to basic practical applications of optical principles, which shows how to set up inexpensive working models of each of the four main types of optical instruments—telescopes, microscopes, photographic lenses, optical projecting systems. Explains in detail the most important experiments for determining their accuracy, resolving power, angular field of view, amounts of aberration, all other necessary facts about the instruments. Formerly "Practical Optics." Index. 234 diagrams. Appendix. 224pp. 5⅜ x 8.
S642 Paperbound **$1.65**

PRINCIPLES OF PHYSICAL OPTICS, Ernst Mach. This classical examination of the propagation of light, color, polarization, etc. offers an historical and philosophical treatment that has never been surpassed for breadth and easy readability. Contents: Rectilinear propagation of light. Reflection, refraction. Early knowledge of vision. Dioptrics. Composition of light. Theory of color and dispersion. Periodicity. Theory of interference. Polarization. Mathematical representation of properties of light. Propagation of waves, etc. 279 illustrations, 10 portraits. Appendix. Indexes. 324pp. 5⅜ x 8.
S178 Paperbound **$1.75**

FUNDAMENTALS OF ELECTRICITY AND MAGNETISM, L. B. Loeb. For students of physics, chemistry, or engineering who want an introduction to electricity and magnetism on a higher level and in more detail than general elementary physics texts provide. Only elementary differential and integral calculus is assumed. Physical laws developed logically, from magnetism to electric currents, Ohm's law, electrolysis, and on to static electricity, induction, etc. Covers an unusual amount of material; one third of book on modern material: solution of wave equation, photoelectric and thermionic effects, etc. Complete statement of the various electrical systems of units and interrelations. 2 Indexes. 75 pages of problems with answers stated. Over 300 figures and diagrams. xix +669pp. 5⅜ x 8.
S745 Paperbound **$2.75**

THE ELECTROMAGNETIC FIELD, Max Mason & Warren Weaver. Used constantly by graduate engineers. Vector methods exclusively: detailed treatment of electrostatics, expansion methods, with tables converting any quantity into absolute electromagnetic, absolute electrostatic, practical units. Discrete charges, ponderable bodies, Maxwell field equations, etc. Introduction. Indexes. 416pp. 5⅜ x 8.
S185 Paperbound **$2.00**

ELECTRICAL THEORY ON THE GIORGI SYSTEM, P. Cornelius. A new clarification of the fundamental concepts of electricity and magnetism, advocating the convenient m.k.s. system of units that is steadily gaining followers in the sciences. Illustrating the use and effectiveness of his terminology with numerous applications to concrete technical problems, the author here expounds the famous Giorgi system of electrical physics. His lucid presentation and well-reasoned, cogent argument for the universal adoption of this system form one of the finest pieces of scientific exposition in recent years. 28 figures. Index. Conversion tables for translating earlier data into modern units. Translated from 3rd Dutch edition by L. J. Jolley. x + 187pp. 5½ x 8¾.
S909 Clothbound **$6.00**

THEORY OF ELECTRONS AND ITS APPLICATION TO THE PHENOMENA OF LIGHT AND RADIANT HEAT, H. Lorentz. Lectures delivered at Columbia University by Nobel laureate Lorentz. Unabridged, they form a historical coverage of the theory of free electrons, motion, absorption of heat, Zeeman effect, propagation of light in molecular bodies, inverse Zeeman effect, optical phenomena in moving bodies, etc. 109 pages of notes explain the more advanced sections. Index. 9 figures. 352pp. 5⅜ x 8.
S173 Paperbound **$1.85**

TREATISE ON ELECTRICITY AND MAGNETISM, James Clerk Maxwell. For more than 80 years a seemingly inexhaustible source of leads for physicists, mathematicians, engineers. Total of 1082pp. on such topics as Measurement of Quantities, Electrostatics, Elementary Mathematical Theory of Electricity, Electrical Work and Energy in a System of Conductors, General Theorems, Theory of Electrical Images, Electrolysis, Conduction, Polarization, Dielectrics, Resistance, etc. "The greatest mathematical physicist since Newton," Sir James Jeans. 3rd edition. 107 figures, 21 plates. 1082pp. 5⅜ x 8.
S636-7, 2 volume set, paperbound **$4.00**

See also: **FUNDAMENTAL FORMULAS OF PHYSICS, D. H. Menzel; MATHEMATICAL ANALYSIS OF ELECTRICAL & OPTICAL WAVE MOTION, H. Bateman.**

Dover publishes books on art, music, philosophy, literature, languages, history, social sciences, psychology, handcrafts, orientalia, puzzles and entertainments, chess, pets and gardens, books explaining science, intermediate and higher mathematics mathematical physics, engineering, biological sciences, earth sciences, classics of science, etc. Write to:

Dept. catrr.
Dover Publications, Inc.
180 Varick Street, N. Y. 14, N. Y.

V